2007 Yearbook of Astronomy

2007 Yearbook of Astronomy

edited by

Patrick Moore

co-editor

John Mason

MACMILLAN

First published 2006 by Macmillan
an imprint of Pan Macmillan Ltd
20 New Wharf Road, London N1 9RR
Basingstoke and Oxford
Associated companies throughout the world
www.panmacmillan.com

ISBN-13: 978-1-4050-5333-4
ISBN-10: 1-4050-5333-x

9 8 7 6 5 4 3 2 1

A CIP catalogue record for this book is available from the British Library.

Typeset by Rowland Phototypesetting Ltd,
Bury St Edmunds, Suffolk
Printed and bound in Great Britain by
Mackays of Chatham plc, Chatham, Kent

Contents

Editors' Foreword

The *2007 Yearbook* follows the usual pattern. Gordon Taylor has provided the data for the invaluable monthly notes, as he has done for so many years now, John Isles has updated the variable-star notes, and Bob Argyle has dealt similarly with the information on double stars.

The new style, with enlarged star charts for both Northern and Southern Hemispheres, drawn by Wil Tirion, and the expanded section summarizing the events for the year, both of which we introduced in 2005, have proved popular additions and have been retained.

We hope that our selection of articles will have something of interest for everyone. There is the usual wide range of subjects, with contributions both from our regular authors and from some welcome newcomers.

PATRICK MOORE
JOHN MASON
Selsey, August 2006

Preface

New readers will find that all the information in this *Yearbook* is given in diagrammatic or descriptive form; the positions of the planets may easily be found from the specially designed star charts, while the monthly notes describe the movements of the planets and give details of other astronomical phenomena visible in both the Northern and Southern Hemispheres. Two sets of star charts are provided. The **Northern Charts** (pp. 17 to 41) are designed for use at latitude 52°N, but may be used without alteration throughout the British Isles, and (except in the case of eclipses and occultations) in other countries of similar northerly latitude. The **Southern Charts** (pp. 43 to 67) are drawn for latitude 35°S, and are suitable for use in South Africa, Australia and New Zealand, and other locations in approximately the same southerly latitude. The reader who needs more detailed information will find *Norton's Star Atlas* an invaluable guide, while more precise positions of the planets and their satellites, together with predictions of occultations, meteor showers and periodic comets, may be found in the *Handbook* of the British Astronomical Association. Readers will also find details of forthcoming events given in the American monthly magazine *Sky & Telescope* and the British periodicals *The Sky at Night*, *Astronomy Now* and *Astronomy and Space*.

Important note

The times given on the star charts and in the Monthly Notes are generally given as local times, using the 24-hour clock, the day beginning at midnight. All the dates, and the times of a few events (e.g. eclipses), are given in Greenwich Mean Time (GMT), which is related to local time by the formula

Local Mean Time = GMT – west longitude

In practice, small differences in longitude are ignored, and the observer will use local clock time, which will be the appropriate Standard (or Zone) Time. As the formula indicates, places in west longitude will have a Standard Time slow on GMT, while places in east longitude will have a Standard Time fast on GMT. As examples we have:

Standard Time in	
New Zealand	GMT + 12 hours
Victoria, NSW	GMT + 10 hours
Western Australia	GMT + 8 hours
South Africa	GMT + 2 hours
British Isles	GMT
Eastern ST	GMT – 5 hours
Central ST	GMT – 6 hours, etc.

If Summer Time is in use, the clocks will have been advanced by one hour, and this hour must be subtracted from the clock time to give Standard Time.

Part I

Monthly Charts and Astronomical Phenomena

Notes on the Star Charts

The stars, together with the Sun, Moon and planets, seem to be set on the surface of the celestial sphere, which appears to rotate about the Earth from east to west. Since it is impossible to represent a curved surface accurately on a plane, any kind of star map is bound to contain some form of distortion.

Most of the monthly star charts which appear in the various journals and some national newspapers are drawn in circular form. This is perfectly accurate, but it can make the charts awkward to use. For the star charts in this volume, we have preferred to give two hemispherical maps for each month of the year, one showing the northern aspect of the sky, and the other showing the southern aspect. Two sets of monthly charts are provided, one for observers in the Northern Hemisphere and one for those in the Southern Hemisphere.

Unfortunately, the constellations near the overhead point (the zenith) on these hemispherical charts can be rather distorted. This would be a serious drawback for precision charts, but what we have done is to give maps which are best suited to star recognition. We have also refrained from putting in too many stars, so that the main patterns stand out clearly. To help observers with any distortions near the zenith, and the lack of overlap between the charts of each pair, we have also included two circular maps, one showing all the constellations in the northern half of the sky, and one those in the southern half. Incidentally, there is a curious illusion that stars at an altitude of 60° or more are actually overhead, and beginners may often feel that they are leaning over backwards in trying to see them.

The charts show all stars down to the fourth magnitude, together with a number of fainter stars which are necessary to define the shapes of constellations. There is no standard system for representing the outlines of the constellations, and triangles and other simple figures have been used to give outlines which are easy to trace with the naked eye. The names of the constellations are given, together with the proper names of the brighter stars. The apparent magnitudes of the stars are indicated roughly by using different sizes of dot, the larger dots representing the brighter stars.

The two sets of star charts – one each for Northern and Southern Hemisphere observers – are similar in design. At each opening there is a single circular chart which shows all the constellations in that hemisphere of the sky. (These two charts are centred on the North and South Celestial Poles, respectively.) Then there are twelve double-page spreads, showing the northern and southern aspects for each month of the year for observers in that hemisphere. In the **Northern Charts** (drawn for latitude 52°N) the left-hand chart of each spread shows the northern half of the sky (lettered 1N, 2N, 3N . . . 12N), and the corresponding right-hand chart shows the southern half of the sky (lettered 1S, 2S, 3S . . . 12S). The arrangement and lettering of the charts is exactly the same for the **Southern Charts** (drawn for latitude 35°S).

Because the sidereal day is shorter than the solar day, the stars appear to rise and set about four minutes earlier each day, and this amounts to two hours in a month. Hence the twelve pairs of charts in each set are sufficient to give the appearance of the sky throughout the day at intervals of two hours, or at the same time of night at monthly intervals throughout the year. For example, charts 1N and 1S here are drawn for 23 hours on 6 January. The view will also be the same on 6 October at 05 hours; 6 November at 03 hours; 6 December at 01 hours and 6 February at 21 hours. The actual range of dates and times when the stars on the charts are visible is indicated on each page. Each pair of charts is numbered in bold type, and the number to be used for any given month and time may be found from the following table:

Local Time	**18^h**	**20^h**	**22^h**	**0^h**	**2^h**	**4^h**	**6^h**
January	11	12	1	2	3	4	5
February	12	1	2	3	4	5	6
March	1	2	3	4	5	6	7
April	2	3	4	5	6	7	8
May	3	4	5	6	7	8	9
June	4	5	6	7	8	9	10
July	5	6	7	8	9	10	11
August	6	7	8	9	10	11	12
September	7	8	9	10	11	12	1

Local Time	**18h**	**20h**	**22h**	**0h**	**2h**	**4h**	**6h**
October	8	9	10	11	12	1	2
November	9	10	11	12	1	2	3
December	10	11	12	1	2	3	4

On these charts, the ecliptic is drawn as a broken line on which longitude is marked every 10°. The positions of the planets are then easily found by reference to the table on p. 74. It will be noticed that on the **Southern Charts** the ecliptic may reach an altitude in excess of 62.5° on the star charts showing the northern aspect (5N to 9N). The continuations of the broken line will be found on the corresponding charts for the southern aspect (5S, 6S, 8S and 9S).

Northern Star Charts

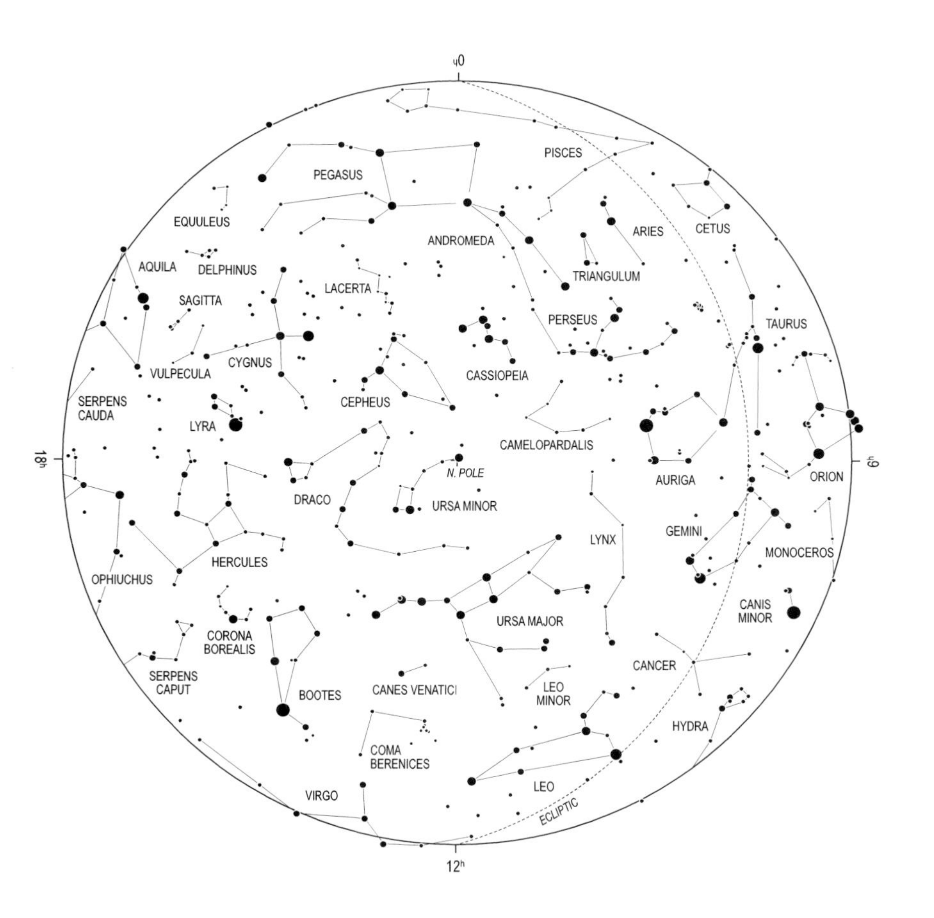

Northern Hemisphere

Note that the markers at 0h, 6h, 12h and 18h indicate hours of Right Ascension.

1N

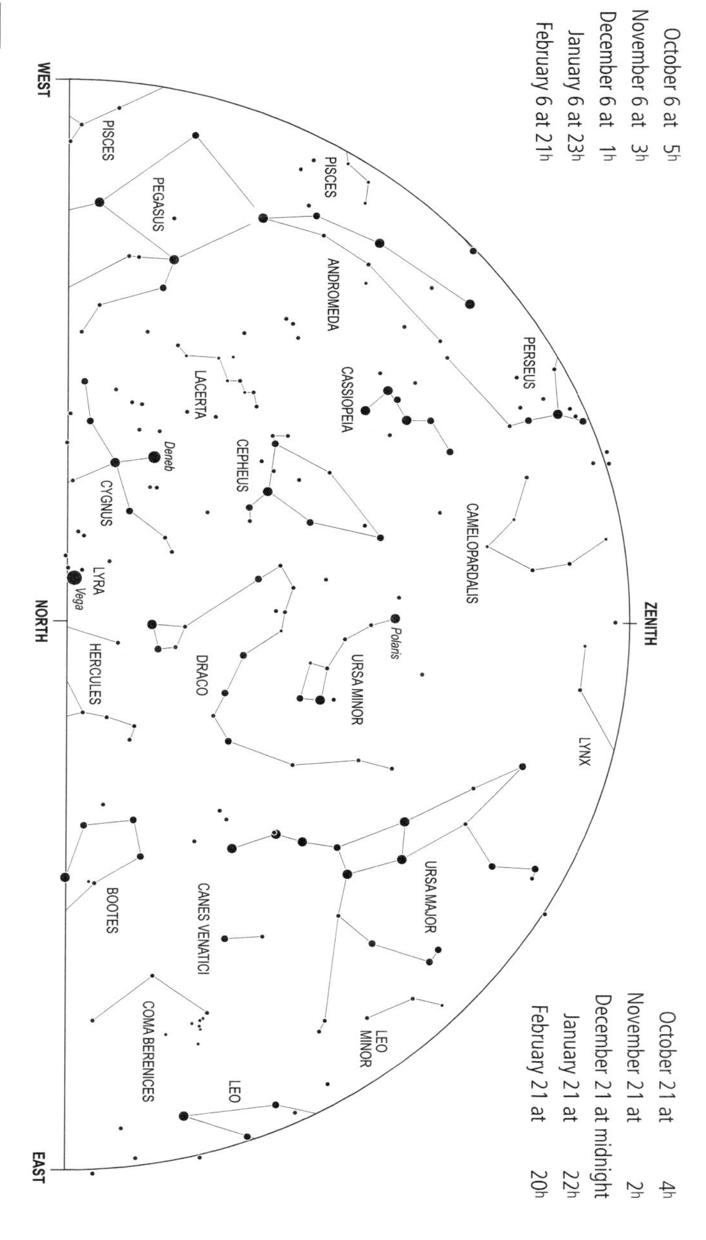
October 6 at 5h
November 6 at 3h
December 6 at 1h
January 6 at 23h
February 6 at 21h
October 21 at 4h
November 21 at 2h
December 21 at midnight
January 21 at 22h
February 21 at 20h
WEST
NORTH
EAST
ZENITH
PISCES
PEGASUS
ANDROMEDA
PERSEUS
CASSIOPEIA
LACERTA
CEPHEUS
Deneb
CYGNUS
LYRA
Vega
CAMELOPARDALIS
Polaris
URSA MINOR
DRACO
HERCULES
LYNX
URSA MAJOR
BOOTES
CANES VENATICI
COMA BERENICES
LEO MINOR
LEO

1S

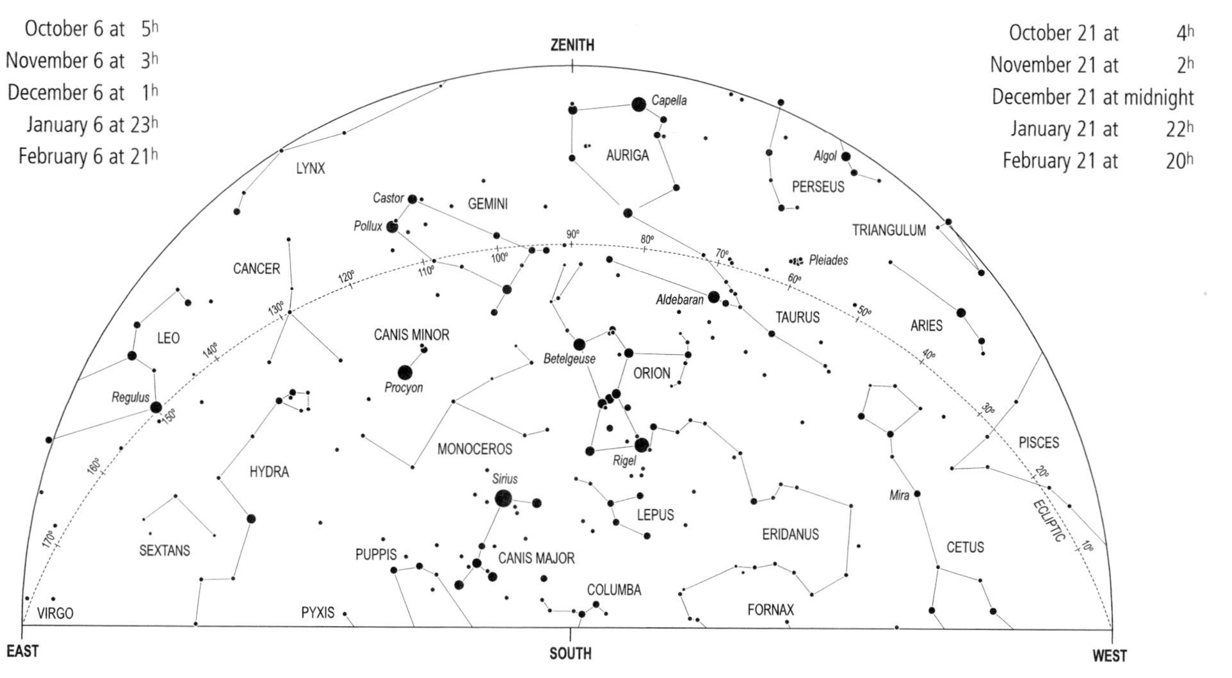
October 6 at 5h
November 6 at 3h
December 6 at 1h
January 6 at 23h
February 6 at 21h
October 21 at 4h
November 21 at 2h
December 21 at midnight
January 21 at 22h
February 21 at 20h
ZENITH
EAST
SOUTH
WEST
ECLIPTIC
10°
20°
30°
40°
50°
60°
70°
80°
90°
100°
110°
120°
130°
140°
150°
160°
170°
LYNX
AURIGA
Capella
PERSEUS
Algol
TRIANGULUM
Pleiades
GEMINI
Castor
Pollux
CANCER
LEO
Regulus
CANIS MINOR
Procyon
Betelgeuse
ORION
Aldebaran
TAURUS
ARIES
PISCES
MONOCEROS
Rigel
HYDRA
Sirius
LEPUS
ERIDANUS
Mira
CETUS
SEXTANS
PUPPIS
CANIS MAJOR
COLUMBA
FORNAX
PYXIS
VIRGO

2N

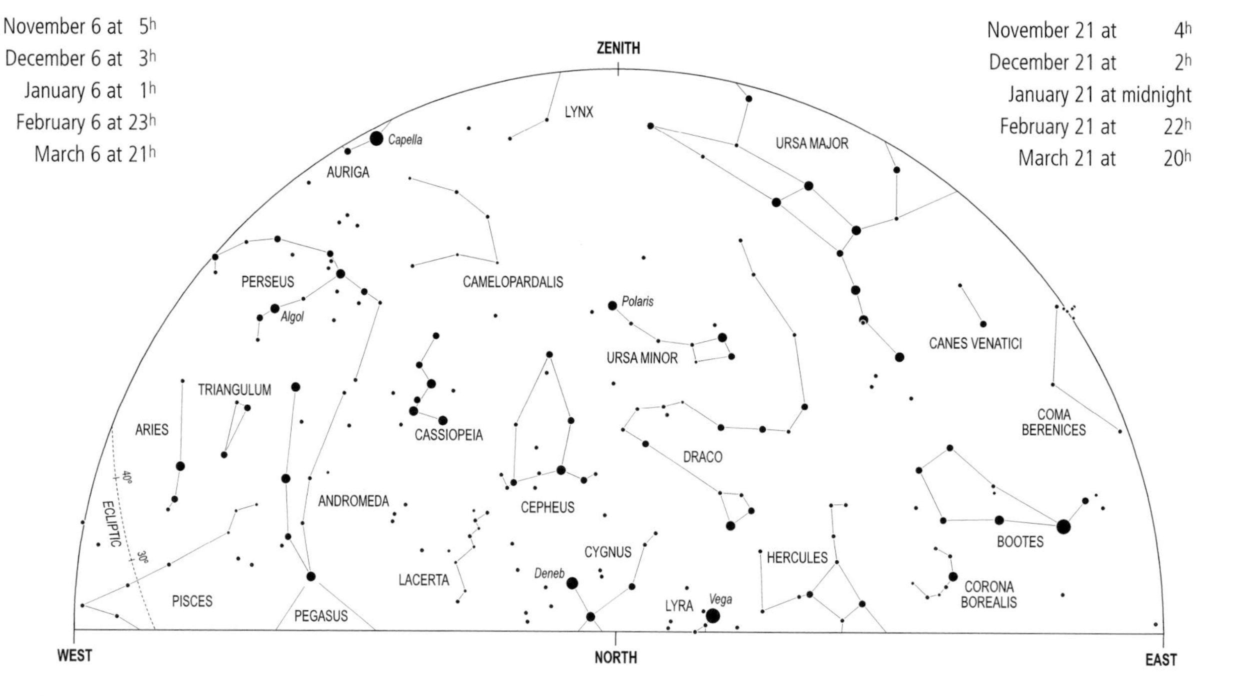
November 6 at 5h
December 6 at 3h
January 6 at 1h
February 6 at 23h
March 6 at 21h
November 21 at 4h
December 21 at 2h
January 21 at midnight
February 21 at 22h
March 21 at 20h
ZENITH
WEST
NORTH
EAST
ECLIPTIC
40°
30°
LYNX
Capella
AURIGA
URSA MAJOR
PERSEUS
Algol
CAMELOPARDALIS
Polaris
URSA MINOR
CANES VENATICI
TRIANGULUM
ARIES
CASSIOPEIA
COMA
BERENICES
DRACO
ANDROMEDA
CEPHEUS
BOOTES
CYGNUS
HERCULES
Deneb
LACERTA
CORONA
BOREALIS
PISCES
LYRA
Vega
PEGASUS

2S

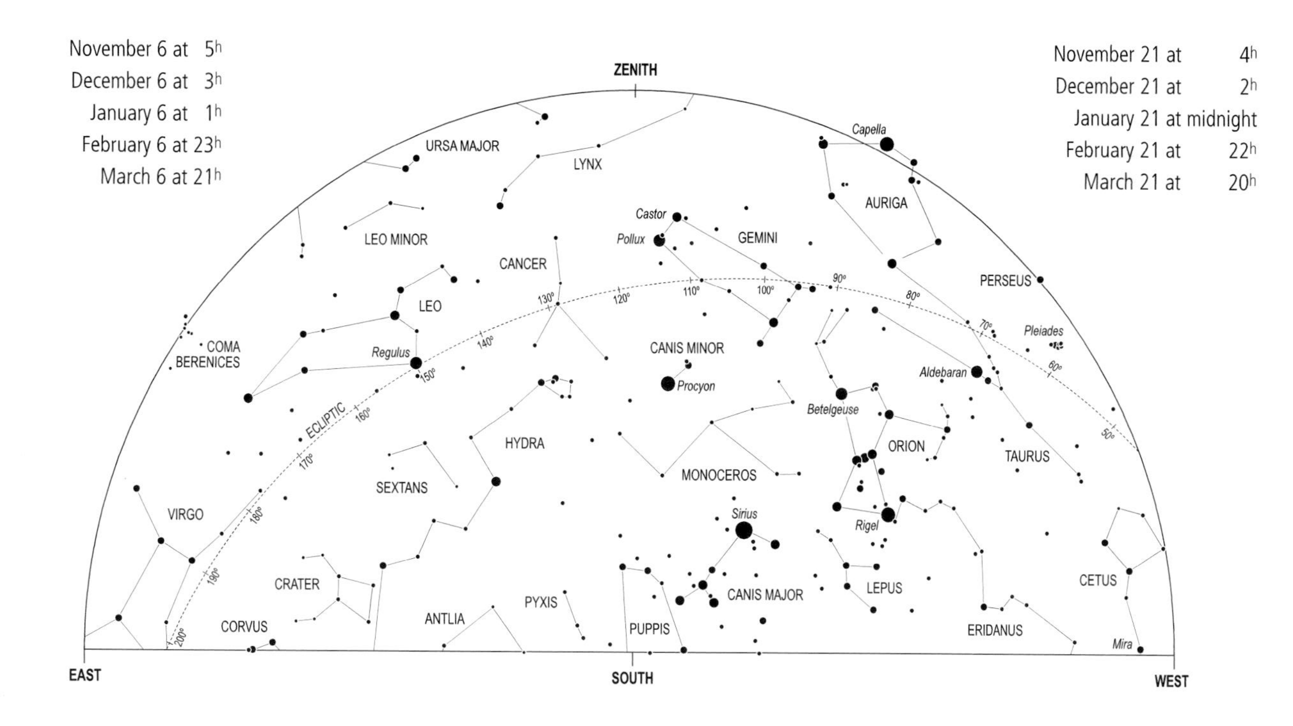
November 6 at 5h
December 6 at 3h
January 6 at 1h
February 6 at 23h
March 6 at 21h
November 21 at 4h
December 21 at 2h
January 21 at midnight
February 21 at 22h
March 21 at 20h
ZENITH
URSA MAJOR
LYNX
Capella
AURIGA
LEO MINOR
CANCER
Castor
Pollux
GEMINI
PERSEUS
LEO
COMA BERENICES
Regulus
CANIS MINOR
Procyon
Pleiades
Aldebaran
Betelgeuse
ORION
TAURUS
ECLIPTIC
HYDRA
SEXTANS
MONOCEROS
VIRGO
Sirius
Rigel
CRATER
CANIS MAJOR
LEPUS
CETUS
PYXIS
ANTLIA
CORVUS
PUPPIS
ERIDANUS
Mira
EAST
SOUTH
WEST
50°
60°
70°
80°
90°
100°
110°
120°
130°
140°
150°
160°
170°
180°
190°
200°

3N

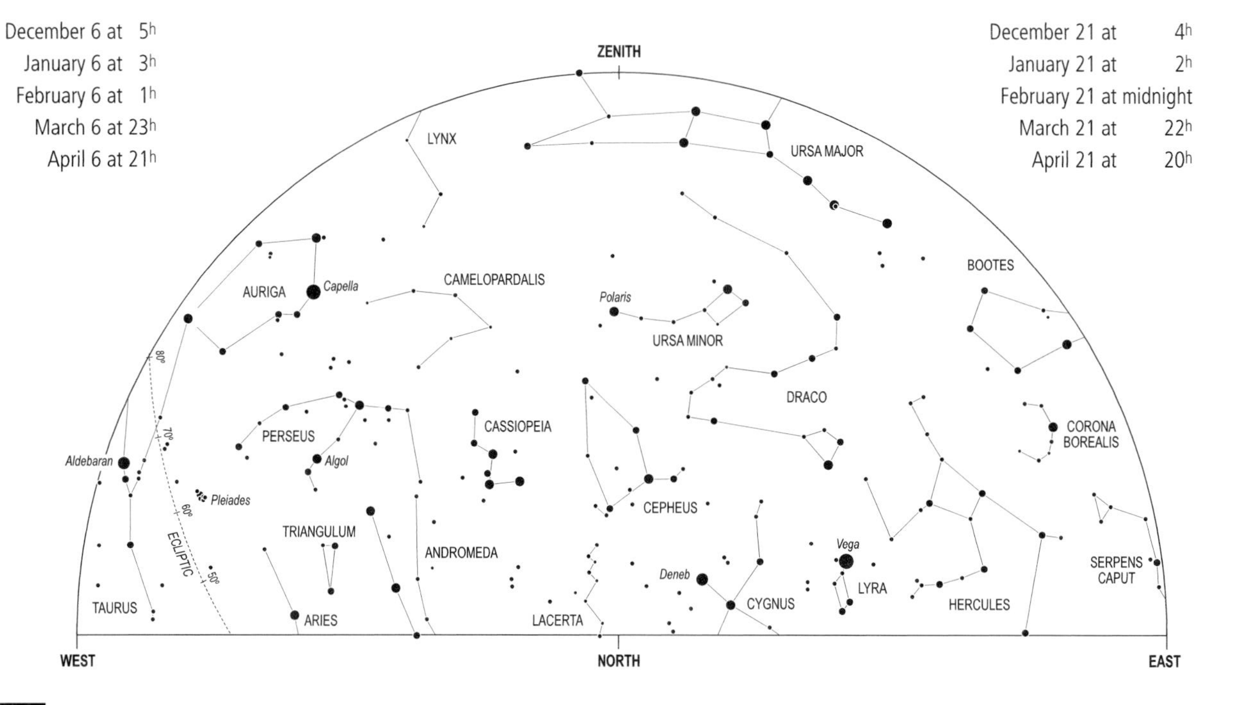
December 6 at 5h
January 6 at 3h
February 6 at 1h
March 6 at 23h
April 6 at 21h
December 21 at 4h
January 21 at 2h
February 21 at midnight
March 21 at 22h
April 21 at 20h
ZENITH
LYNX
URSA MAJOR
AURIGA
Capella
CAMELOPARDALIS
Polaris
URSA MINOR
BOOTES
DRACO
PERSEUS
Algol
CASSIOPEIA
CORONA BOREALIS
Aldebaran
80°
70°
60°
50°
ECLIPTIC
Pleiades
TRIANGULUM
ANDROMEDA
CEPHEUS
Vega
SERPENS CAPUT
Deneb
LYRA
CYGNUS
HERCULES
TAURUS
ARIES
LACERTA
WEST
NORTH
EAST

3S

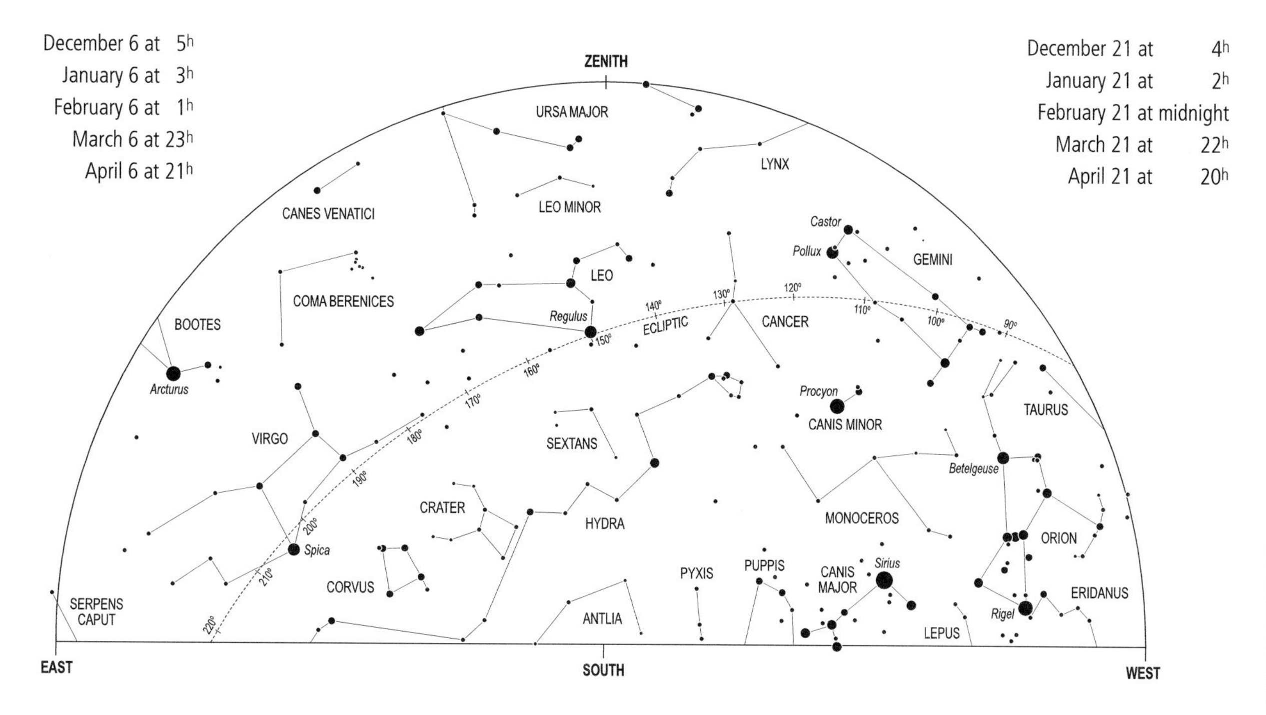

December 6 at 5h
January 6 at 3h
February 6 at 1h
March 6 at 23h
April 6 at 21h
December 21 at 4h
January 21 at 2h
February 21 at midnight
March 21 at 22h
April 21 at 20h
ZENITH
EAST
SOUTH
WEST
URSA MAJOR
LYNX
LEO MINOR
CANES VENATICI
Castor
Pollux
GEMINI
LEO
COMA BERENICES
BOOTES
Regulus
ECLIPTIC
CANCER
Arcturus
Procyon
CANIS MINOR
TAURUS
VIRGO
SEXTANS
Betelgeuse
CRATER
HYDRA
MONOCEROS
ORION
Spica
CORVUS
PYXIS
PUPPIS
CANIS MAJOR
Sirius
ERIDANUS
SERPENS CAPUT
ANTLIA
Rigel
LEPUS
90°
100°
110°
120°
130°
140°
150°
160°
170°
180°
190°
200°
210°
220°

4N

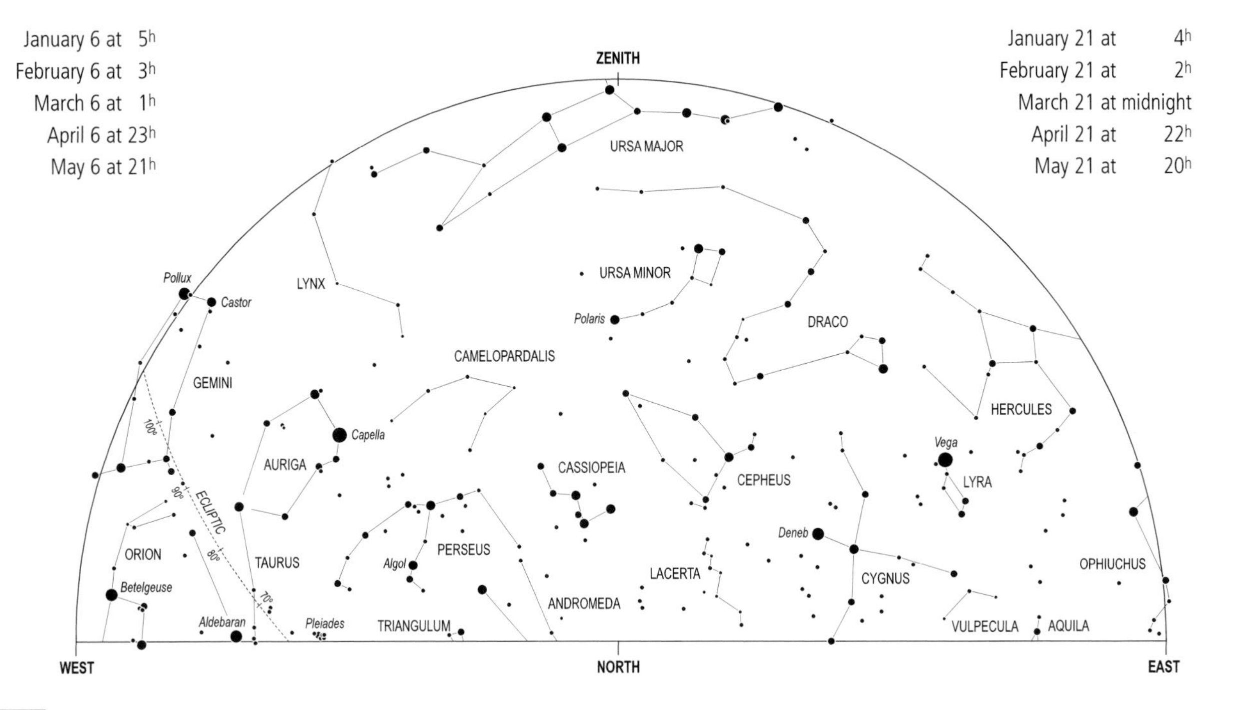
January 6 at 5h
February 6 at 3h
March 6 at 1h
April 6 at 23h
May 6 at 21h
January 21 at 4h
February 21 at 2h
March 21 at midnight
April 21 at 22h
May 21 at 20h
ZENITH
URSA MAJOR
URSA MINOR
Polaris
DRACO
LYNX
Pollux
Castor
GEMINI
CAMELOPARDALIS
Capella
AURIGA
CASSIOPEIA
CEPHEUS
HERCULES
Vega
LYRA
100°
90°
ECLIPTIC
80°
70°
ORION
TAURUS
Algol
PERSEUS
Deneb
LACERTA
CYGNUS
OPHIUCHUS
Betelgeuse
Aldebaran
Pleiades
TRIANGULUM
ANDROMEDA
VULPECULA
AQUILA
WEST
NORTH
EAST

4S

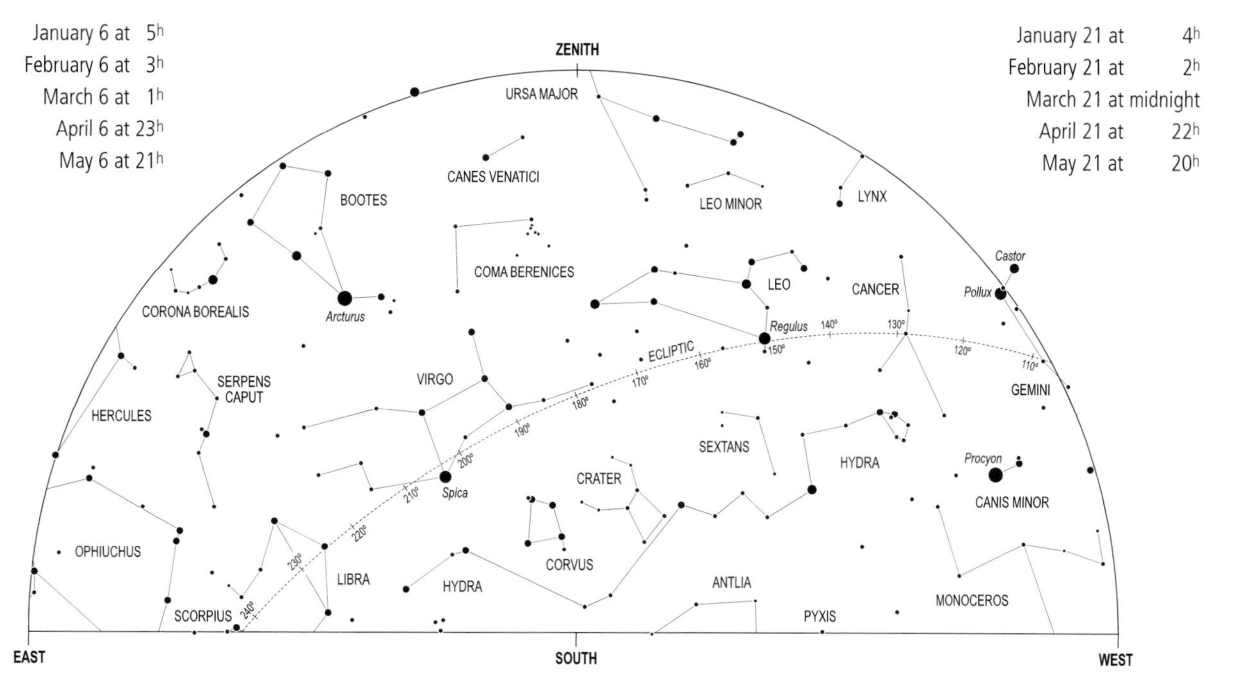
January 6 at 5h
February 6 at 3h
March 6 at 1h
April 6 at 23h
May 6 at 21h
January 21 at 4h
February 21 at 2h
March 21 at midnight
April 21 at 22h
May 21 at 20h
ZENITH
URSA MAJOR
CANES VENATICI
BOOTES
LEO MINOR
LYNX
COMA BERENICES
Castor
Pollux
LEO
CANCER
CORONA BOREALIS
Arcturus
Regulus
140°
130°
150°
ECLIPTIC
160°
170°
120°
110°
GEMINI
SERPENS CAPUT
VIRGO
HERCULES
180°
190°
SEXTANS
HYDRA
200°
Procyon
CRATER
210°
Spica
CANIS MINOR
220°
OPHIUCHUS
230°
CORVUS
LIBRA
HYDRA
ANTLIA
MONOCEROS
SCORPIUS
240°
PYXIS
EAST
SOUTH
WEST

5N

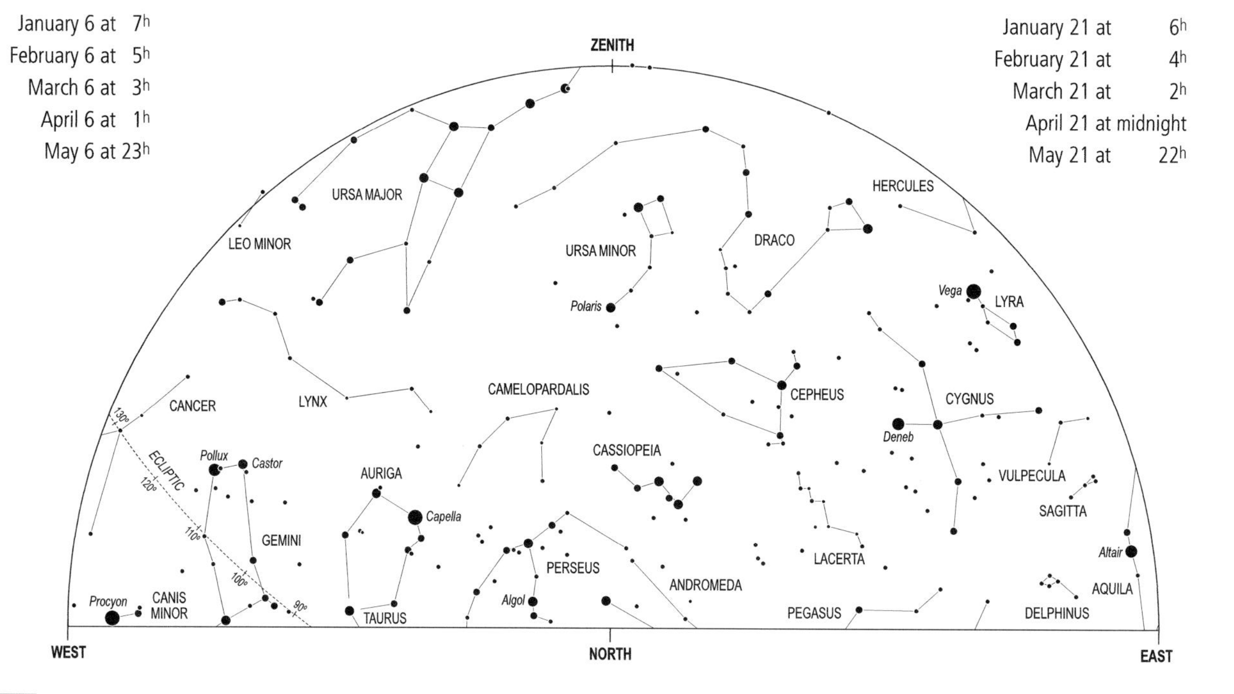

January 6 at 7h
February 6 at 5h
March 6 at 3h
April 6 at 1h
May 6 at 23h
January 21 at 6h
February 21 at 4h
March 21 at 2h
April 21 at midnight
May 21 at 22h
ZENITH
WEST
NORTH
EAST
URSA MAJOR
LEO MINOR
URSA MINOR
Polaris
DRACO
HERCULES
Vega
LYRA
CANCER
LYNX
CAMELOPARDALIS
CEPHEUS
CYGNUS
Deneb
130°
ECLIPTIC
120°
110°
100°
90°
Pollux
Castor
GEMINI
AURIGA
Capella
CASSIOPEIA
VULPECULA
SAGITTA
PERSEUS
Algol
ANDROMEDA
LACERTA
Altair
AQUILA
Procyon
CANIS MINOR
TAURUS
PEGASUS
DELPHINUS

5S

January 6 at 7^h
February 6 at 5^h
March 6 at 3^h
April 6 at 1^h
May 6 at 23^h

January 21 at 6^h
February 21 at 4^h
March 21 at 2^h
April 21 at midnight
May 21 at 22^h

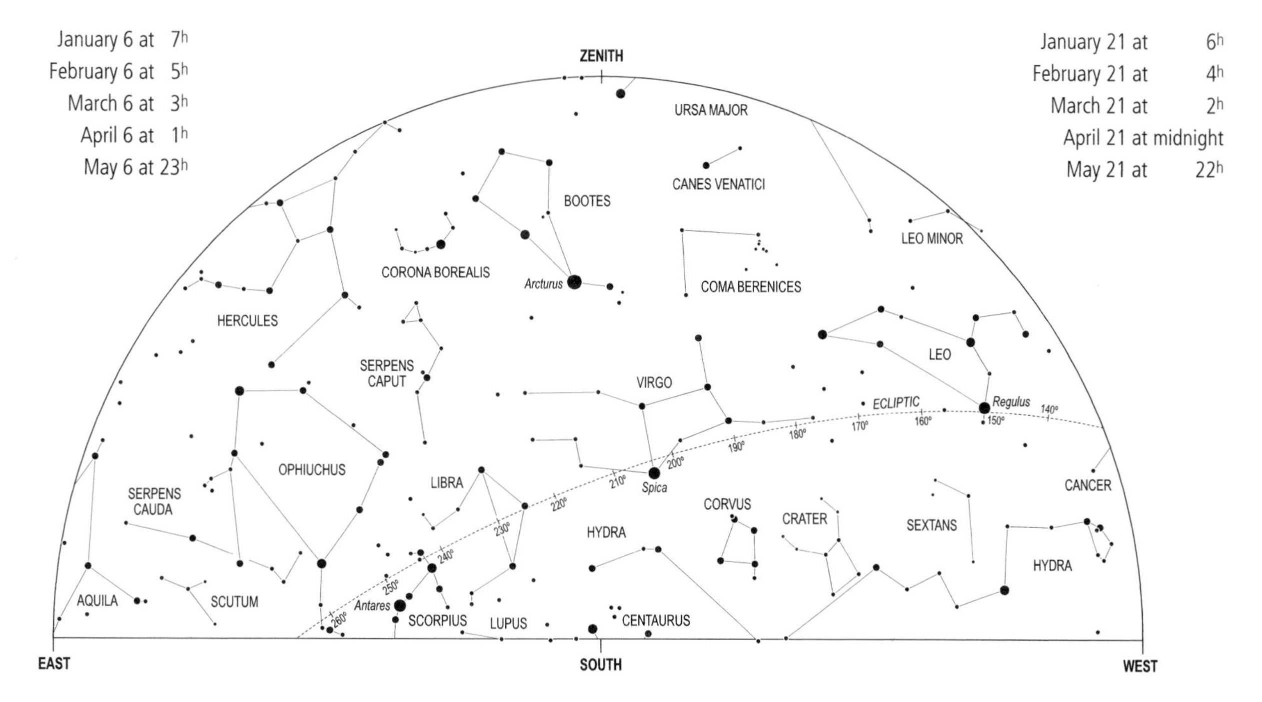

6N

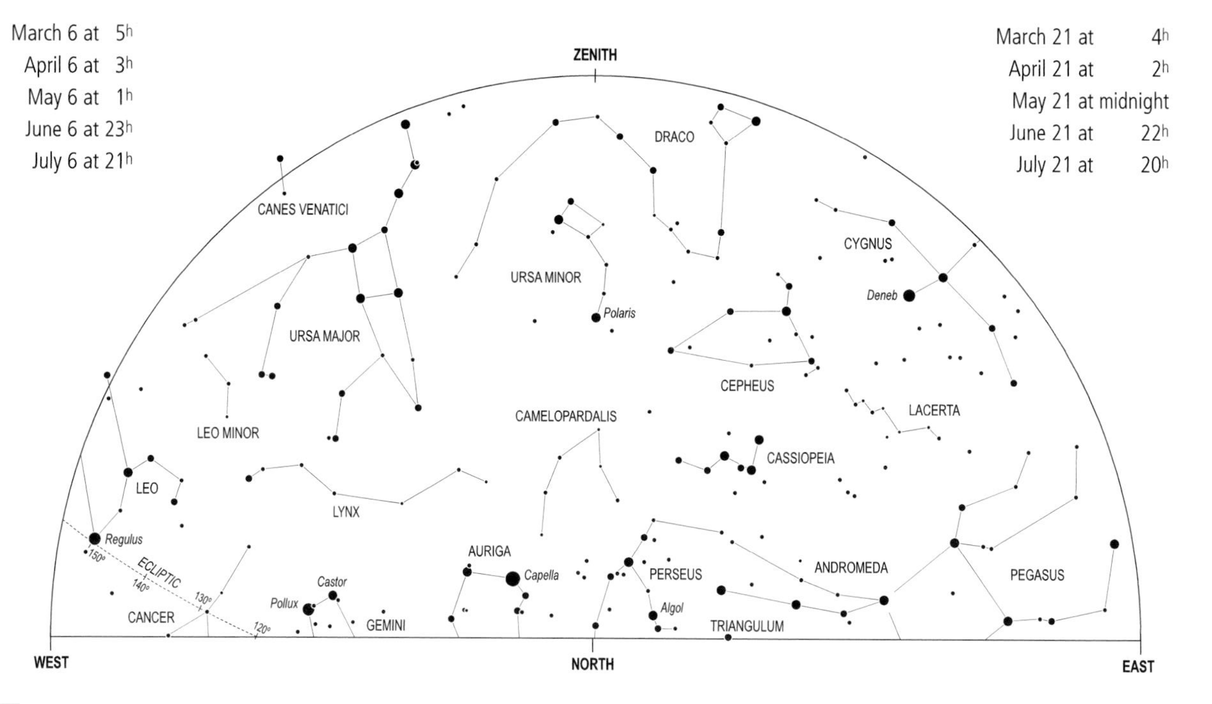
March 6 at 5h
April 6 at 3h
May 6 at 1h
June 6 at 23h
July 6 at 21h
March 21 at 4h
April 21 at 2h
May 21 at midnight
June 21 at 22h
July 21 at 20h
ZENITH
DRACO
CANES VENATICI
URSA MINOR
Polaris
CYGNUS
Deneb
URSA MAJOR
CEPHEUS
LACERTA
LEO MINOR
CAMELOPARDALIS
CASSIOPEIA
LEO
LYNX
Regulus
ECLIPTIC
150°
140°
130°
120°
AURIGA
Capella
PERSEUS
ANDROMEDA
PEGASUS
Castor
Pollux
Algol
CANCER
GEMINI
TRIANGULUM
WEST
NORTH
EAST

6S

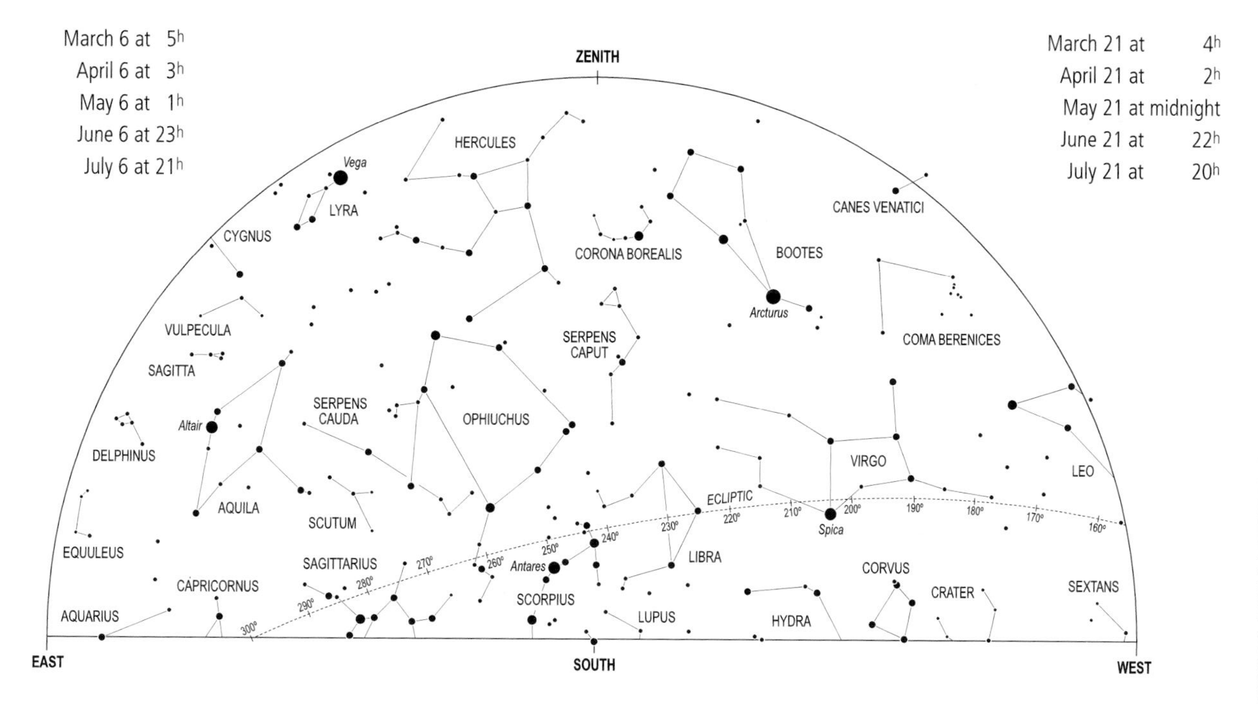
March 6 at 5h
April 6 at 3h
May 6 at 1h
June 6 at 23h
July 6 at 21h
March 21 at 4h
April 21 at 2h
May 21 at midnight
June 21 at 22h
July 21 at 20h
ZENITH
HERCULES
Vega
LYRA
CYGNUS
CORONA BOREALIS
BOOTES
CANES VENATICI
Arcturus
VULPECULA
SAGITTA
SERPENS CAPUT
COMA BERENICES
SERPENS CAUDA
OPHIUCHUS
Altair
DELPHINUS
VIRGO
LEO
AQUILA
SCUTUM
ECLIPTIC
Spica
EQUULEUS
SAGITTARIUS
Antares
LIBRA
CORVUS
CRATER
SEXTANS
CAPRICORNUS
SCORPIUS
LUPUS
HYDRA
AQUARIUS
EAST
SOUTH
WEST
160°
170°
180°
190°
200°
210°
220°
230°
240°
250°
260°
270°
280°
290°
300°

7N

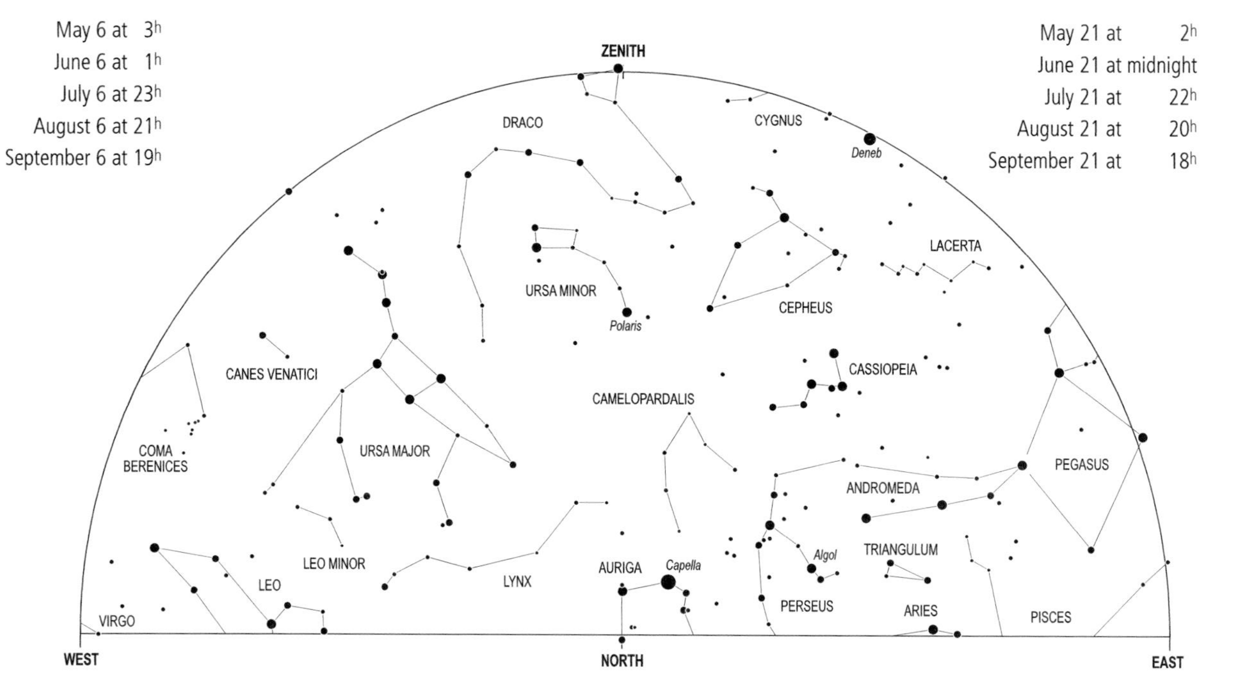
May 6 at 3h
June 6 at 1h
July 6 at 23h
August 6 at 21h
September 6 at 19h
May 21 at 2h
June 21 at midnight
July 21 at 22h
August 21 at 20h
September 21 at 18h
ZENITH
DRACO
CYGNUS
Deneb
URSA MINOR
Polaris
LACERTA
CEPHEUS
CANES VENATICI
CASSIOPEIA
CAMELOPARDALIS
COMA
BERENICES
URSA MAJOR
PEGASUS
ANDROMEDA
LEO MINOR
TRIANGULUM
Algol
AURIGA
Capella
LEO
LYNX
PERSEUS
ARIES
PISCES
VIRGO
WEST
NORTH
EAST

7S

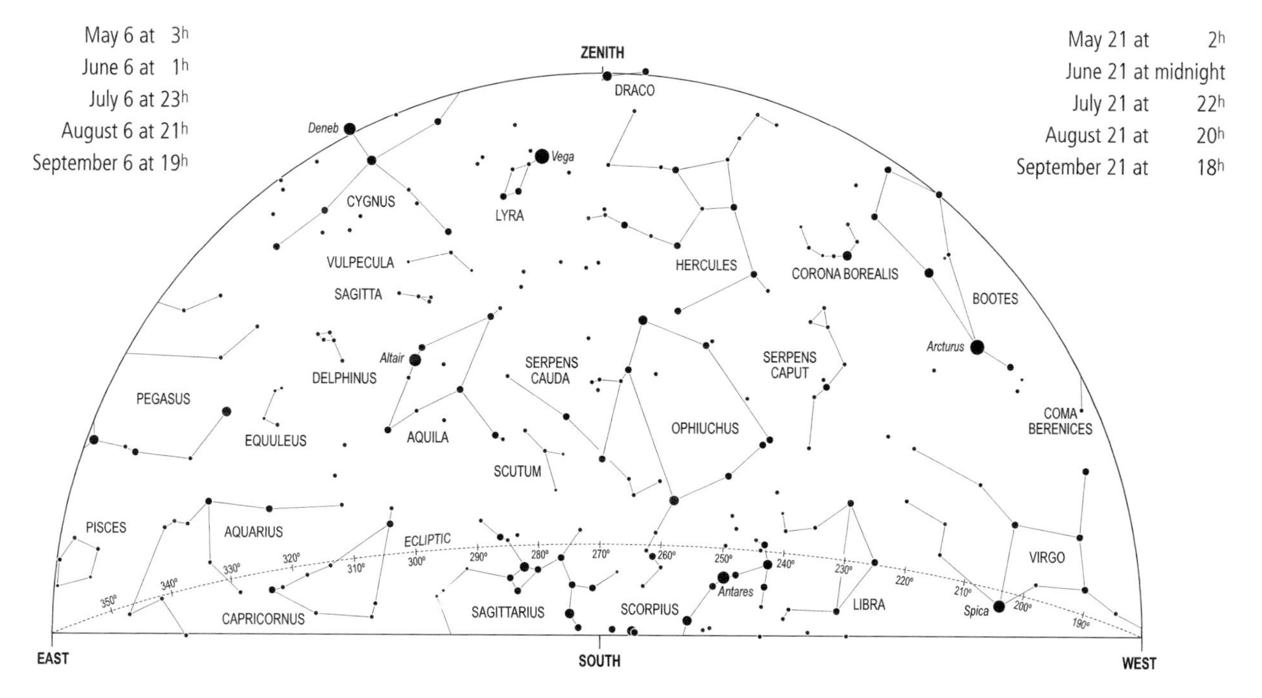
May 6 at 3h
June 6 at 1h
July 6 at 23h
August 6 at 21h
September 6 at 19h
May 21 at 2h
June 21 at midnight
July 21 at 22h
August 21 at 20h
September 21 at 18h
ZENITH
DRACO
Deneb
Vega
CYGNUS
LYRA
HERCULES
CORONA BOREALIS
BOOTES
VULPECULA
SAGITTA
Arcturus
SERPENS CAUDA
SERPENS CAPUT
Altair
DELPHINUS
PEGASUS
EQUULEUS
AQUILA
OPHIUCHUS
COMA BERENICES
SCUTUM
PISCES
AQUARIUS
ECLIPTIC
VIRGO
Antares
LIBRA
Spica
CAPRICORNUS
SAGITTARIUS
SCORPIUS
350°
340°
330°
320°
310°
300°
290°
280°
270°
260°
250°
240°
230°
220°
210°
200°
190°
EAST
SOUTH
WEST

8N

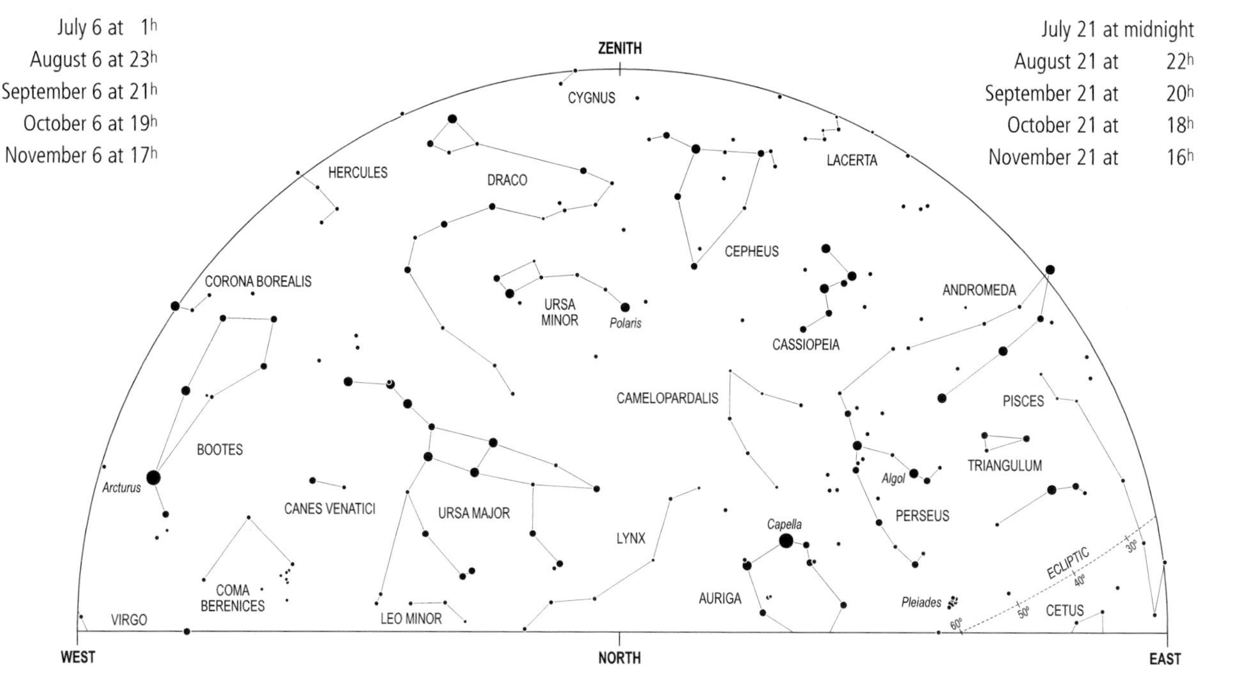
July 6 at 1h
August 6 at 23h
September 6 at 21h
October 6 at 19h
November 6 at 17h
July 21 at midnight
August 21 at 22h
September 21 at 20h
October 21 at 18h
November 21 at 16h
ZENITH
CYGNUS
HERCULES
DRACO
LACERTA
CEPHEUS
CORONA BOREALIS
URSA MINOR
Polaris
ANDROMEDA
CASSIOPEIA
CAMELOPARDALIS
PISCES
BOOTES
Arcturus
Algol
TRIANGULUM
CANES VENATICI
URSA MAJOR
PERSEUS
LYNX
Capella
ECLIPTIC
30°
40°
50°
60°
COMA BERENICES
AURIGA
Pleiades
CETUS
VIRGO
LEO MINOR
WEST
NORTH
EAST

8S

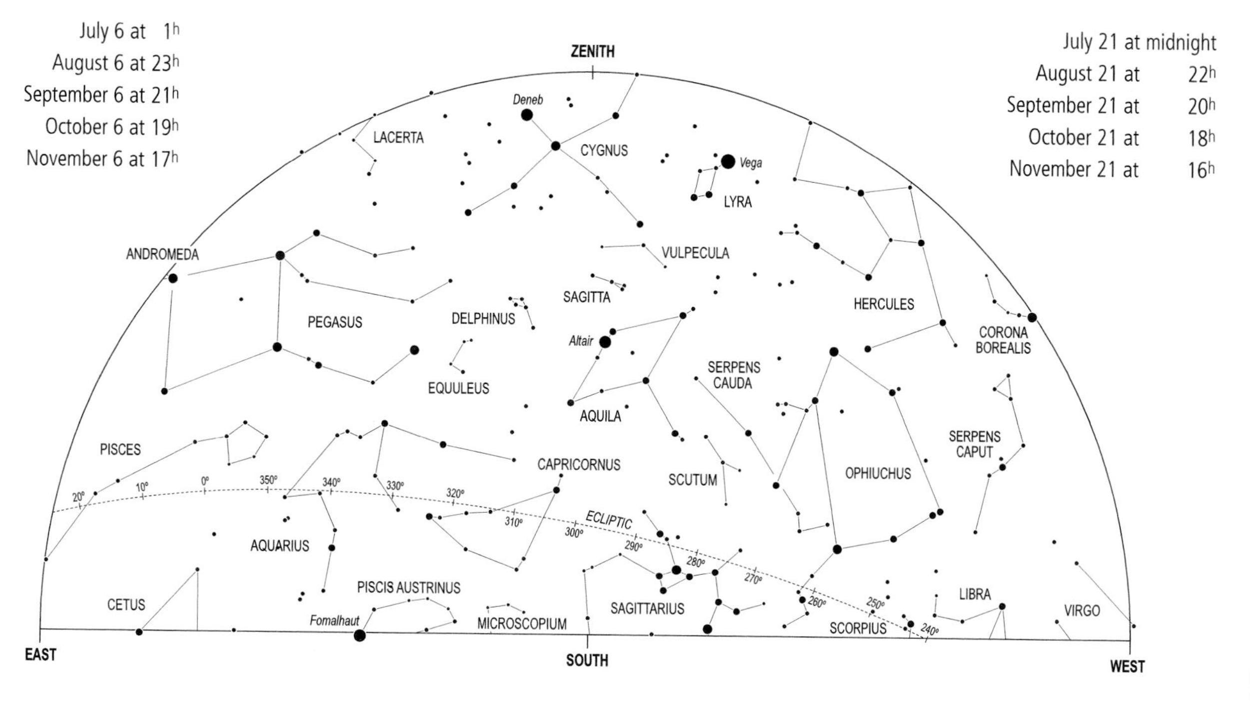
July 6 at 1h
August 6 at 23h
September 6 at 21h
October 6 at 19h
November 6 at 17h
July 21 at midnight
August 21 at 22h
September 21 at 20h
October 21 at 18h
November 21 at 16h
ZENITH
EAST
SOUTH
WEST
LACERTA
Deneb
CYGNUS
Vega
LYRA
ANDROMEDA
VULPECULA
SAGITTA
PEGASUS
DELPHINUS
Altair
HERCULES
CORONA BOREALIS
SERPENS CAUDA
EQUULEUS
AQUILA
SERPENS CAPUT
PISCES
CAPRICORNUS
SCUTUM
OPHIUCHUS
ECLIPTIC
AQUARIUS
PISCIS AUSTRINUS
LIBRA
CETUS
SAGITTARIUS
VIRGO
Fomalhaut
MICROSCOPIUM
SCORPIUS
20°
10°
0°
350°
340°
330°
320°
310°
300°
290°
280°
270°
260°
250°
240°

9N

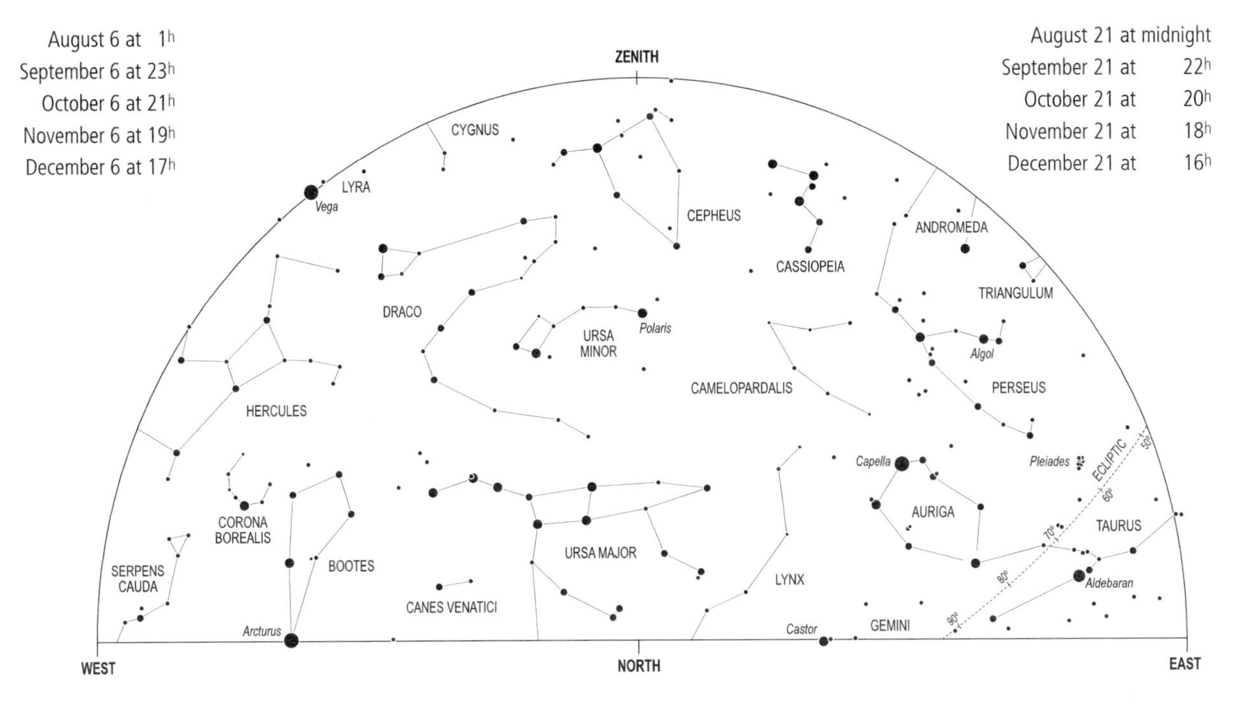
August 6 at 1h
September 6 at 23h
October 6 at 21h
November 6 at 19h
December 6 at 17h
August 21 at midnight
September 21 at 22h
October 21 at 20h
November 21 at 18h
December 21 at 16h
ZENITH
WEST
NORTH
EAST
CYGNUS
LYRA
Vega
CEPHEUS
CASSIOPEIA
ANDROMEDA
TRIANGULUM
DRACO
URSA MINOR
Polaris
CAMELOPARDALIS
Algol
PERSEUS
HERCULES
Capella
Pleiades
ECLIPTIC
50°
60°
70°
80°
90°
AURIGA
TAURUS
CORONA BOREALIS
BOOTES
URSA MAJOR
LYNX
Aldebaran
SERPENS CAUDA
CANES VENATICI
GEMINI
Arcturus
Castor

9S

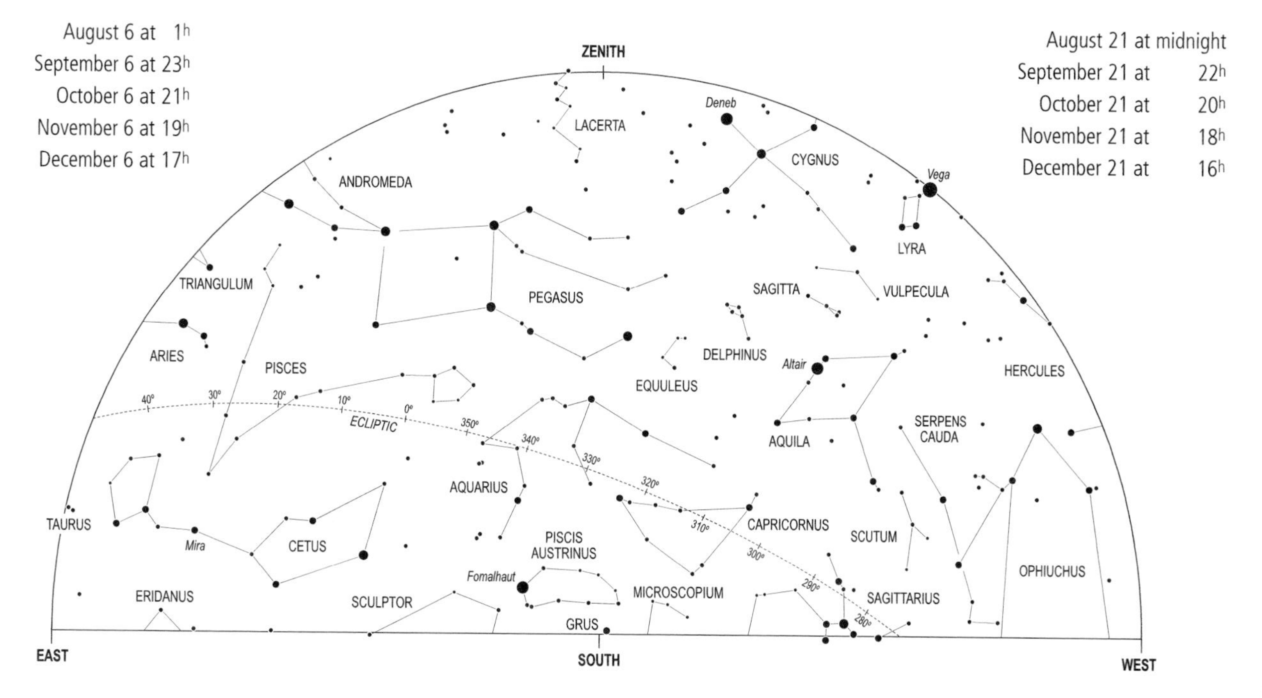

August 6 at 1h
September 6 at 23h
October 6 at 21h
November 6 at 19h
December 6 at 17h
August 21 at midnight
September 21 at 22h
October 21 at 20h
November 21 at 18h
December 21 at 16h
ZENITH
LACERTA
Deneb
CYGNUS
Vega
LYRA
ANDROMEDA
TRIANGULUM
PEGASUS
SAGITTA
VULPECULA
ARIES
PISCES
DELPHINUS
Altair
HERCULES
EQUULEUS
40°
30°
20°
10°
0°
ECLIPTIC
350°
340°
330°
320°
310°
300°
290°
280°
AQUILA
SERPENS CAUDA
AQUARIUS
TAURUS
Mira
CETUS
PISCIS AUSTRINUS
CAPRICORNUS
SCUTUM
OPHIUCHUS
Fomalhaut
ERIDANUS
SCULPTOR
MICROSCOPIUM
SAGITTARIUS
GRUS
EAST
SOUTH
WEST

10N

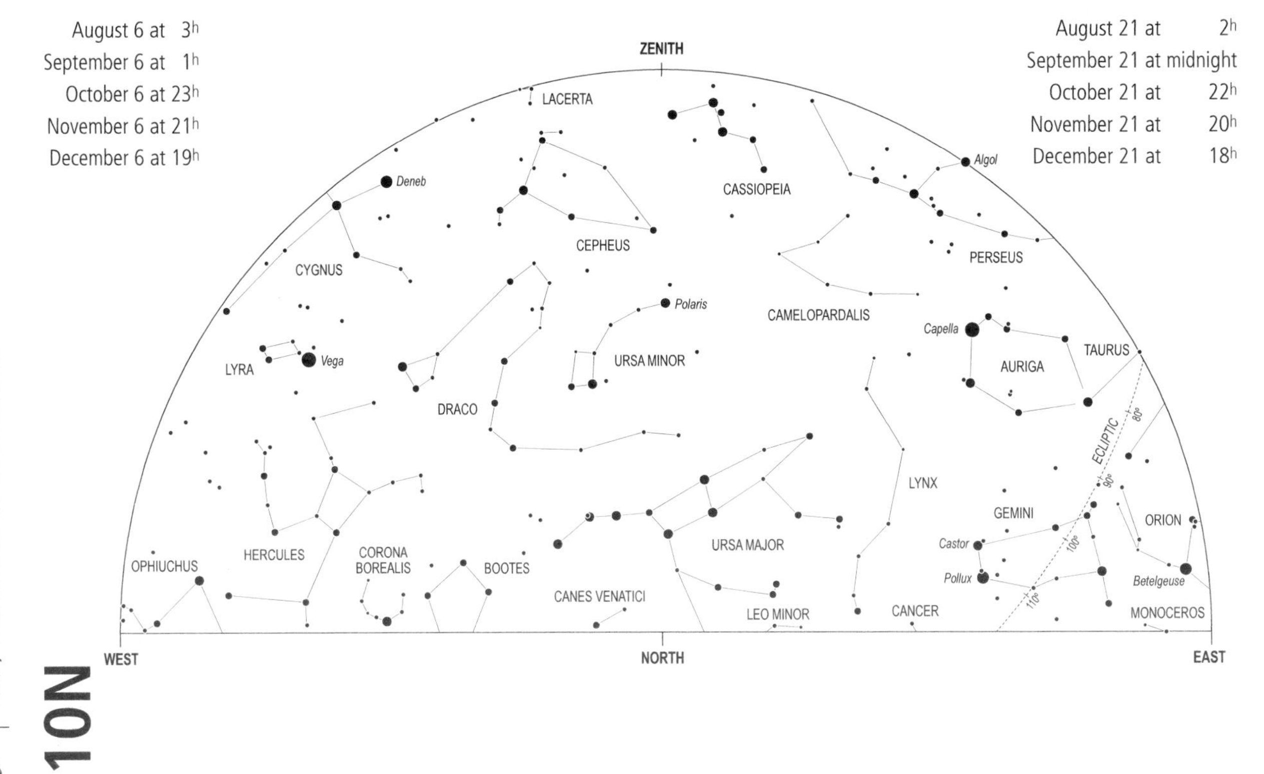

August 6 at 3h
September 6 at 1h
October 6 at 23h
November 6 at 21h
December 6 at 19h
August 21 at 2h
September 21 at midnight
October 21 at 22h
November 21 at 20h
December 21 at 18h
WEST
NORTH
EAST
ZENITH
OPHIUCHUS
HERCULES
LYRA
Vega
CYGNUS
Deneb
CORONA BOREALIS
DRACO
BOOTES
LACERTA
CEPHEUS
CANES VENATICI
URSA MINOR
Polaris
CASSIOPEIA
URSA MAJOR
LEO MINOR
CAMELOPARDALIS
LYNX
CANCER
Capella
PERSEUS
Algol
Castor
Pollux
GEMINI
AURIGA
110°
100°
90°
ECLIPTIC
80°
TAURUS
Betelgeuse
ORION
MONOCEROS

10S

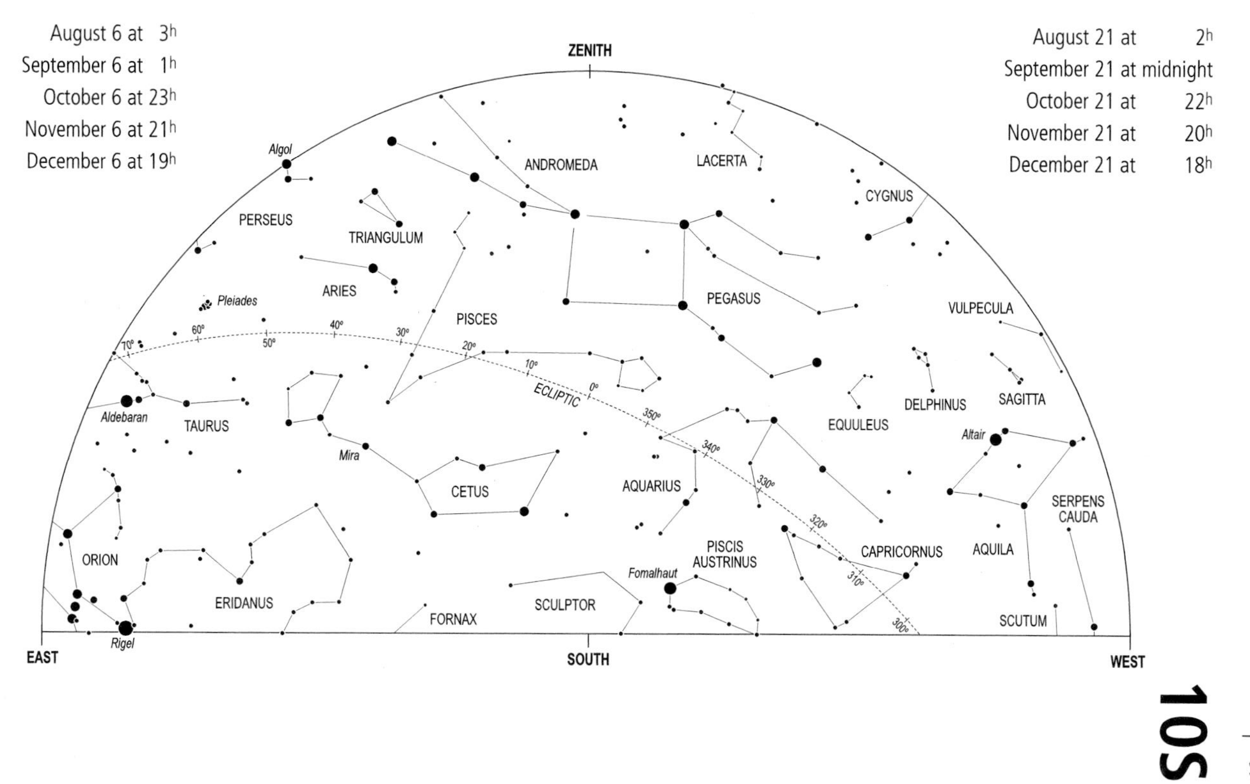

August 6 at 3h
September 6 at 1h
October 6 at 23h
November 6 at 21h
December 6 at 19h
August 21 at 2h
September 21 at midnight
October 21 at 22h
November 21 at 20h
December 21 at 18h
ZENITH
EAST
SOUTH
WEST
Algol
PERSEUS
TRIANGULUM
ANDROMEDA
LACERTA
CYGNUS
ARIES
Pleiades
PISCES
PEGASUS
VULPECULA
70°
60°
50°
40°
30°
20°
10°
0°
350°
340°
330°
320°
310°
300°
ECLIPTIC
Aldebaran
TAURUS
Mira
DELPHINUS
SAGITTA
EQUULEUS
Altair
CETUS
AQUARIUS
SERPENS CAUDA
ORION
PISCIS AUSTRINUS
CAPRICORNUS
AQUILA
Fomalhaut
ERIDANUS
SCULPTOR
FORNAX
SCUTUM
Rigel

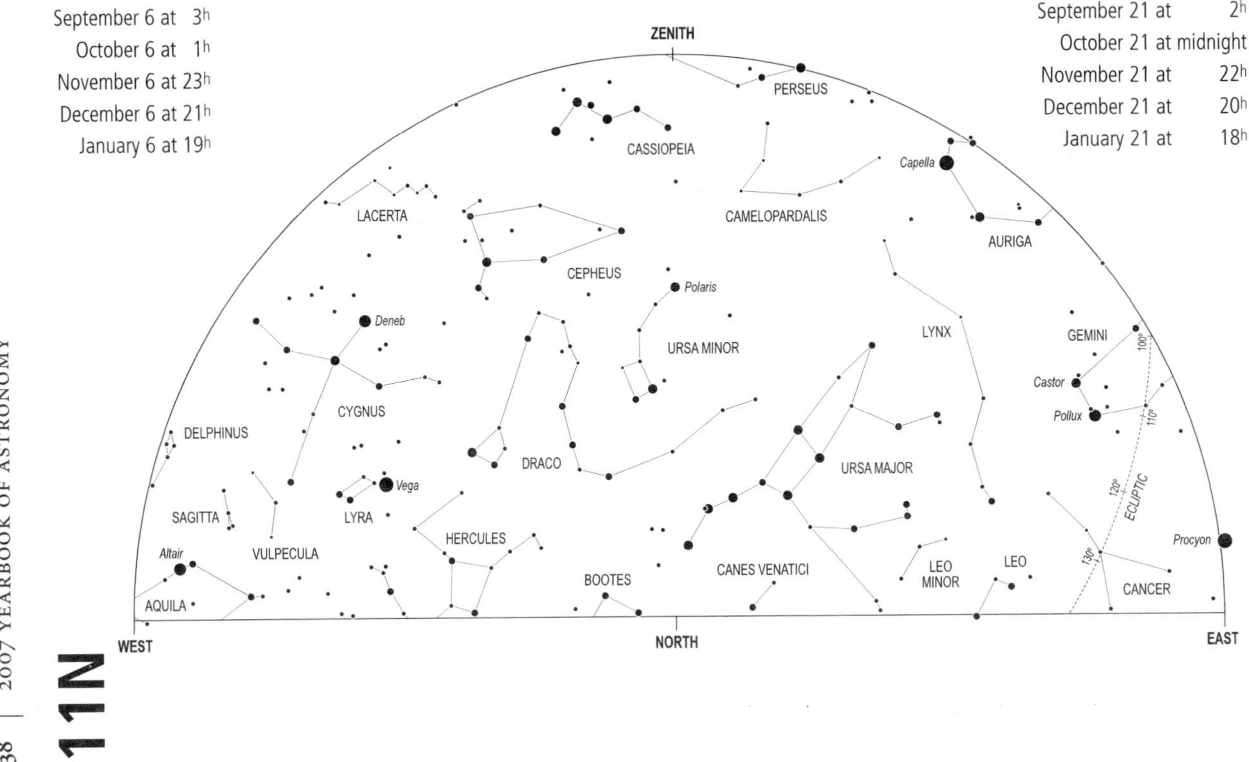
11N
September 6 at 3h
October 6 at 1h
November 6 at 23h
December 6 at 21h
January 6 at 19h
September 21 at 2h
October 21 at midnight
November 21 at 22h
December 21 at 20h
January 21 at 18h
ZENITH
PERSEUS
CASSIOPEIA
Capella
CAMELOPARDALIS
LACERTA
AURIGA
CEPHEUS
Polaris
Deneb
URSA MINOR
LYNX
GEMINI
Castor
Pollux
CYGNUS
DELPHINUS
DRACO
URSA MAJOR
Vega
LYRA
SAGITTA
HERCULES
ECLIPTIC
100°
110°
120°
130°
Procyon
Altair
VULPECULA
BOOTES
CANES VENATICI
LEO MINOR
LEO
CANCER
AQUILA
WEST
NORTH
EAST

11S

September 6 at 3^h
October 6 at 1^h
November 6 at 23^h
December 6 at 21^h
January 6 at 19^h

September 21 at 2^h
October 21 at midnight
November 21 at 22^h
December 21 at 20^h
January 21 at 18^h

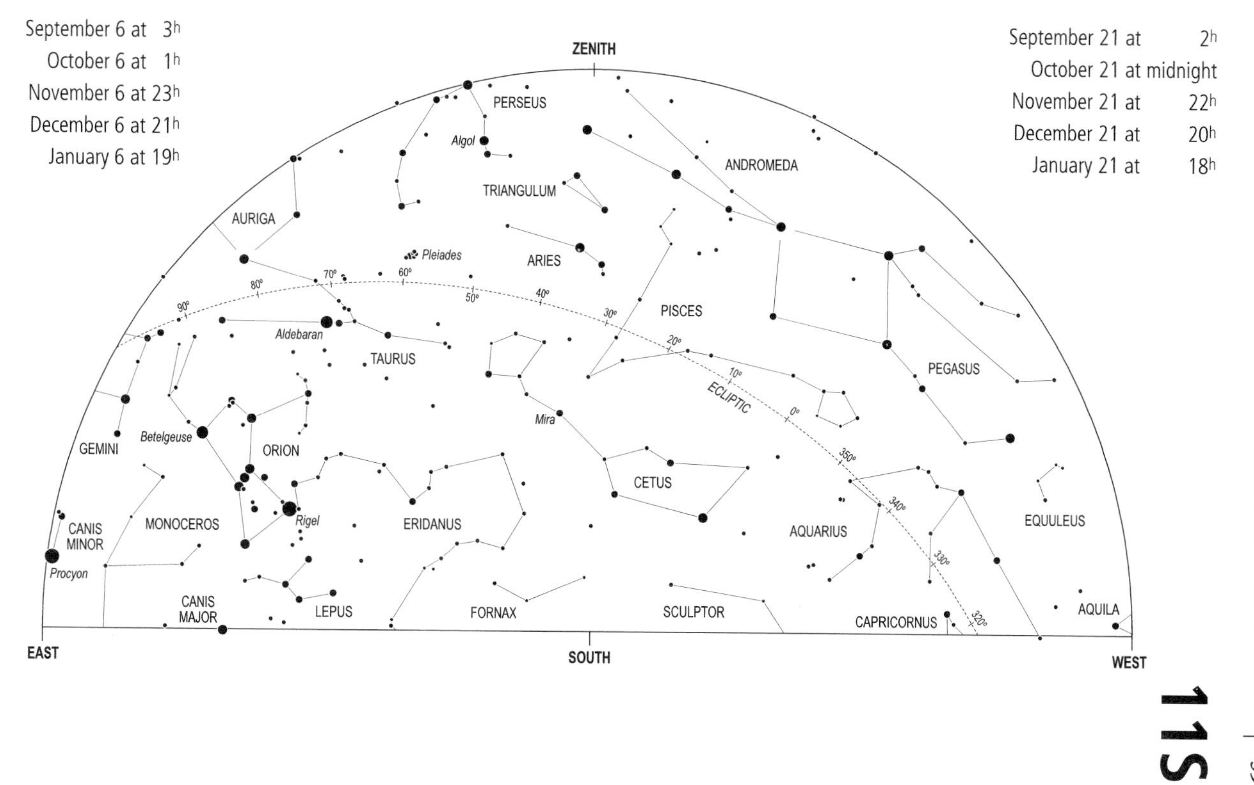

12N

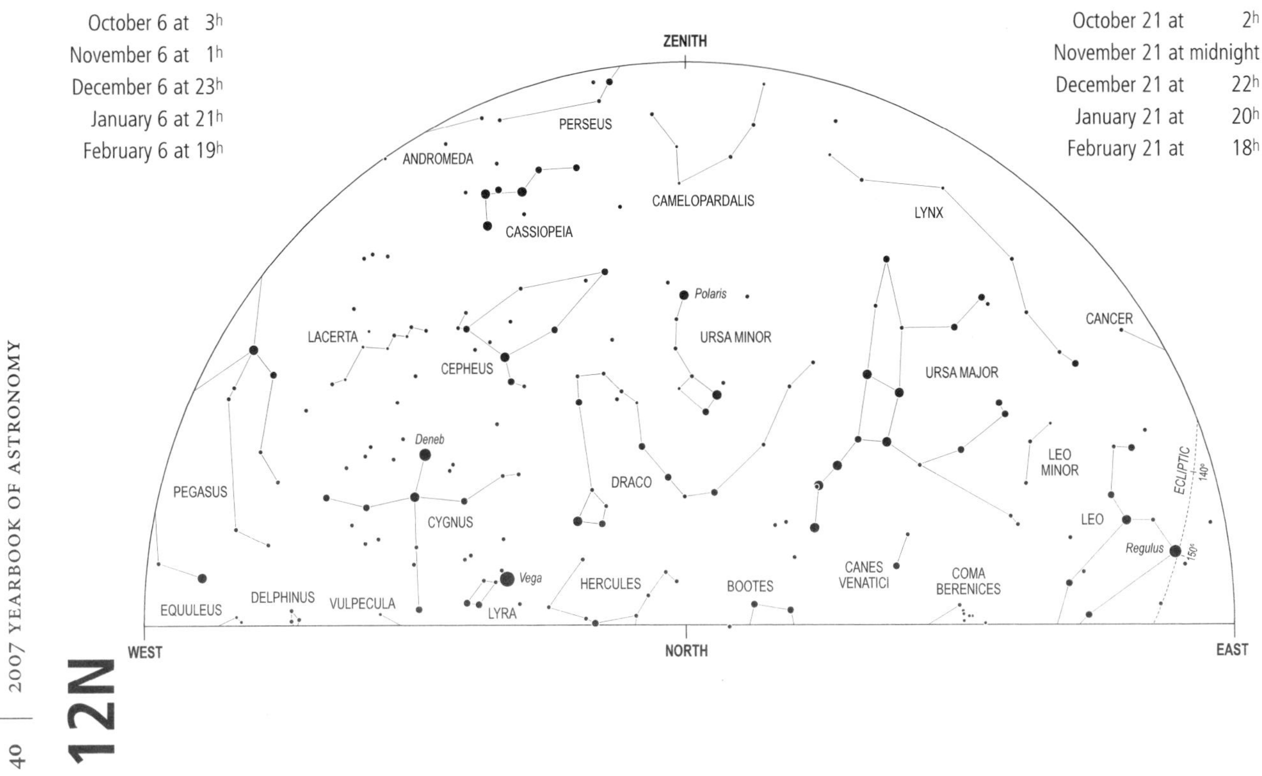
October 6 at 3h
November 6 at 1h
December 6 at 23h
January 6 at 21h
February 6 at 19h
October 21 at 2h
November 21 at midnight
December 21 at 22h
January 21 at 20h
February 21 at 18h
ZENITH
PERSEUS
ANDROMEDA
CAMELOPARDALIS
LYNX
CASSIOPEIA
Polaris
LACERTA
URSA MINOR
CANCER
CEPHEUS
URSA MAJOR
Deneb
LEO MINOR
DRACO
PEGASUS
CYGNUS
ECLIPTIC
140°
LEO
Regulus
150°
CANES VENATICI
COMA BERENICES
Vega
HERCULES
BOOTES
DELPHINUS
VULPECULA
EQUULEUS
LYRA
WEST
NORTH
EAST

12S

October 6 at 3h
November 6 at 1h
December 6 at 23h
January 6 at 21h
February 6 at 19h

October 21 at 2h
November 21 at midnight
December 21 at 22h
January 21 at 20h
February 21 at 18h

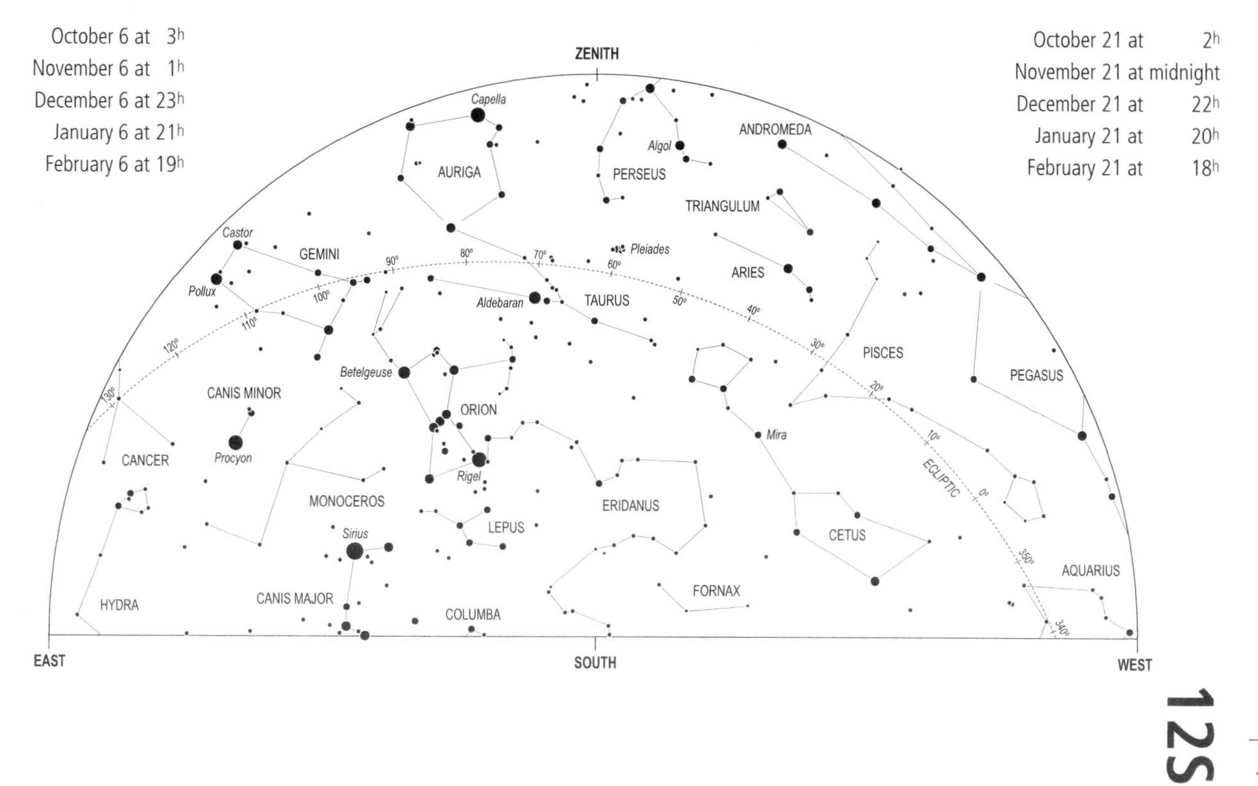

Southern Star Charts

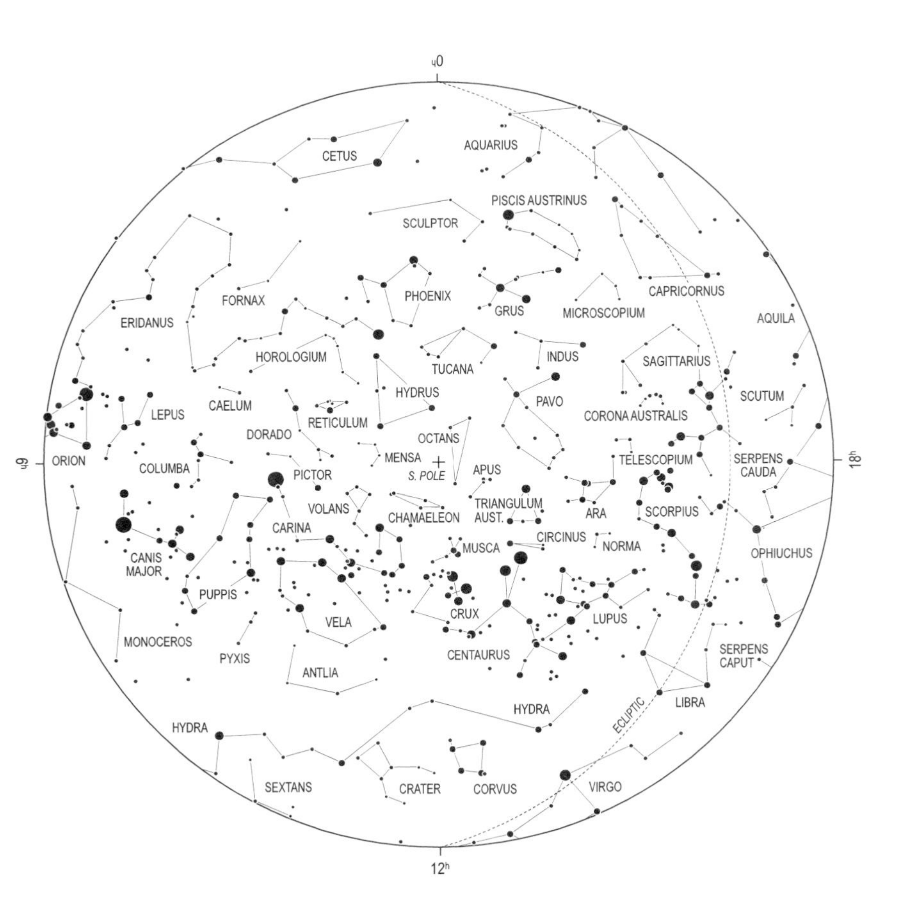

Southern Hemisphere

Note that the markers at 0h, 6h, 12h and 18h indicate hours of Right Ascension.

1N

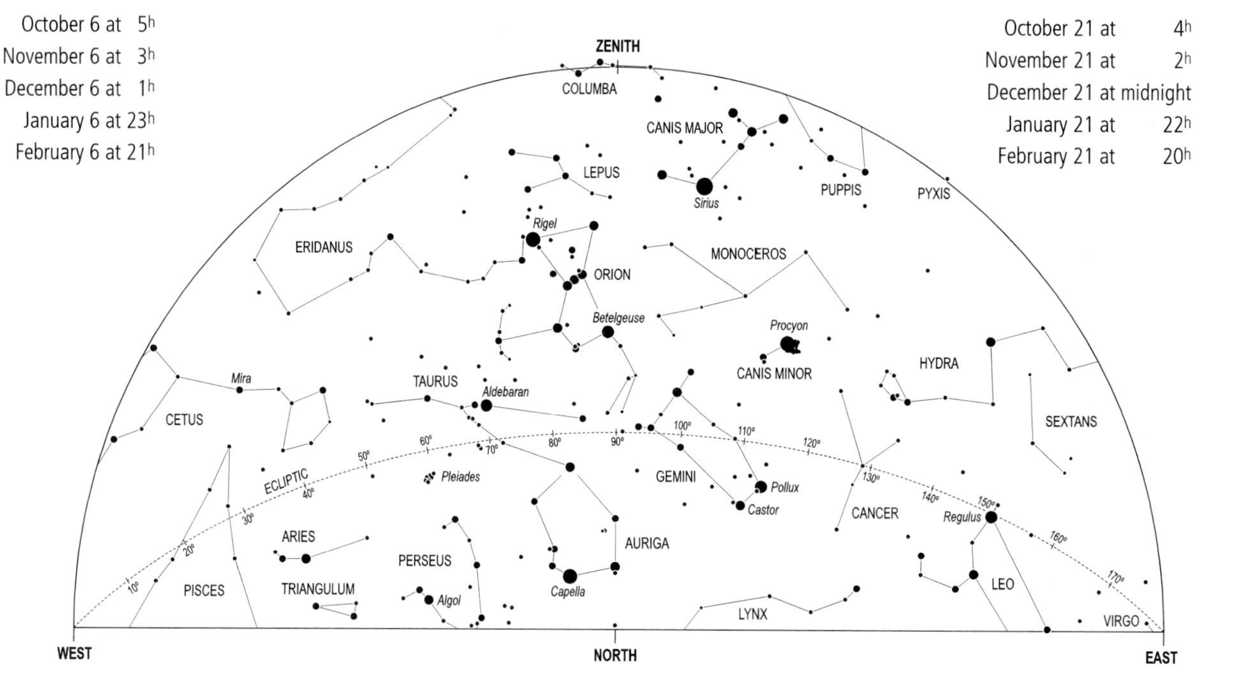
October 6 at 5h
November 6 at 3h
December 6 at 1h
January 6 at 23h
February 6 at 21h
October 21 at 4h
November 21 at 2h
December 21 at midnight
January 21 at 22h
February 21 at 20h
ZENITH
COLUMBA
CANIS MAJOR
LEPUS
Sirius
PUPPIS
PYXIS
ERIDANUS
Rigel
ORION
MONOCEROS
Betelgeuse
Procyon
CANIS MINOR
HYDRA
Mira
CETUS
TAURUS
Aldebaran
SEXTANS
ECLIPTIC
Pleiades
GEMINI
Pollux
Castor
CANCER
Regulus
ARIES
PERSEUS
AURIGA
PISCES
TRIANGULUM
Algol
Capella
LEO
LYNX
VIRGO
WEST
NORTH
EAST

1S

October 6 at 5h
November 6 at 3h
December 6 at 1h
January 6 at 23h
February 6 at 21h

October 21 at 4h
November 21 at 2h
December 21 at midnight
January 21 at 22h
February 21 at 20h

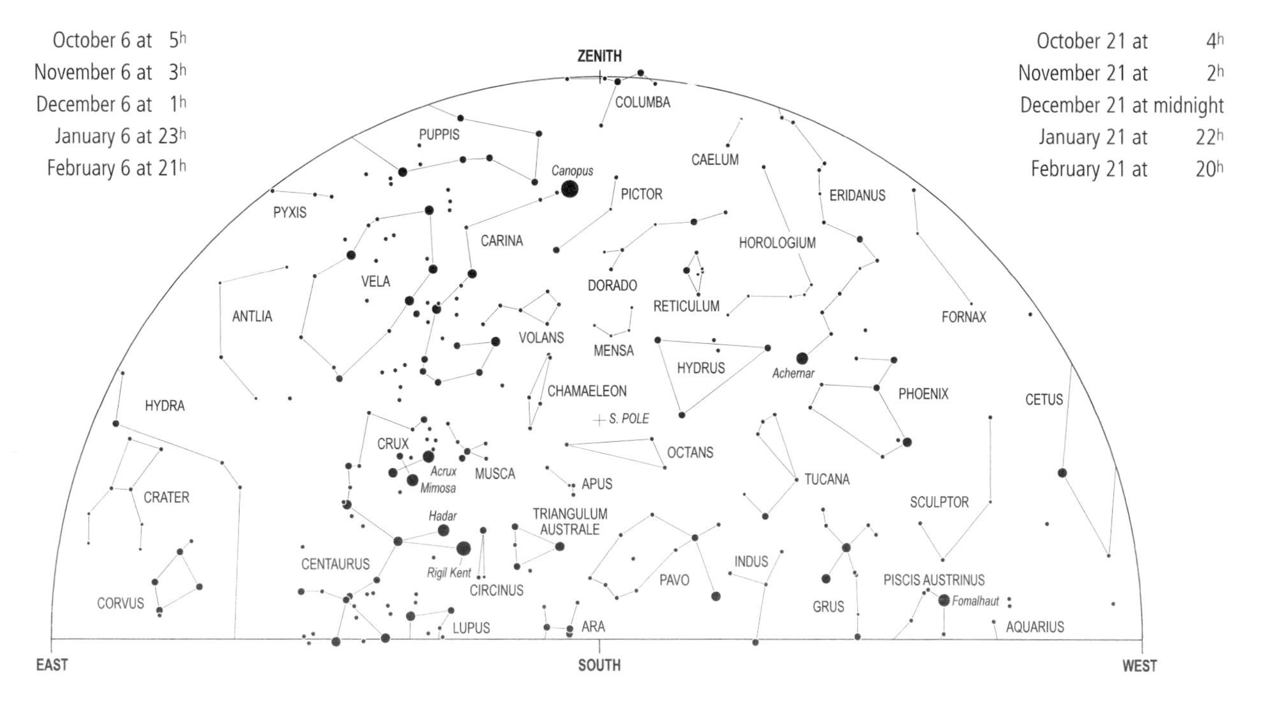

2N

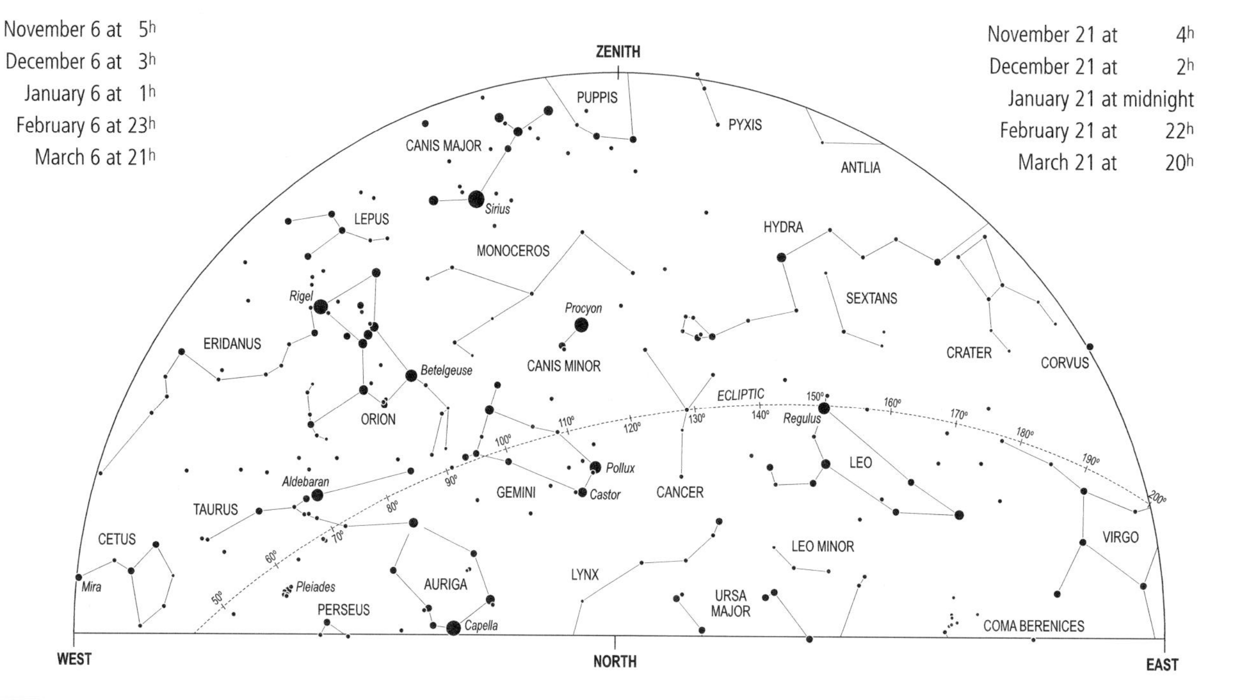
November 6 at 5h
December 6 at 3h
January 6 at 1h
February 6 at 23h
March 6 at 21h
November 21 at 4h
December 21 at 2h
January 21 at midnight
February 21 at 22h
March 21 at 20h
ZENITH
WEST
NORTH
EAST
PUPPIS
PYXIS
CANIS MAJOR
ANTLIA
Sirius
LEPUS
HYDRA
MONOCEROS
SEXTANS
Rigel
Procyon
ERIDANUS
CRATER
CORVUS
Betelgeuse
CANIS MINOR
ECLIPTIC
ORION
Regulus
Pollux
LEO
Aldebaran
GEMINI
Castor
CANCER
TAURUS
CETUS
LEO MINOR
VIRGO
LYNX
Mira
Pleiades
AURIGA
URSA MAJOR
PERSEUS
Capella
COMA BERENICES
50°
60°
70°
80°
90°
100°
110°
120°
130°
140°
150°
160°
170°
180°
190°
200°

2S

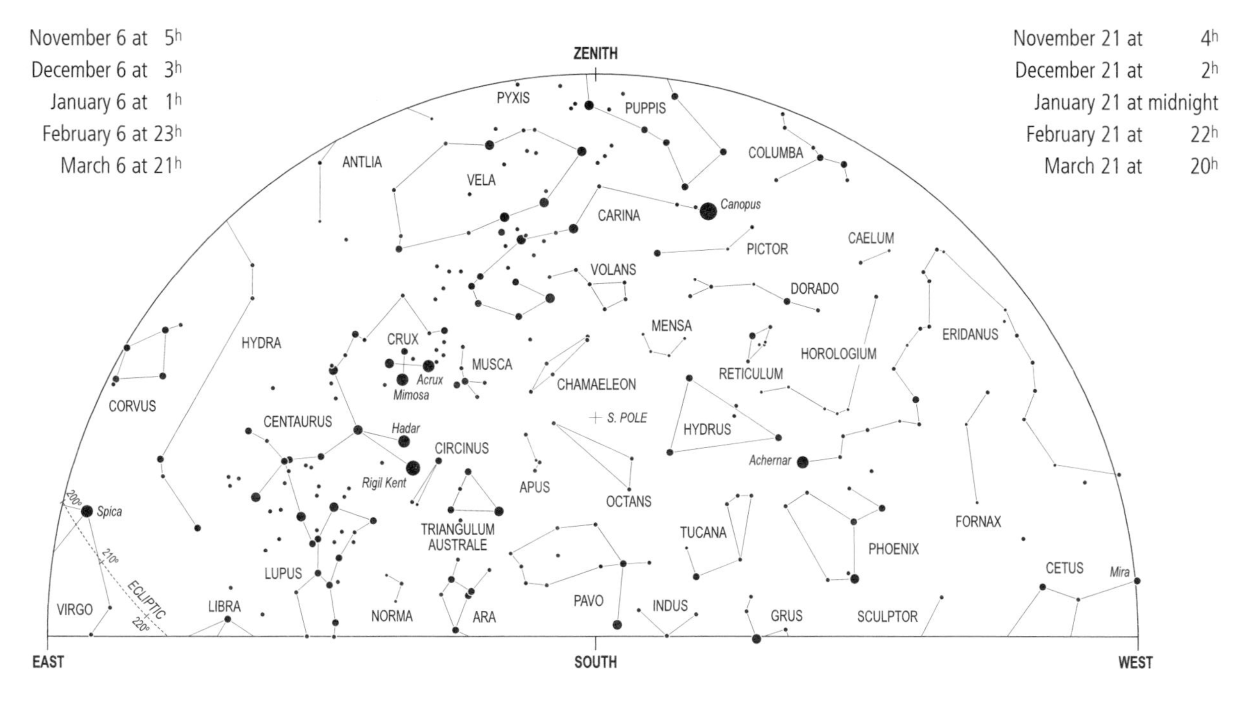
November 6 at 5h
December 6 at 3h
January 6 at 1h
February 6 at 23h
March 6 at 21h
November 21 at 4h
December 21 at 2h
January 21 at midnight
February 21 at 22h
March 21 at 20h
ZENITH
PYXIS
PUPPIS
COLUMBA
ANTLIA
VELA
Canopus
CARINA
CAELUM
PICTOR
VOLANS
DORADO
HYDRA
CRUX
MUSCA
MENSA
RETICULUM
HOROLOGIUM
ERIDANUS
Acrux
Mimosa
CHAMAELEON
CORVUS
CENTAURUS
S. POLE
HYDRUS
Hadar
CIRCINUS
Achernar
Rigil Kent
APUS
OCTANS
Spica
TRIANGULUM AUSTRALE
TUCANA
PHOENIX
FORNAX
200°
210°
LUPUS
CETUS
Mira
ECLIPTIC
220°
VIRGO
LIBRA
NORMA
ARA
PAVO
INDUS
GRUS
SCULPTOR
EAST
SOUTH
WEST

3N

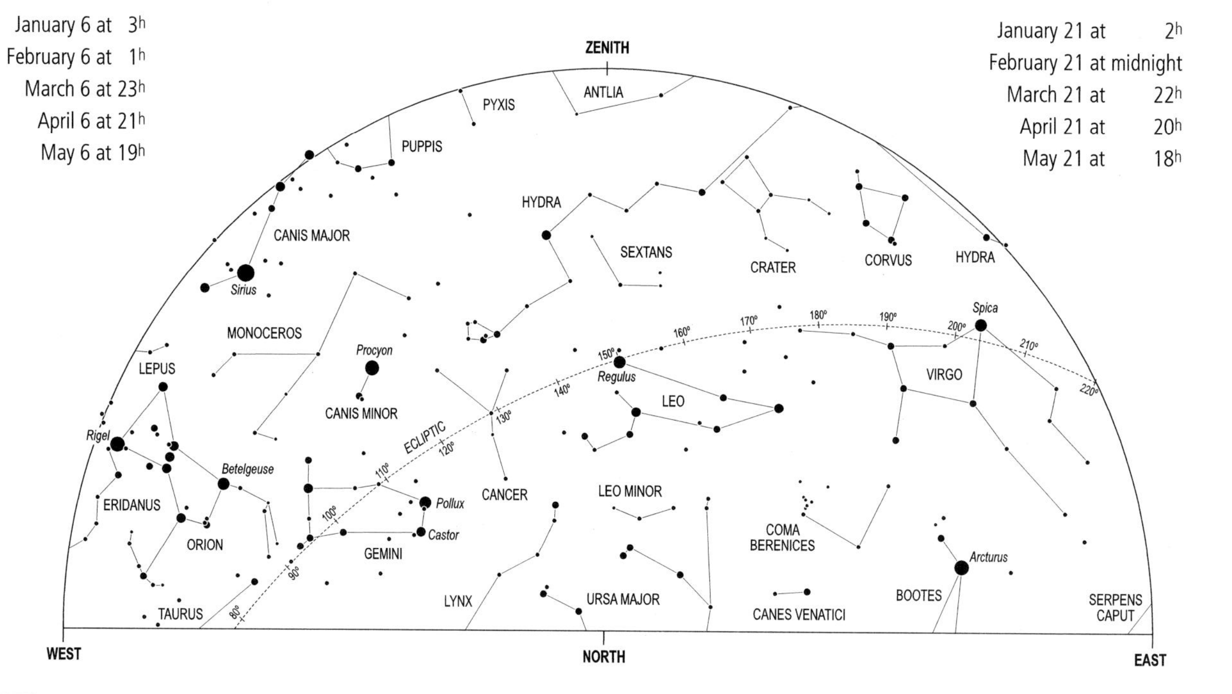
January 6 at 3h
February 6 at 1h
March 6 at 23h
April 6 at 21h
May 6 at 19h
January 21 at 2h
February 21 at midnight
March 21 at 22h
April 21 at 20h
May 21 at 18h
ZENITH
ANTLIA
PYXIS
PUPPIS
HYDRA
CANIS MAJOR
Sirius
SEXTANS
CRATER
CORVUS
HYDRA
MONOCEROS
Procyon
CANIS MINOR
LEPUS
Rigel
ERIDANUS
ORION
Betelgeuse
TAURUS
ECLIPTIC
GEMINI
Pollux
Castor
CANCER
Regulus
LEO
LEO MINOR
LYNX
URSA MAJOR
COMA
BERENICES
CANES VENATICI
Spica
VIRGO
Arcturus
BOOTES
SERPENS
CAPUT
WEST
NORTH
EAST
80°
90°
100°
110°
120°
130°
140°
150°
160°
170°
180°
190°
200°
210°
220°

3S

January 6 at 3h
February 6 at 1h
March 6 at 23h
April 6 at 21h
May 6 at 19h

January 21 at 2h
February 21 at midnight
March 21 at 22h
April 21 at 20h
May 21 at 18h

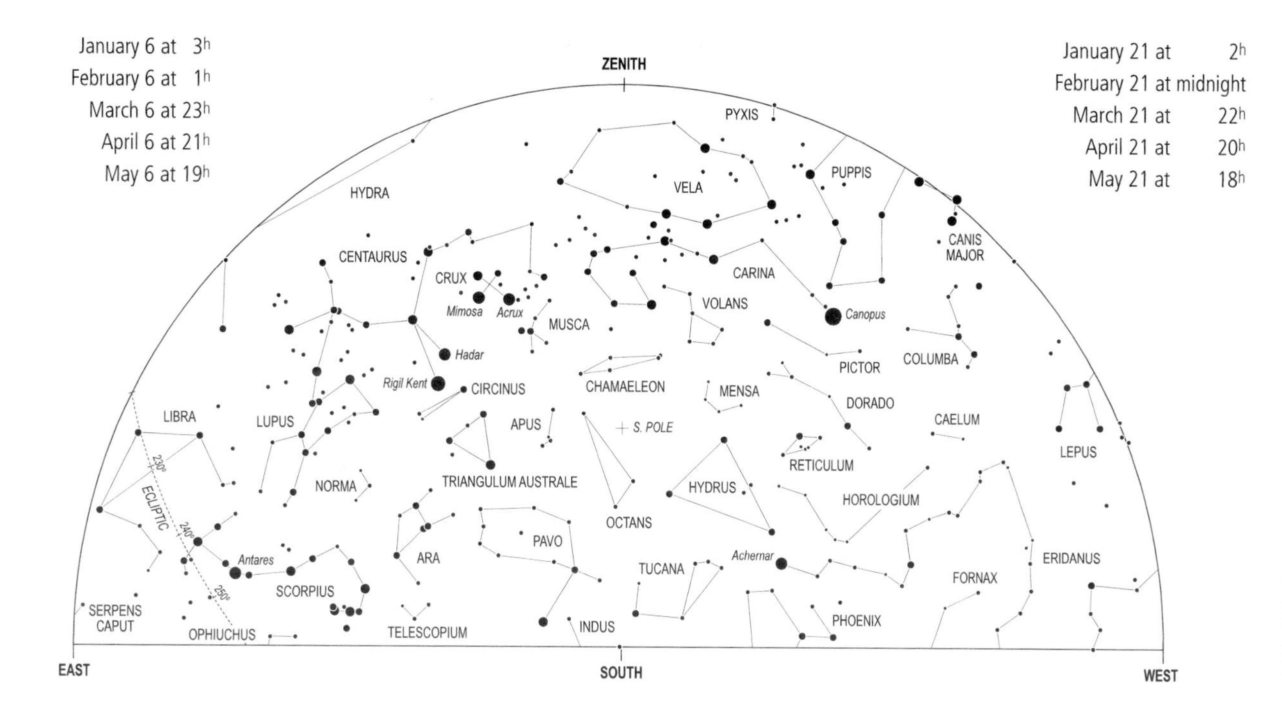

4N

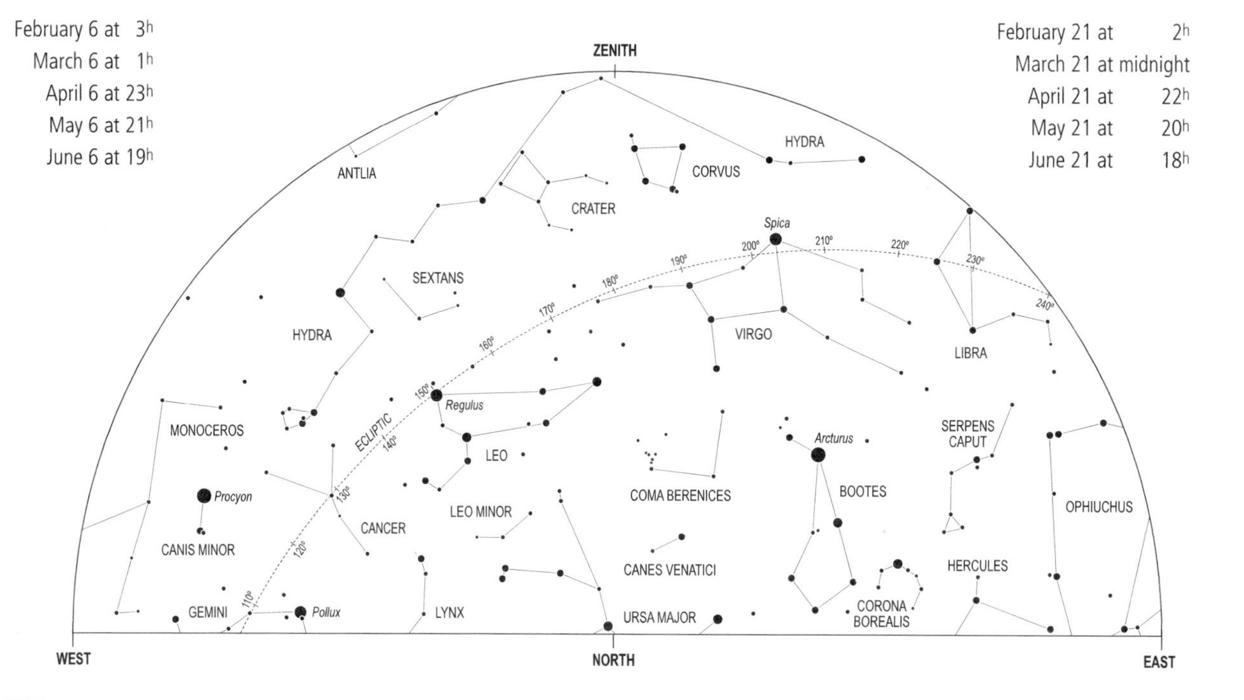
February 6 at 3h
March 6 at 1h
April 6 at 23h
May 6 at 21h
June 6 at 19h
February 21 at 2h
March 21 at midnight
April 21 at 22h
May 21 at 20h
June 21 at 18h
ZENITH
WEST
NORTH
EAST
ECLIPTIC
110°
120°
130°
140°
150°
160°
170°
180°
190°
200°
210°
220°
230°
240°
ANTLIA
CRATER
CORVUS
HYDRA
SEXTANS
Spica
HYDRA
VIRGO
LIBRA
MONOCEROS
Regulus
LEO
Arcturus
SERPENS
CAPUT
Procyon
CANIS MINOR
CANCER
LEO MINOR
COMA BERENICES
BOOTES
OPHIUCHUS
CANES VENATICI
HERCULES
GEMINI
Pollux
LYNX
URSA MAJOR
CORONA
BOREALIS

4S

February 6 at 3^h
March 6 at 1^h
April 6 at 23^h
May 6 at 21^h
June 6 at 19^h

February 21 at 2^h
March 21 at midnight
April 21 at 22^h
May 21 at 20^h
June 21 at 18^h

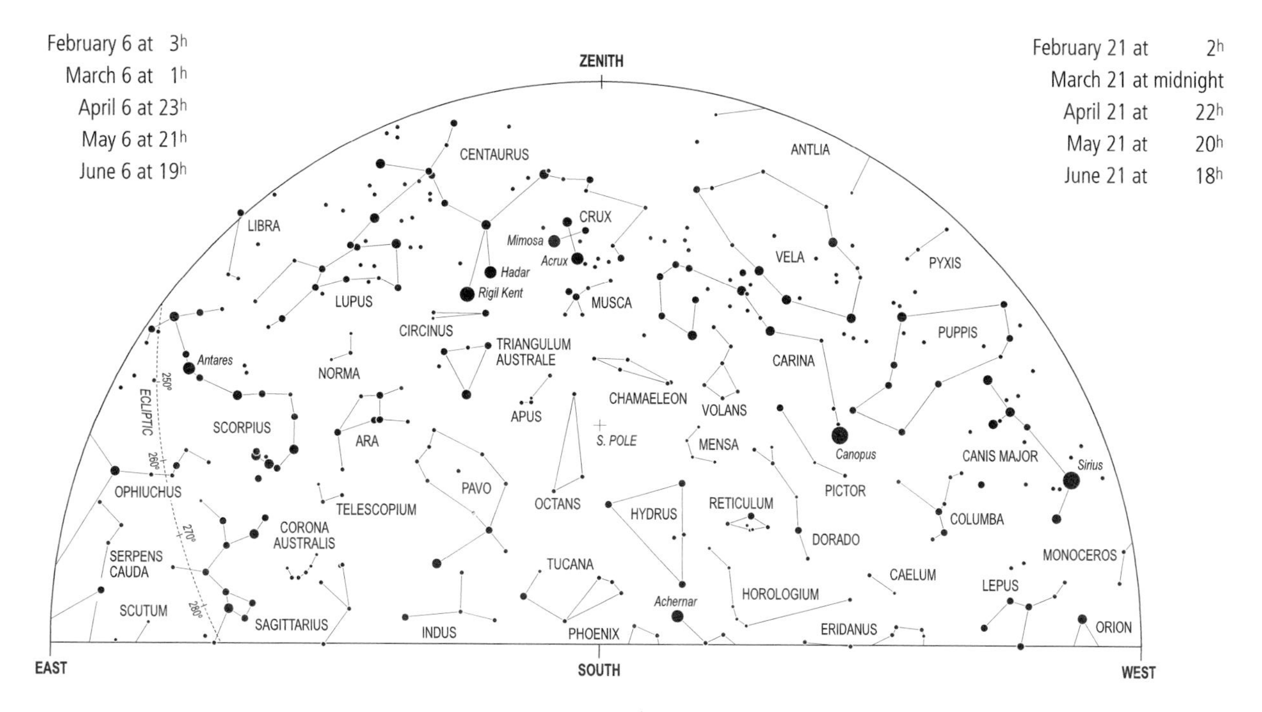

5N

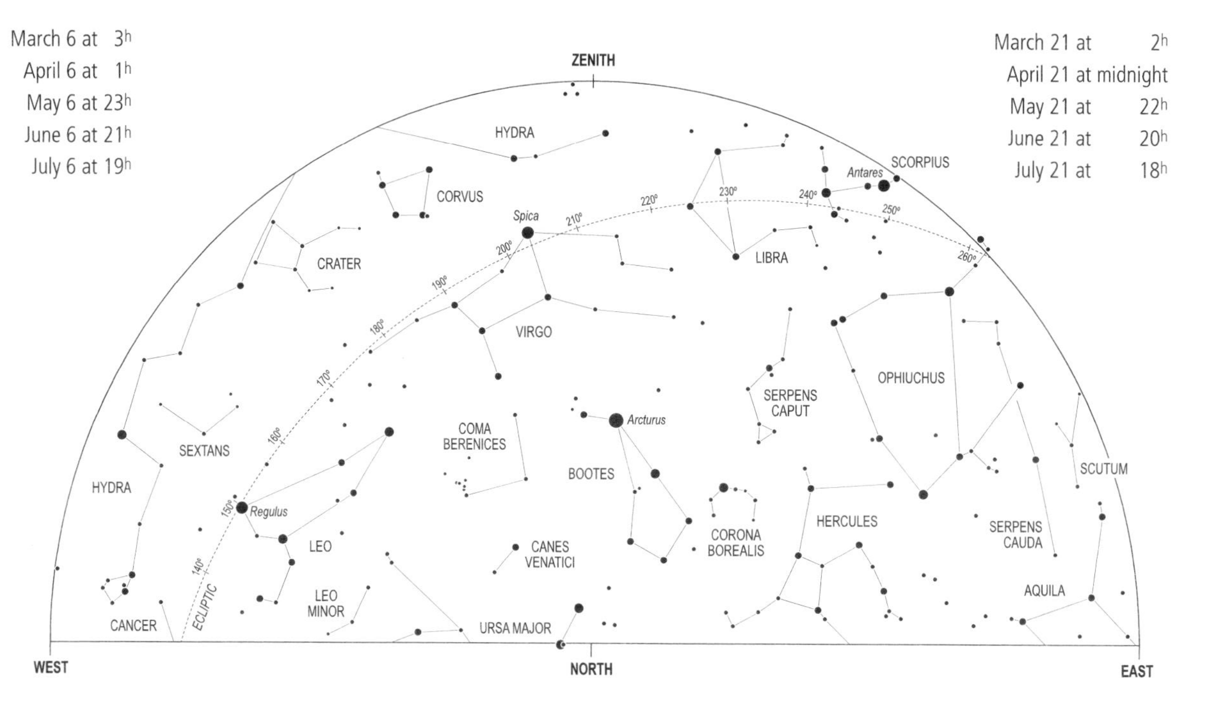
March 6 at 3h
April 6 at 1h
May 6 at 23h
June 6 at 21h
July 6 at 19h
March 21 at 2h
April 21 at midnight
May 21 at 22h
June 21 at 20h
July 21 at 18h
ZENITH
WEST
NORTH
EAST
ECLIPTIC
140°
150°
160°
170°
180°
190°
200°
210°
220°
230°
240°
250°
260°
HYDRA
CORVUS
Spica
CRATER
VIRGO
LIBRA
Antares
SCORPIUS
SEXTANS
HYDRA
Regulus
LEO
LEO MINOR
CANCER
COMA BERENICES
BOOTES
Arcturus
CANES VENATICI
URSA MAJOR
SERPENS CAPUT
CORONA BOREALIS
OPHIUCHUS
HERCULES
SCUTUM
SERPENS CAUDA
AQUILA

5S

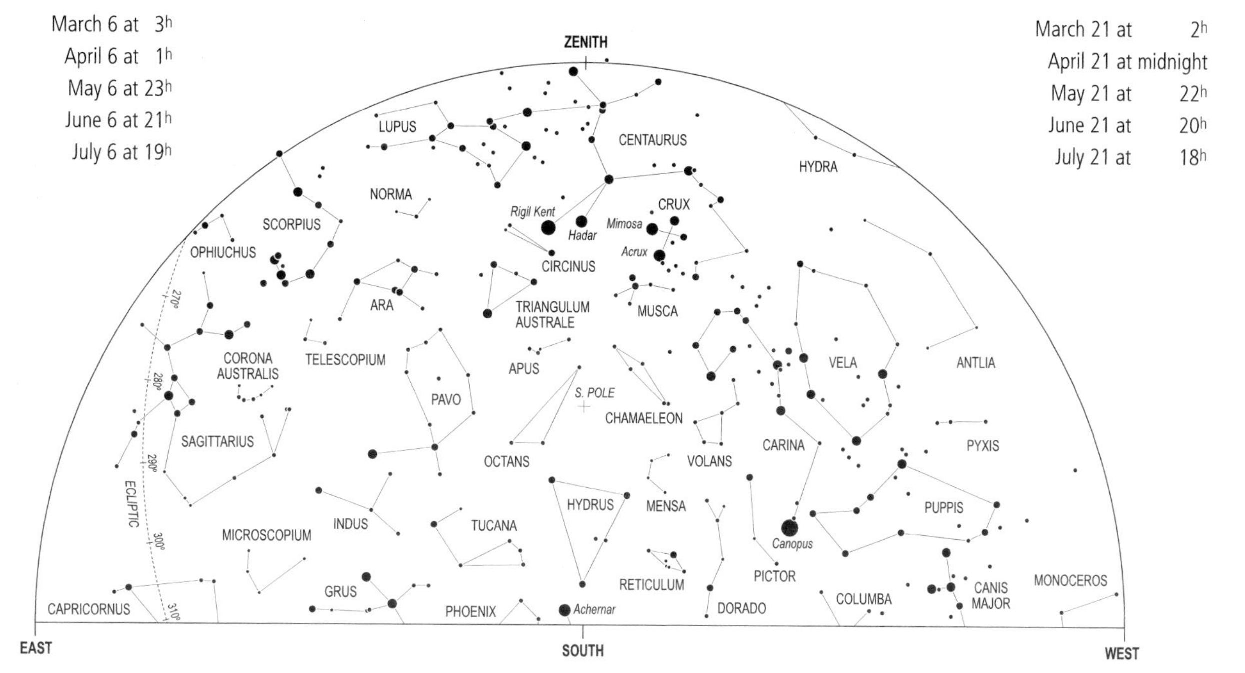
March 6 at 3h
April 6 at 1h
May 6 at 23h
June 6 at 21h
July 6 at 19h
March 21 at 2h
April 21 at midnight
May 21 at 22h
June 21 at 20h
July 21 at 18h
ZENITH
EAST
SOUTH
WEST
S. POLE
ECLIPTIC
270°
280°
290°
300°
310°
LUPUS
CENTAURUS
HYDRA
NORMA
Rigil Kent
Hadar
Mimosa
CRUX
Acrux
SCORPIUS
OPHIUCHUS
CIRCINUS
ARA
TRIANGULUM AUSTRALE
MUSCA
CORONA AUSTRALIS
TELESCOPIUM
APUS
VELA
ANTLIA
PAVO
CHAMAELEON
SAGITTARIUS
OCTANS
VOLANS
CARINA
PYXIS
HYDRUS
MENSA
PUPPIS
INDUS
TUCANA
MICROSCOPIUM
Canopus
RETICULUM
PICTOR
GRUS
CANIS MAJOR
MONOCEROS
COLUMBA
CAPRICORNUS
PHOENIX
Achernar
DORADO

6N

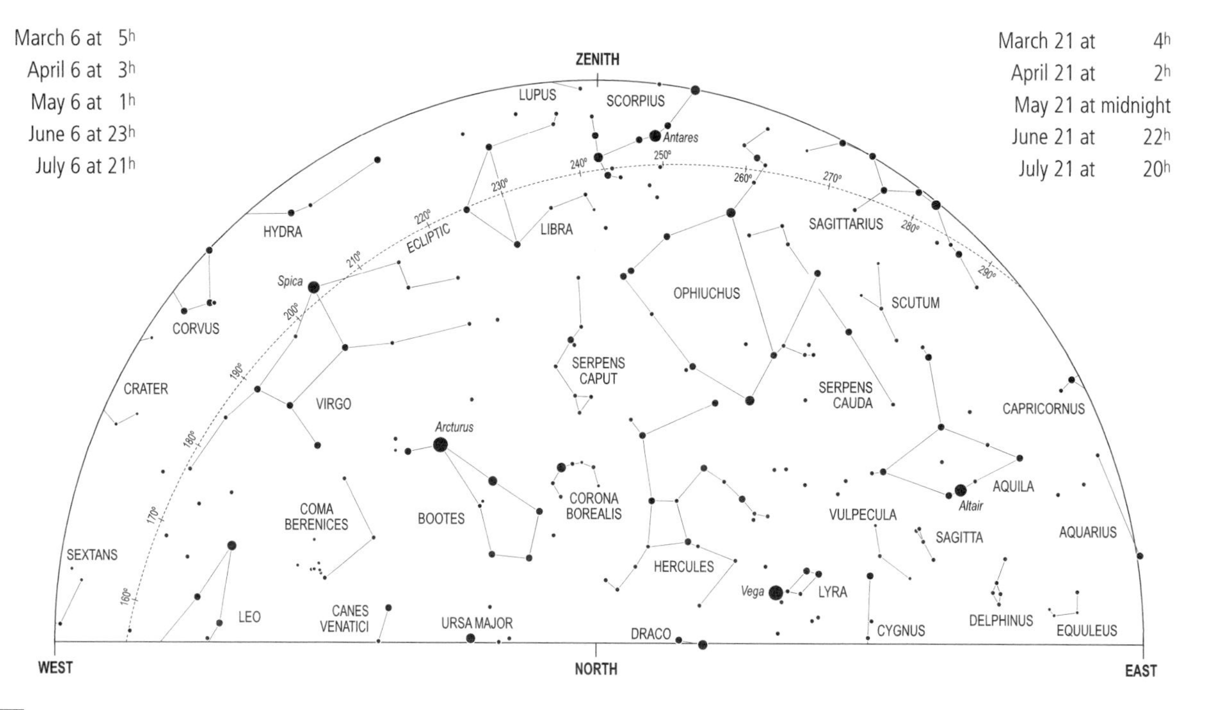
March 6 at 5h
April 6 at 3h
May 6 at 1h
June 6 at 23h
July 6 at 21h
March 21 at 4h
April 21 at 2h
May 21 at midnight
June 21 at 22h
July 21 at 20h
ZENITH
LUPUS
SCORPIUS
Antares
HYDRA
LIBRA
ECLIPTIC
SAGITTARIUS
Spica
CORVUS
OPHIUCHUS
SCUTUM
SERPENS CAPUT
CRATER
VIRGO
SERPENS CAUDA
CAPRICORNUS
Arcturus
AQUILA
Altair
COMA BERENICES
BOOTES
CORONA BOREALIS
VULPECULA
AQUARIUS
SAGITTA
SEXTANS
HERCULES
Vega
LYRA
LEO
CANES VENATICI
URSA MAJOR
DRACO
CYGNUS
DELPHINUS
EQUULEUS
WEST
NORTH
EAST
160°
170°
180°
190°
200°
210°
220°
230°
240°
250°
260°
270°
280°
290°

6S

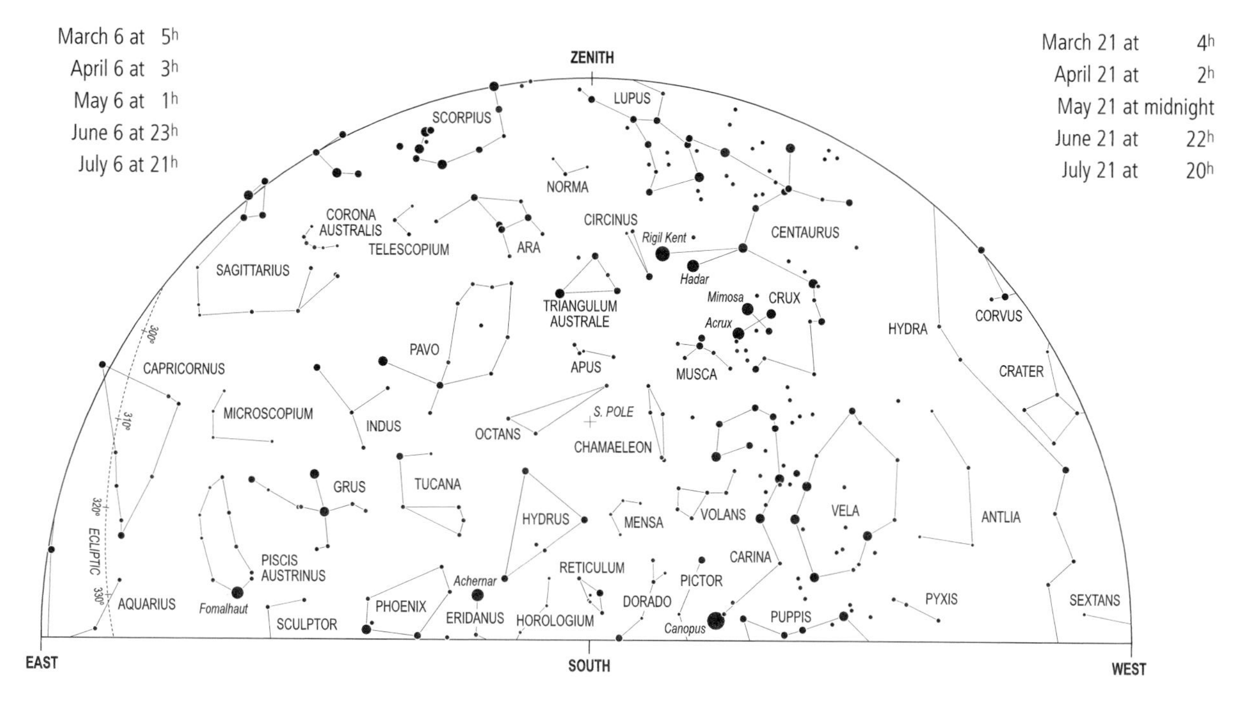
March 6 at 5h
April 6 at 3h
May 6 at 1h
June 6 at 23h
July 6 at 21h
March 21 at 4h
April 21 at 2h
May 21 at midnight
June 21 at 22h
July 21 at 20h
ZENITH
SCORPIUS
LUPUS
NORMA
CORONA AUSTRALIS
TELESCOPIUM
ARA
CIRCINUS
Rigil Kent
CENTAURUS
Hadar
SAGITTARIUS
Mimosa
CRUX
Acrux
TRIANGULUM AUSTRALE
PAVO
APUS
MUSCA
HYDRA
CORVUS
CRATER
CAPRICORNUS
300°
310°
320°
330°
ECLIPTIC
MICROSCOPIUM
INDUS
OCTANS
S. POLE
CHAMAELEON
GRUS
TUCANA
HYDRUS
MENSA
VOLANS
VELA
ANTLIA
PISCIS AUSTRINUS
RETICULUM
CARINA
PICTOR
Achernar
AQUARIUS
Fomalhaut
SCULPTOR
PHOENIX
ERIDANUS
HOROLOGIUM
DORADO
Canopus
PUPPIS
PYXIS
SEXTANS
EAST
SOUTH
WEST

7N

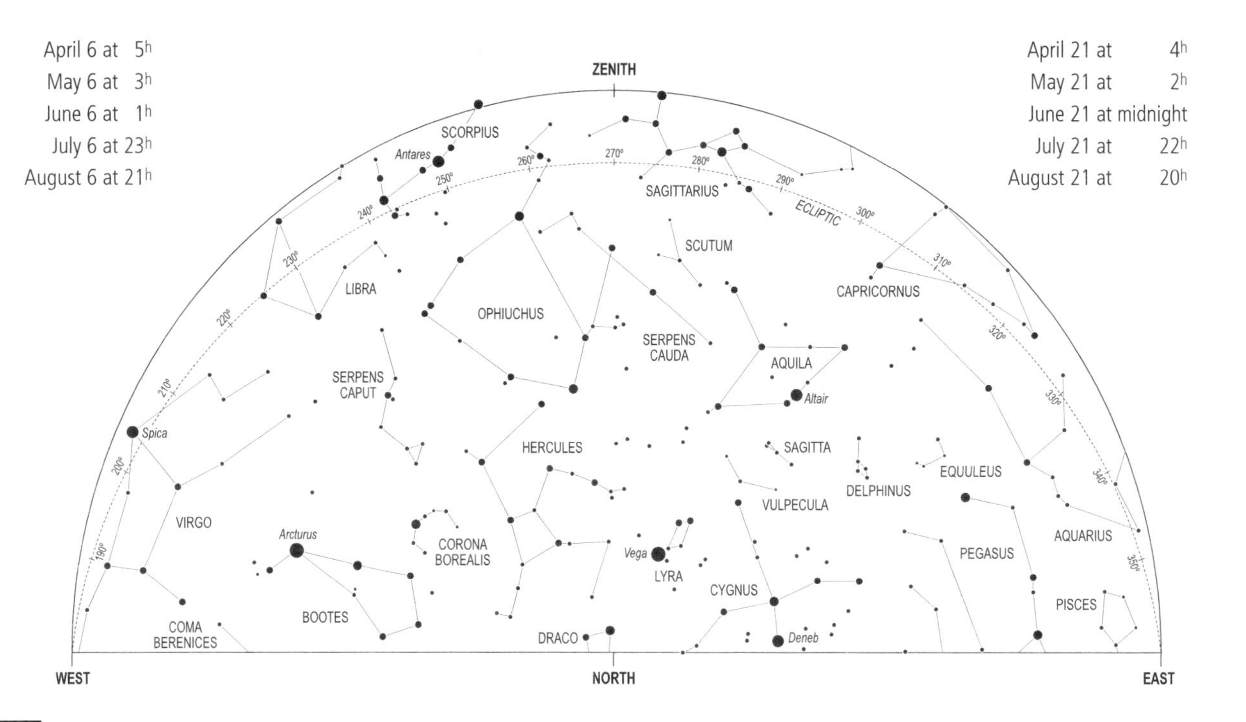
April 6 at 5h
May 6 at 3h
June 6 at 1h
July 6 at 23h
August 6 at 21h
April 21 at 4h
May 21 at 2h
June 21 at midnight
July 21 at 22h
August 21 at 20h
ZENITH
WEST
NORTH
EAST
ECLIPTIC
190°
200°
210°
220°
230°
240°
250°
260°
270°
280°
290°
300°
310°
320°
330°
340°
350°
SCORPIUS
Antares
SAGITTARIUS
SCUTUM
LIBRA
OPHIUCHUS
CAPRICORNUS
SERPENS CAUDA
AQUILA
Altair
SERPENS CAPUT
Spica
HERCULES
SAGITTA
EQUULEUS
DELPHINUS
VULPECULA
VIRGO
Arcturus
CORONA BOREALIS
Vega
LYRA
PEGASUS
AQUARIUS
CYGNUS
PISCES
COMA BERENICES
BOOTES
DRACO
Deneb

7S

April 6 at 5h
May 6 at 3h
June 6 at 1h
July 6 at 23h
August 6 at 21h

April 21 at 4h
May 21 at 2h
June 21 at midnight
July 21 at 22h
August 21 at 20h

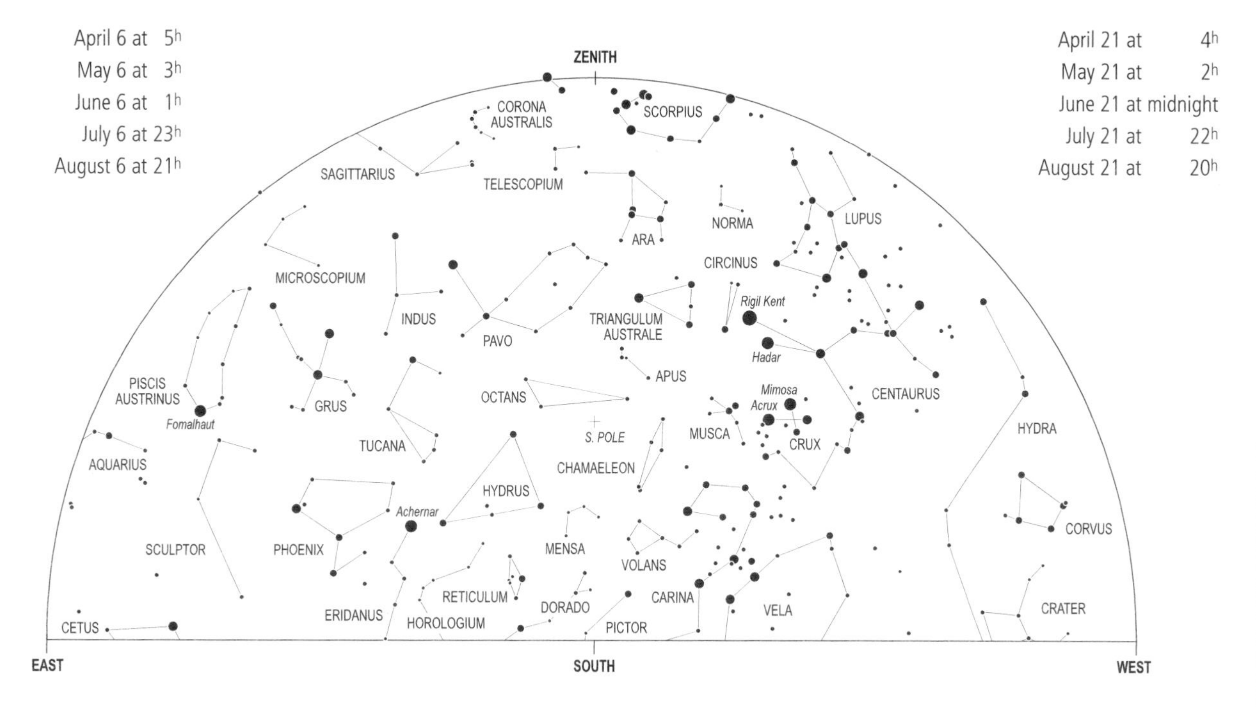

8N

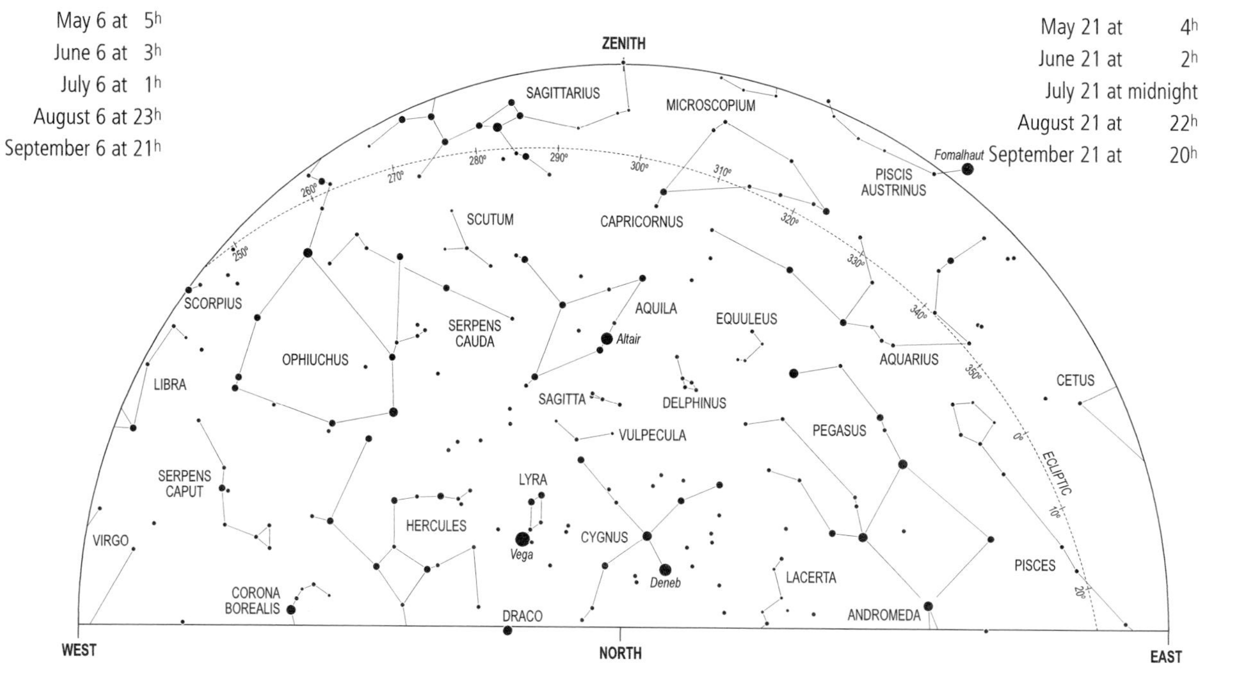
May 6 at 5h
June 6 at 3h
July 6 at 1h
August 6 at 23h
September 6 at 21h
May 21 at 4h
June 21 at 2h
July 21 at midnight
August 21 at 22h
September 21 at 20h
ZENITH
WEST
NORTH
EAST
ECLIPTIC
SAGITTARIUS
MICROSCOPIUM
PISCIS AUSTRINUS
Fomalhaut
SCUTUM
CAPRICORNUS
SCORPIUS
SERPENS CAUDA
AQUILA
Altair
EQUULEUS
OPHIUCHUS
AQUARIUS
LIBRA
SAGITTA
DELPHINUS
CETUS
VULPECULA
PEGASUS
SERPENS CAPUT
LYRA
HERCULES
Vega
CYGNUS
VIRGO
Deneb
LACERTA
PISCES
CORONA BOREALIS
DRACO
ANDROMEDA
250°
260°
270°
280°
290°
300°
310°
320°
330°
340°
350°
0°
10°
20°

8S

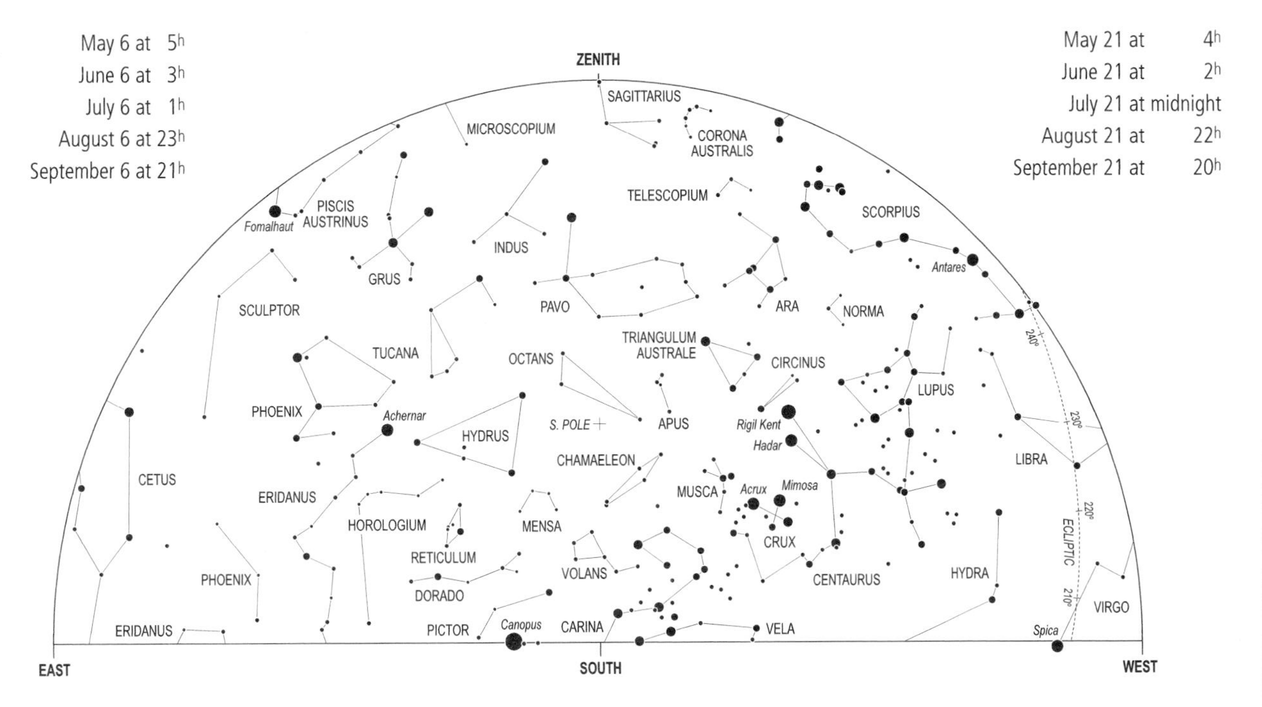
May 6 at 5h
June 6 at 3h
July 6 at 1h
August 6 at 23h
September 6 at 21h
May 21 at 4h
June 21 at 2h
July 21 at midnight
August 21 at 22h
September 21 at 20h
ZENITH
EAST
SOUTH
WEST
SAGITTARIUS
MICROSCOPIUM
CORONA AUSTRALIS
TELESCOPIUM
SCORPIUS
Antares
PISCIS AUSTRINUS
Fomalhaut
INDUS
GRUS
PAVO
ARA
NORMA
SCULPTOR
TUCANA
OCTANS
TRIANGULUM AUSTRALE
CIRCINUS
LUPUS
240°
PHOENIX
Achernar
HYDRUS
S. POLE
APUS
Rigil Kent
Hadar
230°
LIBRA
CHAMAELEON
CETUS
ERIDANUS
MUSCA
Acrux
Mimosa
HOROLOGIUM
MENSA
CRUX
220°
ECLIPTIC
RETICULUM
VOLANS
CENTAURUS
HYDRA
210°
PHOENIX
DORADO
VIRGO
ERIDANUS
PICTOR
Canopus
CARINA
VELA
Spica

9N

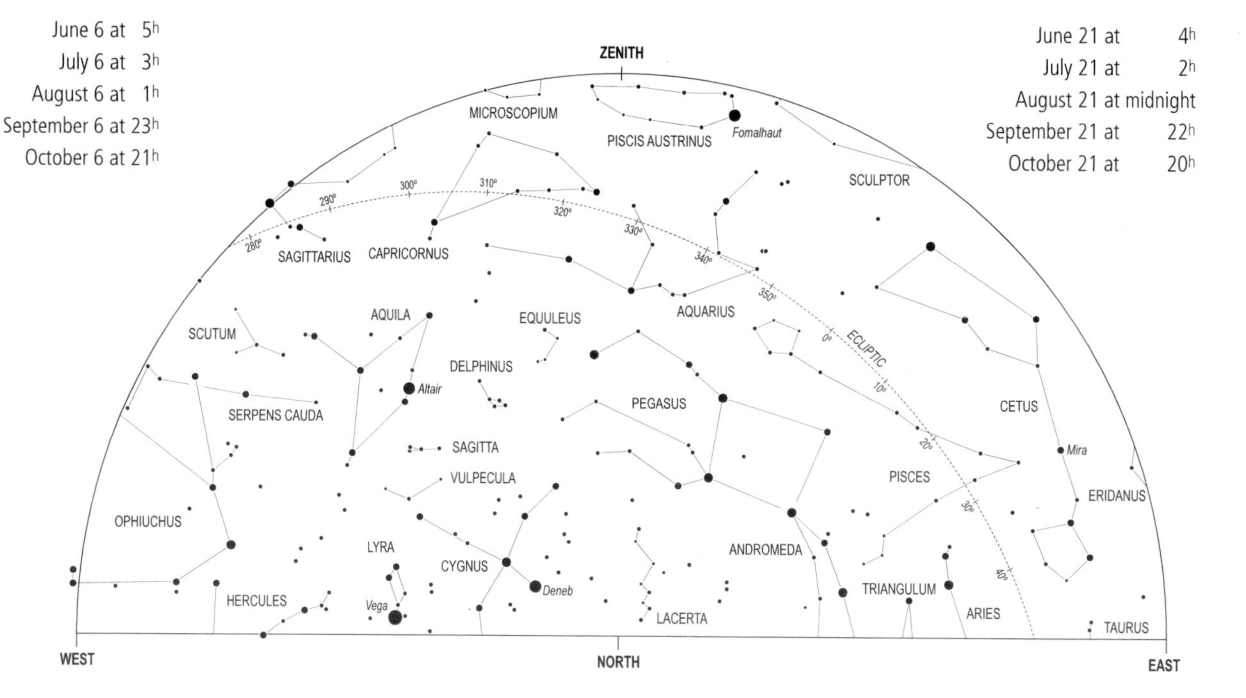
June 6 at 5h
July 6 at 3h
August 6 at 1h
September 6 at 23h
October 6 at 21h
June 21 at 4h
July 21 at 2h
August 21 at midnight
September 21 at 22h
October 21 at 20h
ZENITH
MICROSCOPIUM
PISCIS AUSTRINUS
Fomalhaut
SCULPTOR
SAGITTARIUS
CAPRICORNUS
AQUILA
SCUTUM
EQUULEUS
AQUARIUS
DELPHINUS
Altair
SERPENS CAUDA
PEGASUS
SAGITTA
VULPECULA
OPHIUCHUS
LYRA
CYGNUS
Deneb
Vega
HERCULES
LACERTA
ANDROMEDA
TRIANGULUM
ARIES
PISCES
CETUS
Mira
ERIDANUS
TAURUS
ECLIPTIC
280°
290°
300°
310°
320°
330°
340°
350°
0°
10°
20°
30°
40°
WEST
NORTH
EAST

9S

June 6 at 5h
July 6 at 3h
August 6 at 1h
September 6 at 23h
October 6 at 21h

June 21 at 4h
July 21 at 2h
August 21 at midnight
September 21 at 22h
October 21 at 20h

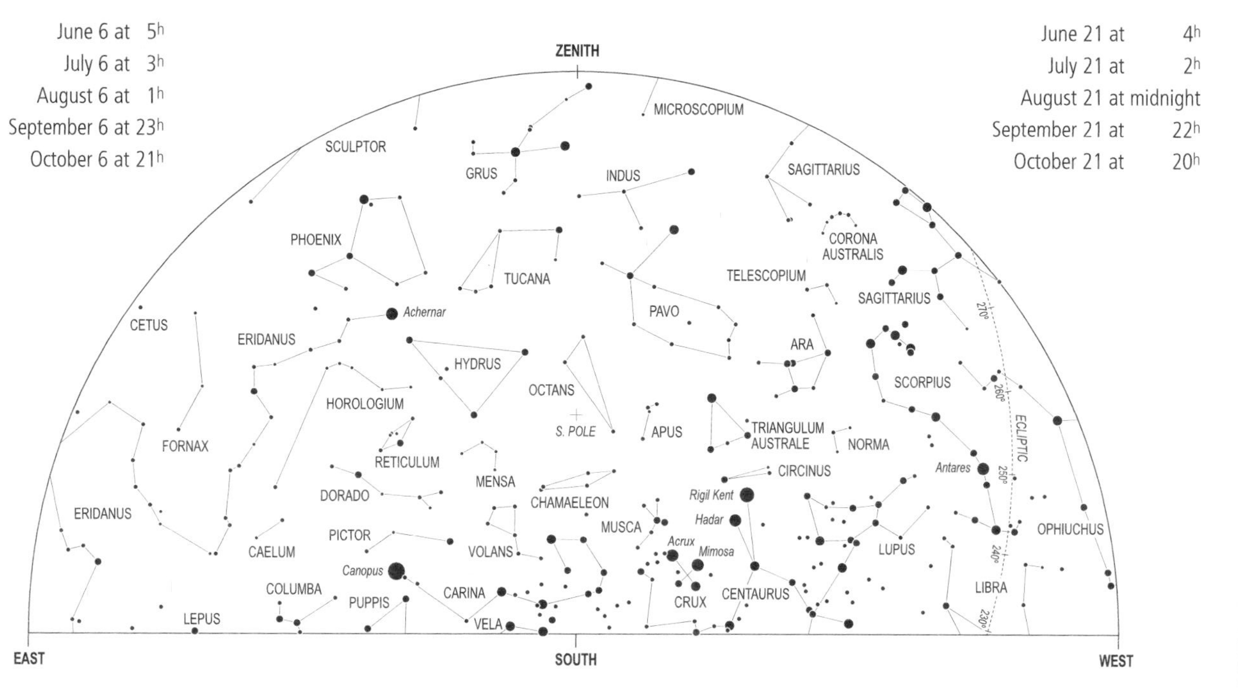

10N

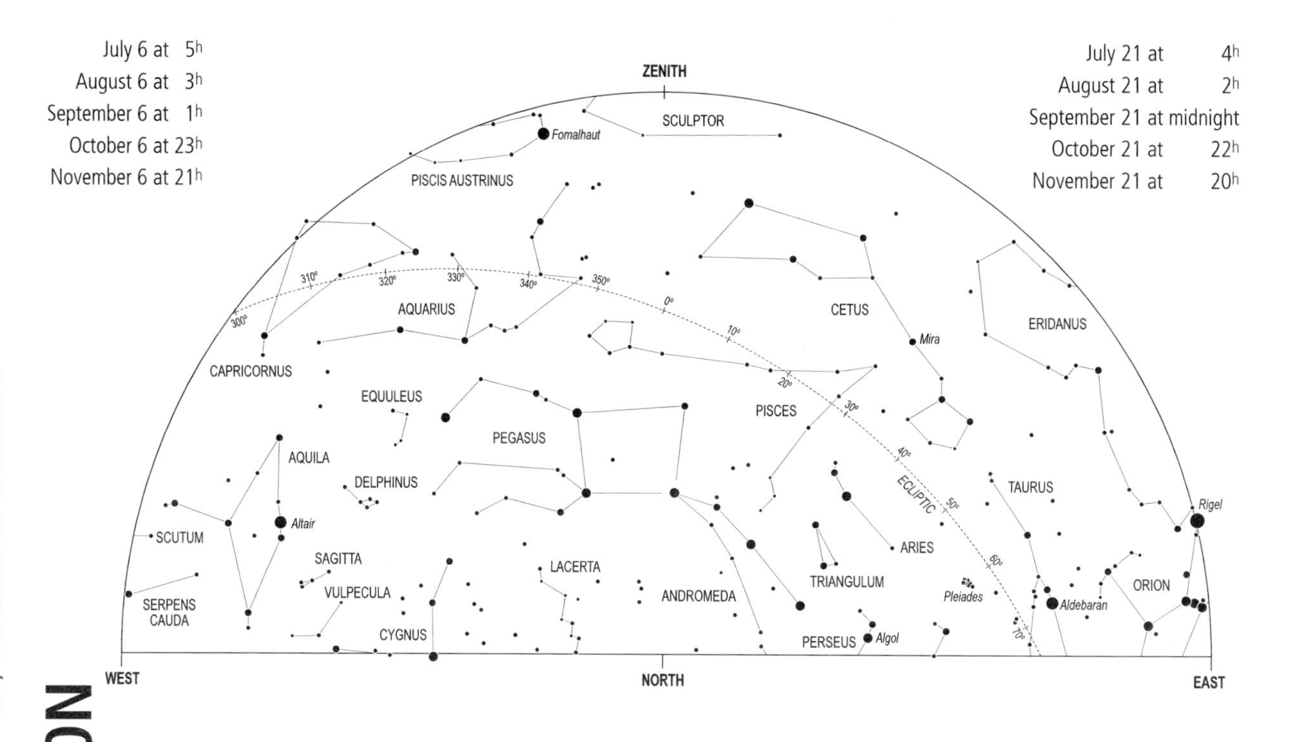

July 6 at 5h
August 6 at 3h
September 6 at 1h
October 6 at 23h
November 6 at 21h
July 21 at 4h
August 21 at 2h
September 21 at midnight
October 21 at 22h
November 21 at 20h
ZENITH
WEST
NORTH
EAST
SCULPTOR
Fomalhaut
PISCIS AUSTRINUS
CETUS
Mira
ERIDANUS
AQUARIUS
CAPRICORNUS
EQUULEUS
PEGASUS
PISCES
AQUILA
DELPHINUS
Altair
SCUTUM
SAGITTA
VULPECULA
SERPENS CAUDA
CYGNUS
LACERTA
ANDROMEDA
TRIANGULUM
ARIES
ECLIPTIC
TAURUS
Rigel
ORION
Pleiades
Aldebaran
PERSEUS
Algol
300°
310°
320°
330°
340°
350°
0°
10°
20°
30°
40°
50°
60°
70°

10S

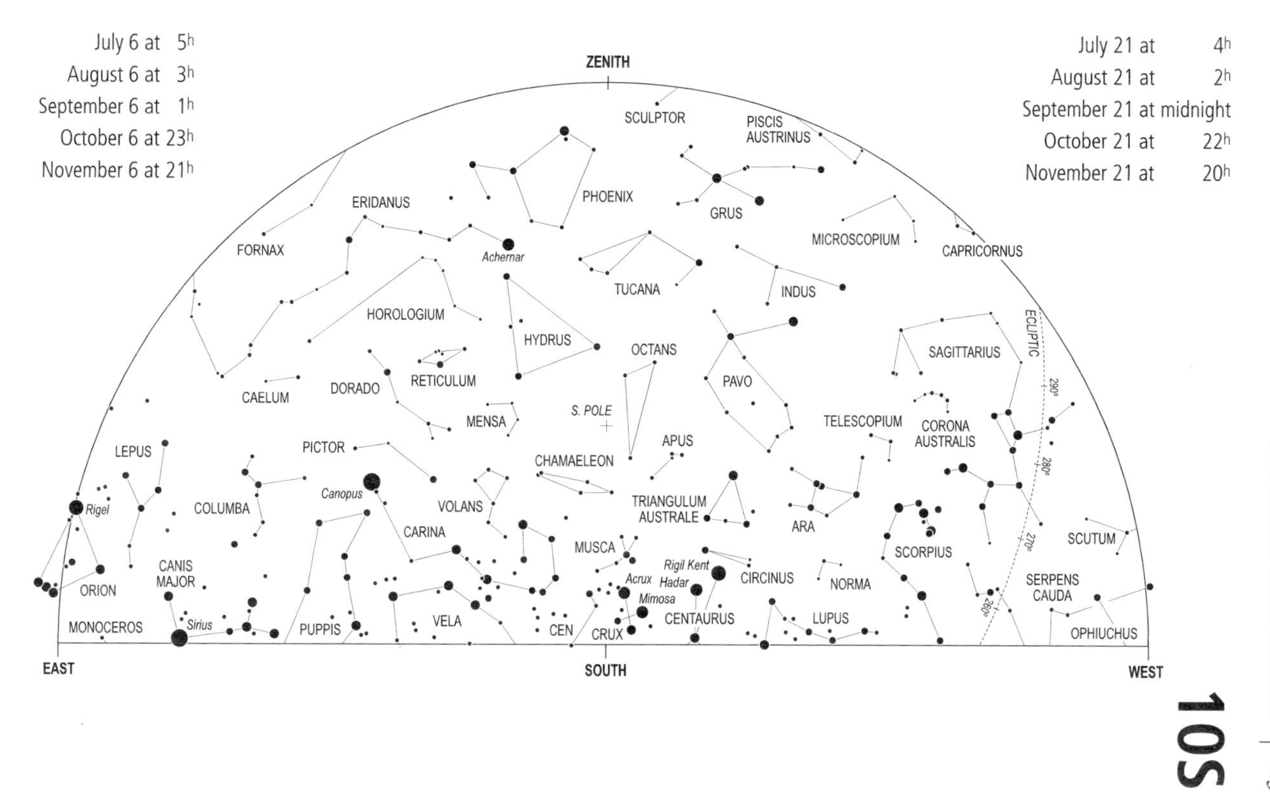
July 6 at 5h
August 6 at 3h
September 6 at 1h
October 6 at 23h
November 6 at 21h
July 21 at 4h
August 21 at 2h
September 21 at midnight
October 21 at 22h
November 21 at 20h
ZENITH
EAST
SOUTH
WEST
ECLIPTIC
290°
280°
270°
260°
S. POLE
SCULPTOR
PISCIS AUSTRINUS
PHOENIX
GRUS
ERIDANUS
MICROSCOPIUM
CAPRICORNUS
FORNAX
Achernar
TUCANA
INDUS
HOROLOGIUM
HYDRUS
OCTANS
SAGITTARIUS
RETICULUM
PAVO
CAELUM
DORADO
MENSA
TELESCOPIUM
CORONA AUSTRALIS
APUS
LEPUS
PICTOR
CHAMAELEON
Canopus
TRIANGULUM AUSTRALE
Rigel
COLUMBA
VOLANS
ARA
CARINA
SCUTUM
MUSCA
SCORPIUS
Rigil Kent
CANIS MAJOR
Acrux
Hadar
CIRCINUS
SERPENS CAUDA
ORION
NORMA
Mimosa
VELA
CENTAURUS
LUPUS
MONOCEROS
Sirius
PUPPIS
CEN
CRUX
OPHIUCHUS

11N

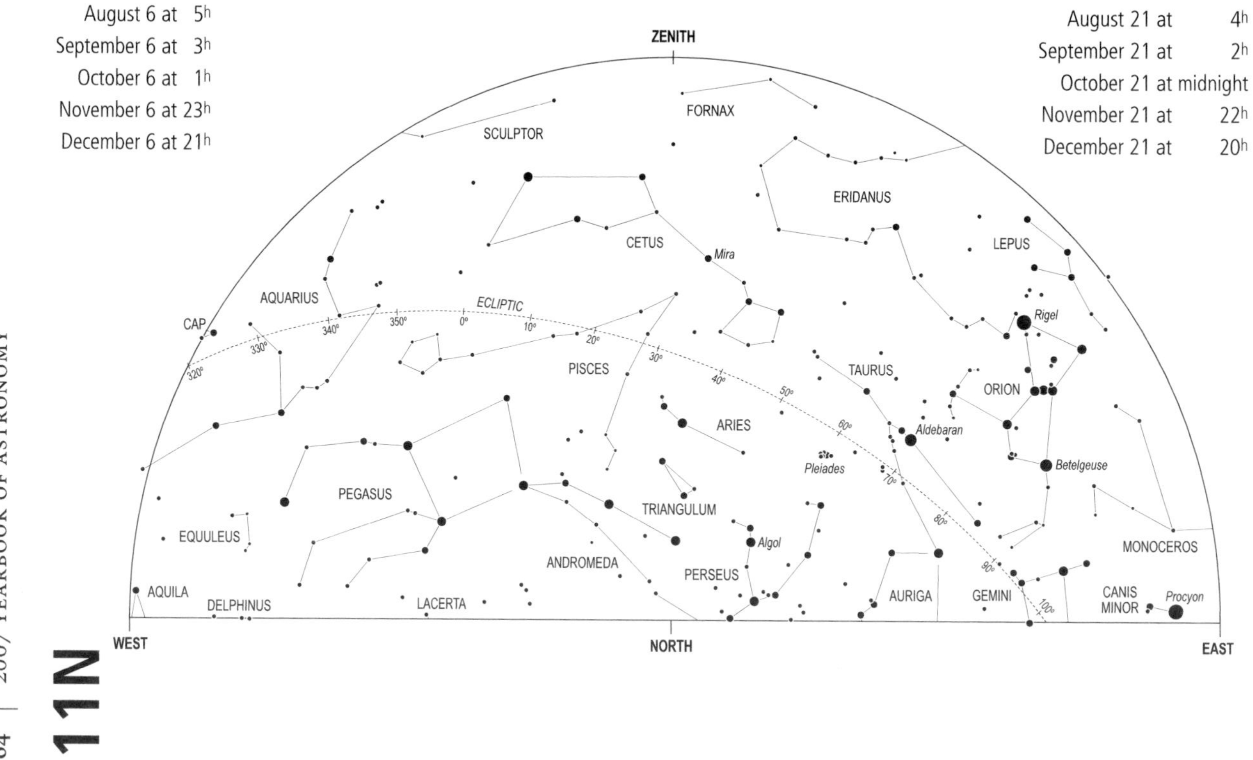
August 6 at 5h
September 6 at 3h
October 6 at 1h
November 6 at 23h
December 6 at 21h
August 21 at 4h
September 21 at 2h
October 21 at midnight
November 21 at 22h
December 21 at 20h
ZENITH
SCULPTOR
FORNAX
ERIDANUS
CETUS
Mira
LEPUS
AQUARIUS
ECLIPTIC
CAP
Rigel
PISCES
TAURUS
ORION
ARIES
Aldebaran
Pleiades
Betelgeuse
PEGASUS
TRIANGULUM
EQUULEUS
Algol
MONOCEROS
ANDROMEDA
PERSEUS
AQUILA
DELPHINUS
LACERTA
AURIGA
GEMINI
CANIS MINOR
Procyon
WEST
NORTH
EAST

11S

August 6 at 5h
September 6 at 3h
October 6 at 1h
November 6 at 23h
December 6 at 21h

August 21 at 4h
September 21 at 2h
October 21 at midnight
November 21 at 22h
December 21 at 20h

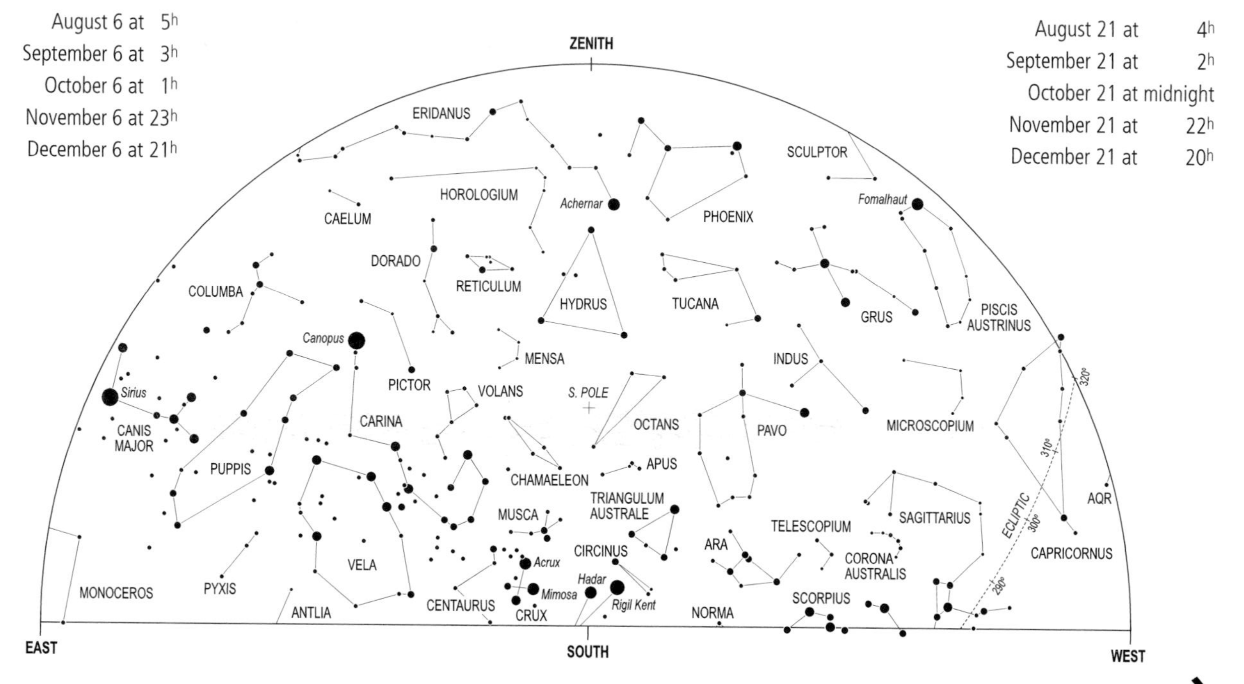

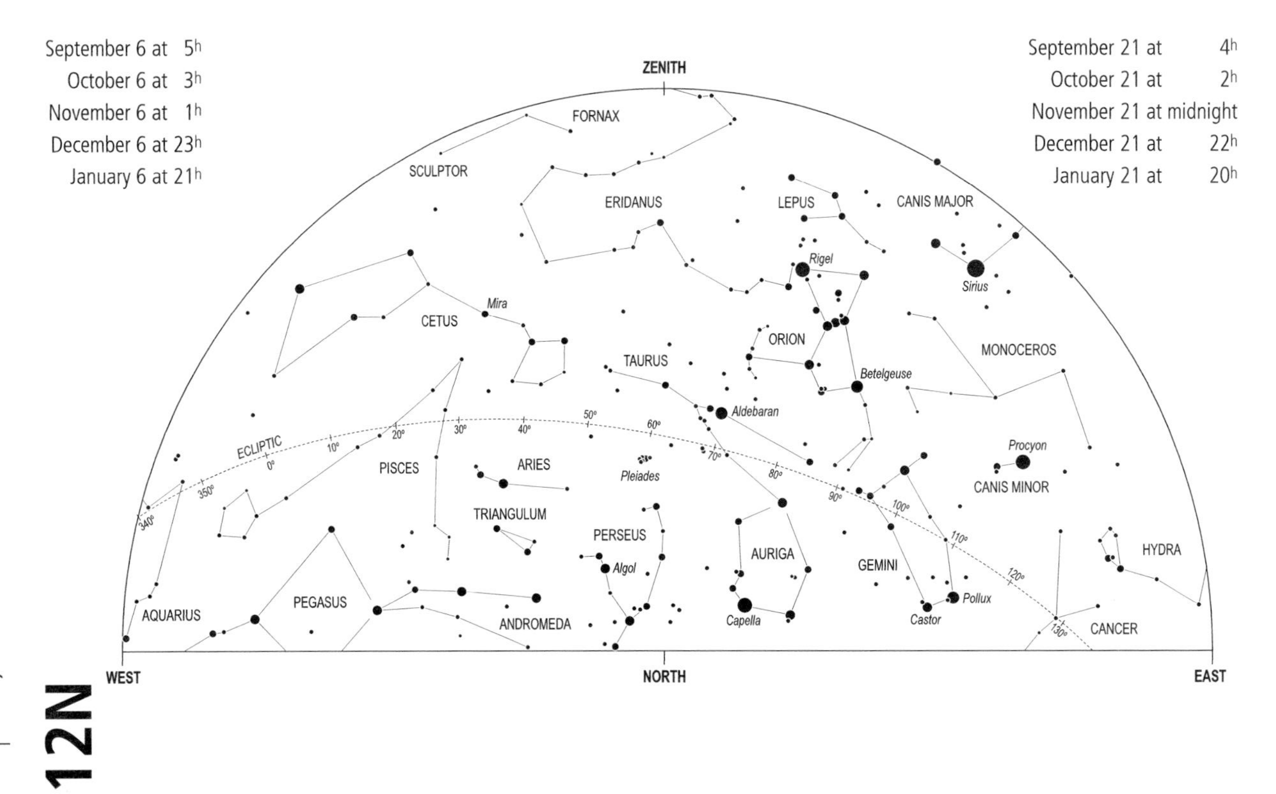
12N
September 6 at 5h
October 6 at 3h
November 6 at 1h
December 6 at 23h
January 6 at 21h
September 21 at 4h
October 21 at 2h
November 21 at midnight
December 21 at 22h
January 21 at 20h
ZENITH
WEST
NORTH
EAST
ECLIPTIC
340°
350°
0°
10°
20°
30°
40°
50°
60°
70°
80°
90°
100°
110°
120°
130°
FORNAX
SCULPTOR
ERIDANUS
LEPUS
CANIS MAJOR
Rigel
Sirius
CETUS
Mira
ORION
TAURUS
MONOCEROS
Betelgeuse
Aldebaran
Procyon
PISCES
ARIES
Pleiades
CANIS MINOR
TRIANGULUM
PERSEUS
AURIGA
GEMINI
HYDRA
Algol
PEGASUS
AQUARIUS
ANDROMEDA
Capella
Castor
Pollux
CANCER

12S

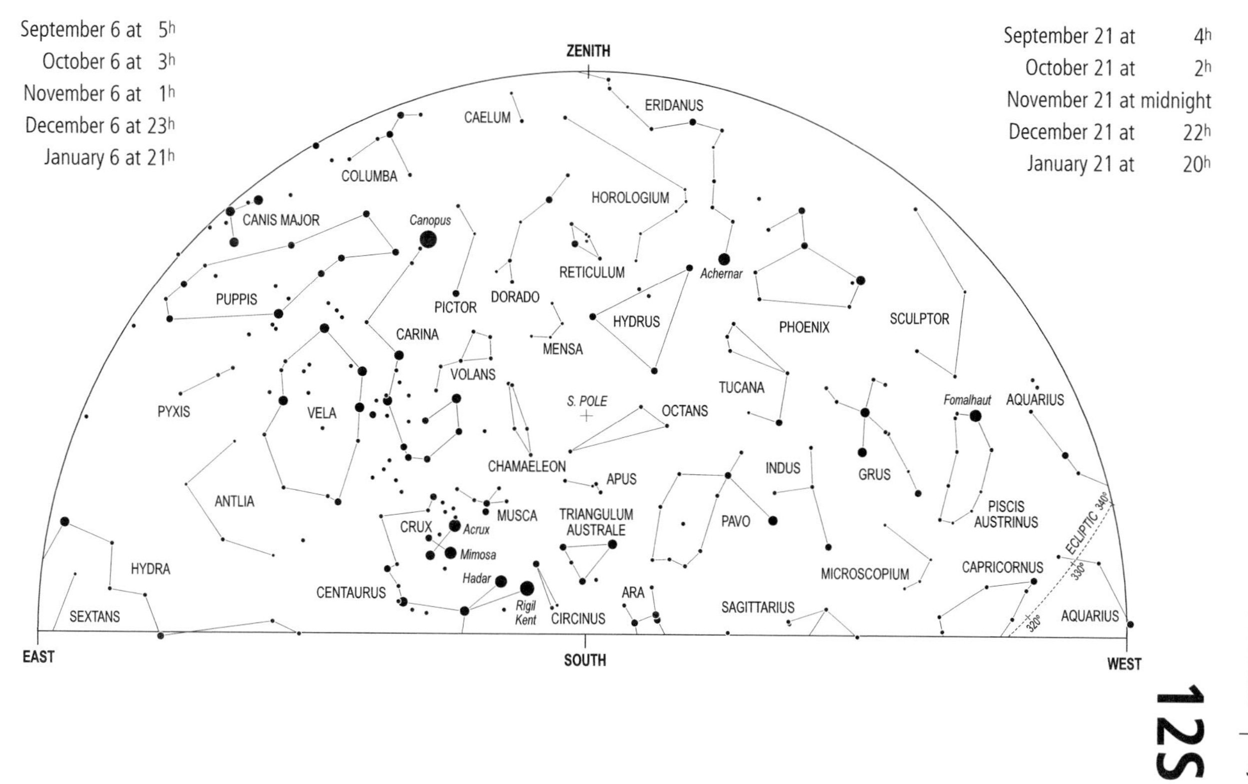
September 6 at 5h
October 6 at 3h
November 6 at 1h
December 6 at 23h
January 6 at 21h
September 21 at 4h
October 21 at 2h
November 21 at midnight
December 21 at 22h
January 21 at 20h
ZENITH
EAST
SOUTH
WEST
CAELUM
ERIDANUS
COLUMBA
HOROLOGIUM
CANIS MAJOR
Canopus
RETICULUM
Achernar
PUPPIS
PICTOR
DORADO
HYDRUS
PHOENIX
SCULPTOR
CARINA
MENSA
VOLANS
TUCANA
PYXIS
VELA
S. POLE
OCTANS
Fomalhaut
AQUARIUS
CHAMAELEON
APUS
INDUS
GRUS
ANTLIA
CRUX
Acrux
MUSCA
TRIANGULUM AUSTRALE
PAVO
PISCIS AUSTRINUS
Mimosa
ECLIPTIC 340°
330°
320°
HYDRA
Hadar
MICROSCOPIUM
CAPRICORNUS
CENTAURUS
Rigil Kent
ARA
SAGITTARIUS
SEXTANS
CIRCINUS
AQUARIUS

The Planets and the Ecliptic

The paths of the planets about the Sun all lie close to the plane of the ecliptic, which is marked for us in the sky by the apparent path of the Sun among the stars, and is shown on the star charts by a broken line. The Moon and naked-eye planets will always be found close to this line, never departing from it by more than about 7°. Thus the planets are most favourably placed for observation when the ecliptic is well displayed, and this means that it should be as high in the sky as possible. This avoids the difficulty of finding a clear horizon, and also overcomes the problem of atmospheric absorption, which greatly reduces the light of the stars. Thus a star at an altitude of 10° suffers a loss of 60 per cent of its light, which corresponds to a whole magnitude; at an altitude of only 4°, the loss may amount to two magnitudes.

The position of the ecliptic in the sky is therefore of great importance, and since it is tilted at about 23.5° to the Equator, it is only at certain times of the day or year that it is displayed to the best advantage. It will be realized that the Sun (and therefore the ecliptic) is at its highest in the sky at noon in midsummer, and at its lowest at noon in midwinter. Allowing for the daily motion of the sky, it follows that the ecliptic is highest at midnight in winter, at sunset in the spring, at noon in summer and at sunrise in the autumn. Hence these are the best times to see the planets. Thus, if Venus is an evening object in the western sky after sunset, it will be seen to best advantage if this occurs in the spring, when the ecliptic is high in the sky and slopes down steeply to the horizon. This means that the planet is not only higher in the sky, but will remain for a much longer period above the horizon. For similar reasons, a morning object will be seen at its best on autumn mornings before sunrise, when the ecliptic is high in the east. The outer planets, which can come to opposition (i.e. opposite the Sun), are best seen when opposition occurs in the winter months, when the ecliptic is high in the sky at midnight.

The seasons are reversed in the Southern Hemisphere, spring beginning at the September Equinox, when the Sun crosses the Equator on its way south, summer beginning at the December Solstice, when the

Sun is highest in the southern sky, and so on. Thus, the times when the ecliptic is highest in the sky, and therefore best placed for observing the planets, may be summarized as follows:

	Midnight	**Sunrise**	**Noon**	**Sunset**
Northern latitudes	December	September	June	March
Southern latitudes	June	March	December	September

In addition to the daily rotation of the celestial sphere from east to west, the planets have a motion of their own among the stars. The apparent movement is generally *direct*, i.e. to the east, in the direction of increasing longitude, but for a certain period (which depends on the distance of the planet) this apparent motion is reversed. With the outer planets this *retrograde* motion occurs about the time of opposition. Owing to the different inclination of the orbits of these planets, the actual effect is to cause the apparent path to form a loop, or sometimes an S-shaped curve. The same effect is present in the motion of the inferior planets, Mercury and Venus, but it is not so obvious, since it always occurs at the time of inferior conjunction.

The *inferior planets*, Mercury and Venus, move in smaller orbits than that of the Earth, and so are always seen near the Sun. They are most obvious at the times of greatest angular distance from the Sun (greatest elongation), which may reach 28° for Mercury, and 47° for Venus. They are seen as evening objects in the western sky after sunset (at eastern elongations) or as morning objects in the eastern sky before sunrise (at western elongations). The succession of phenomena, conjunctions and elongations always follows the same order, but the intervals between them are not equal. Thus, if either planet is moving round the far side of its orbit its motion will be to the east, in the same direction in which the Sun appears to be moving. It therefore takes much longer for the planet to overtake the Sun – that is, to come to superior conjunction – than it does when moving round to inferior conjunction, between Sun and Earth. The intervals given in the following table are average values; they remain fairly constant in the case of Venus, which travels in an almost circular orbit. In the case of Mercury, however, conditions vary widely because of the great eccentricity and inclination of the planet's orbit.

		Mercury	Venus
Inferior Conjunction	to Elongation West	22 days	72 days
Elongation West	to Superior Conjunction	36 days	220 days
Superior Conjunction	to Elongation East	35 days	220 days
Elongation East	to Inferior Conjunction	22 days	72 days

The greatest brilliancy of Venus always occurs about 36 days before or after inferior conjunction. This will be about a month after greatest eastern elongation (as an evening object), or a month before greatest western elongation (as a morning object). No such rule can be given for Mercury, because its distances from the Earth and the Sun can vary over a wide range.

Mercury is not likely to be seen unless a clear horizon is available. It is seldom as much as 10° above the horizon in the twilight sky in northern temperate latitudes, but this figure is often exceeded in the Southern Hemisphere. This favourable condition arises because the maximum elongation of 28° can occur only when the planet is at aphelion (furthest from the Sun), and it then lies well south of the Equator. Northern observers must be content with smaller elongations, which may be as little as 18° at perihelion (when closest to the Sun). In general, it may be said that the most favourable times for seeing Mercury as an evening object will be in spring, some days before greatest eastern elongation; in autumn, it may be seen as a morning object some days after greatest western elongation.

Venus is the brightest of the planets and may be seen on occasions in broad daylight. Like Mercury, it is alternately a morning and an evening object, and it will be highest in the sky when it is a morning object in autumn, or an evening object in spring. Venus is to be seen at its best as an evening object in northern latitudes when eastern elongation occurs in June. The planet is then well north of the Sun in the preceding spring months, and is a brilliant object in the evening sky over a long period. In the Southern Hemisphere a November elongation is best. For similar reasons, Venus gives a prolonged display as a morning object in the months following western elongation in October (in northern latitudes) or in June (in the Southern Hemisphere).

The *superior planets*, which travel in orbits larger than that of the Earth, differ from Mercury and Venus in that they can be seen opposite the Sun in the sky. The superior planets are morning objects after conjunction with the Sun, rising earlier each day until they come to opposition. They will then be nearest to the Earth (and therefore at their brightest), and will be on the meridian at midnight, due south in northern latitudes, but due north in the Southern Hemisphere. After opposition they are evening objects, setting earlier each evening until they set in the west with the Sun at the next conjunction. The difference in brightness from one opposition to another is most noticeable in the case of Mars, whose distance from Earth can vary considerably and rapidly. The other superior planets are at such great distances that there is very little change in brightness from one opposition to the next. The effect of altitude is, however, of some importance, for at a December opposition in northern latitudes the planets will be among the stars of Taurus or Gemini, and can then be at an altitude of more than 60° in southern England. At a summer opposition, when the planet is in Sagittarius, it may only rise to about 15° above the southern horizon, and so makes a less impressive appearance. In the Southern Hemisphere the reverse conditions apply, a June opposition being the best, with the planet in Sagittarius at an altitude which can reach 80° above the northern horizon for observers in South Africa.

Mars, whose orbit is appreciably eccentric, comes nearest to the Earth at oppositions at the end of August. It may then be brighter even than Jupiter, but rather low in the sky in Aquarius for northern observers, though very well placed for those in southern latitudes. These favourable oppositions occur every fifteen or seventeen years (e.g. in 1988, 2003 and 2018). In the Northern Hemisphere the planet is probably better seen at oppositions in the autumn or winter months, when it is higher in the sky – such as in 2005 when opposition was in early November. Oppositions of Mars occur at an average interval of 780 days, and during this time the planet makes a complete circuit of the sky.

Jupiter is always a bright planet, and comes to opposition a month later each year, having moved, roughly speaking, from one zodiacal constellation to the next.

Saturn moves much more slowly than Jupiter, and may remain in the same constellation for several years. The brightness of Saturn depends on the aspects of its rings, as well as on the distance from Earth and Sun. The Earth passed through the plane of Saturn's rings in 1995 and 1996, when they appeared edge-on; we saw them at maximum opening, and Saturn at its brightest, in 2002. The rings will next appear edge-on in 2009.

Uranus and *Neptune* are both visible with binoculars or a small telescope, but you will need a finder chart to help locate them (such as those reproduced in this *Yearbook* on pages 123 and 129). *Pluto* is hardly likely to attract the attention of observers without adequate telescopes.

Phases of the Moon in 2007

New Moon				First Quarter				Full Moon				Last Quarter			
	d	h	m		d	h	m		d	h	m		d	h	m
								Jan	3	13	57	Jan	11	12	45
Jan	19	04	01	Jan	25	23	01	Feb	2	05	45	Feb	10	09	51
Feb	17	16	14	Feb	24	07	56	Mar	3	23	17	Mar	12	03	54
Mar	19	02	43	Mar	25	18	16	Apr	2	17	15	Apr	10	18	04
Apr	17	11	36	Apr	24	06	36	May	2	10	09	May	10	04	27
May	16	19	27	May	23	21	03	June	1	01	04	June	8	11	43
June	15	03	13	June	22	13	15	June	30	13	49	July	7	16	54
July	14	12	04	July	22	06	29	July	30	00	48	Aug	5	21	20
Aug	12	23	03	Aug	20	23	54	Aug	28	10	35	Sept	4	02	32
Sept	11	12	44	Sept	19	16	48	Sept	26	19	45	Oct	3	10	06
Oct	11	05	01	Oct	19	08	33	Oct	26	04	52	Nov	1	21	18
Nov	9	23	03	Nov	17	22	33	Nov	24	14	30	Dec	1	12	44
Dec	9	17	40	Dec	17	10	18	Dec	24	01	16	Dec	31	07	51

All times are GMT

Longitudes of the Sun, Moon and Planets in 2007

Date		Sun	Moon	Venus	Mars	Jupiter	Saturn
		°	°	°	°	°	°
January	6	285	134	302	262	249	144
	21	301	325	321	273	252	143
February	6	317	179	341	285	255	142
	21	332	18	0	296	257	141
March	6	345	187	16	306	258	140
	21	0	27	34	317	259	139
April	6	16	232	53	330	260	138
	21	31	80	70	341	259	138
May	6	45	265	87	353	258	138
	21	60	116	104	4	257	139
June	6	75	314	120	16	255	140
	21	89	162	134	27	253	141
July	6	104	351	145	38	251	143
	21	118	194	152	48	250	145
August	6	133	45	151	59	250	147
	21	148	238	143	69	250	148
September	6	163	97	137	78	251	150
	21	178	283	139	86	253	152
October	6	192	134	148	93	255	154
	21	207	317	161	98	258	156
November	6	223	180	177	102	261	157
	21	238	7	193	102	264	158
December	6	253	213	211	99	267	158
	21	269	46	228	94	270	159

Longitude of *Uranus* 346°
Neptune 320°

Moon: Longitude of ascending node
Jan 1: 350° Dec 31: 330°

Mercury moves so quickly among the stars that it is not possible to indicate its position on the star charts at convenient intervals. The Monthly Notes must be consulted for the best times at which the planet may be seen.

The positions of the other planets are given in the table on p. 74. This gives the apparent longitudes on dates which correspond to those of the star charts, and the position of the planet may at once be found near the ecliptic at the given longitude.

EXAMPLES

In a northern tropical latitude two planets are seen in the evening about an hour after sunset, in the north-western sky early in July. Identify them.

> The northern chart 6N shows longitudes 120° to 155° along the ecliptic. Reference to the table on p. 74 for 6 July gives the longitude of Venus as 145° and that of Saturn as 143°, Venus being further left (west) in the sky than Saturn, and also much brighter than Saturn.

The positions of the Sun and Moon can be plotted on the star maps in the same manner as for the planets. The average daily motion of the Sun is 1°, and of the Moon 13°. For the Moon an indication of its position relative to the ecliptic may be obtained from a consideration of its longitude relative to that of the ascending node. The latter changes only slowly during the year, as will be seen from the values given on p. 74. Let us denote by d the difference in longitude between the Moon and its ascending node. Then if $d = 0°$, 180° or 360°, the Moon is on the ecliptic. If $d = 90°$ the Moon is 5° north of the ecliptic, and if $d = 270°$ the Moon is 5° south of the ecliptic.

On 21 April the Moon's longitude is given in the table on p. 74 as 80° and the longitude of the ascending node is found by interpolation to be about 344°. Thus $d = 96°$ and the Moon is about 5° north of the ecliptic. Its position may be plotted on northern star charts 1S, 2S, 11S and 12S, and on southern star charts 1N, 2N, 3N, 11N and 12N.

Some Events in 2007

Jan	3	Full Moon
	3	*Earth* at Perihelion
	7	*Mercury* at Superior Conjunction
	19	New Moon
Feb	2	Full Moon
	7	*Mercury* at Greatest Eastern Elongation (18°)
	8	*Neptune* in Conjunction with Sun
	10	*Saturn* at Opposition in Leo
	17	New Moon
	23	*Mercury* at Inferior Conjunction
Mar	3	Full Moon, Total Eclipse of Moon
	5	*Uranus* in Conjunction with Sun
	19	New Moon, Partial Eclipse of Sun
	21	Equinox (Spring Equinox in Northern Hemisphere)
	22	*Mercury* at Greatest Western Elongation (28°)
Apr	2	Full Moon
	17	New Moon
May	2	Full Moon
	3	*Mercury* at Superior Conjunction
	16	New Moon
Jun	1	Full Moon
	2	*Mercury* at Greatest Eastern Elongation (23°)
	5	*Jupiter* at Opposition in Ophiuchus
	9	*Venus* at Greatest Eastern Elongation (45°)
	15	New Moon
	19	*Pluto* at Opposition in Sagittarius
	21	Solstice (Summer Solstice in Northern Hemisphere)

	28	*Mercury* at Inferior Conjunction
	30	Full Moon
Jul	7	*Earth* at Aphelion
	14	New Moon
	20	*Mercury* at Greatest Western Elongation (20°)
	30	Full Moon
Aug	12	New Moon
	13	*Neptune* at Opposition in Capricornus
	15	*Mercury* at Superior Conjunction
	18	*Venus* at Inferior Conjunction
	21	*Saturn* in Conjunction with Sun
	28	Full Moon, Total Eclipse of Moon
Sep	9	*Uranus* at opposition in Aquarius
	11	New Moon, Partial Eclipse of Sun
	23	Equinox (Autumnal Equinox in Northern Hemisphere)
	26	Full Moon
	29	*Mercury* at Greatest Eastern Elongation (26°)
Oct	11	New Moon
	23	*Mercury* at Inferior Conjunction
	26	Full Moon
Nov	8	*Mercury* at Greatest Western Elongation (19°)
	9	New Moon
	24	Full Moon
Dec	9	New Moon
	17	*Mercury* at Superior Conjunction
	21	*Pluto* in Conjunction with Sun
	22	Solstice (Winter Solstice in Northern Hemisphere)
	23	*Jupiter* in Conjunction with Sun
	24	Full Moon
	24	*Mars* at Opposition in Gemini

Monthly Notes 2007

January

New Moon: **19 January** *Full Moon:* **3 January**

EARTH is at perihelion (nearest to the Sun) on 3 January at a distance of 147 million kilometres (91 million miles).

MERCURY is unsuitably placed for observation at first as it passes through superior conjunction on the 7th. During the last week of the month observers in tropical latitudes will be able to see it as an evening object, magnitude −1.0, low above the west-south-western horizon about half an hour after sunset. Observers further north will only have any hope of seeing it during the last few days of January, while those in southern temperate latitudes will not be able to see it before March.

VENUS is an evening object but only visible for a short while after sunset, low above the south-western horizon for observers in the latitudes of the British Isles, but slightly more westerly for observers south of the equator. Its magnitude is −3.9. Venus is slowly moving out from the Sun, though even by the end of January it is not visible for much more than an hour after sunset.

MARS, magnitude +1.4, is a morning object and is visible low above the eastern horizon about an hour before sunrise, though not for observers as far north as the latitude of the British Isles. Mars commences the year in the constellation of Ophiuchus but soon moves eastwards into Sagittarius. Figure 7, given with the notes for April, shows the path of Mars against the background stars during the early part of the year.

JUPITER is a brilliant morning object, visible in the eastern sky for about two hours before dawn, magnitude −1.8. Jupiter passes 5° north of Antares, which is in the constellation of Scorpius, on 5 January, though the planet itself is in Ophiuchus. Figure 12, given with the notes for June, shows the path of Jupiter against the background stars during the year.

SATURN does not come to opposition until next month but it is already visible in the mid to late evening onwards in the eastern sky, magnitude +0.1. Saturn is moving slowly retrograde in the constellation of Leo, as will be seen in Figure 3, given with the notes for February, which shows the path of Saturn against the background stars during the year.

The Great Dog. The evening skies in winter are dominated by Orion and his retinue. In particular, the Hunter is attended by his two dogs. Canis Major, the Great Dog, is distinguished by the presence of Sirius, much the brightest star in the sky, but Canis Major is a large constellation, covering 380 square degrees, and there are several objects of interest (Figure 1). Look, for example, at the lovely open cluster M41 (the only Messier object in Canis Major), also known as NGC 2287, located about 4° directly south of Sirius. It is on the fringe of naked

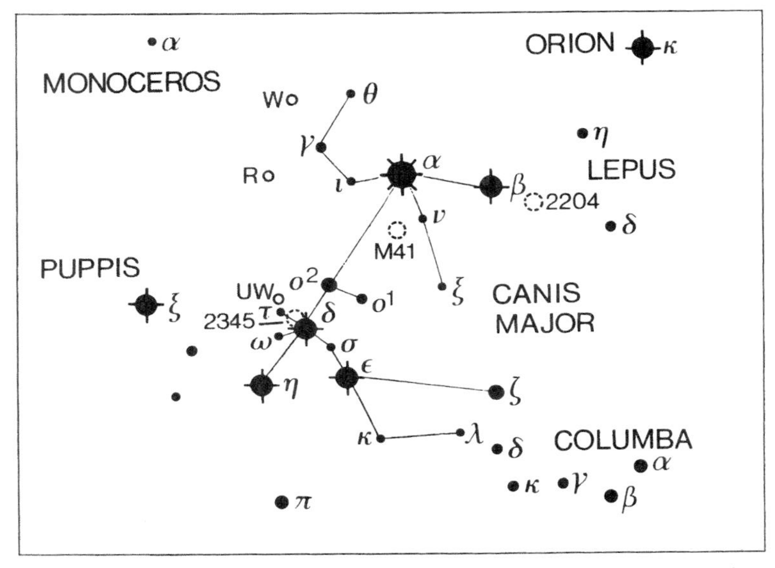

Figure 1. The principal stars of Canis Major, the Great Dog. The brilliant Sirius is above centre, with the open cluster M41 immediately below it.

eye visibility (magnitude 4.6), and binoculars show it well. It is 38 arcminutes in diameter, and lies in the same binocular field as the rather reddish fourth magnitude star Nu^2, forming a triangle with Nu^2 and Sirius. M41 contains about 100 stars, including several red/orange giant stars, the brightest being of seventh magnitude, orange in colour, and situated near the cluster's centre.

You cannot mistake Canis Major's brightest star Sirius (magnitude −1.4) whenever it is above the horizon, because it far outshines any other star of the night sky. Indeed it dominates the evening sky all through late winter and early spring in the Northern Hemisphere. As the leading star of Canis Major, Sirius is popularly known as the Dog Star. Today, in the Northern Hemisphere summer months, from early June until early August, the Dog Star is more or less in conjunction with the Sun, and long ago observers in countries bordering the Mediterranean believed (quite wrongly, of course) that its heat was added to the heat of the Sun creating a period of hot, sultry and rather uncomfortable weather. They named this period of time the 'Dog Days' of summer after the Dog Star. To the ancient Egyptians, Sirius was also of special importance, because they used it to regulate their calendar. When they first saw Sirius in the dawn twilight sky, just before sunrise, they knew that the River Nile was about to flood and in this desert land such an event was vital to their whole economy.

The other bright stars in the Great Dog are Epsilon or Adhara (magnitude 1.5), Delta or Wezen (1.8), Beta or Mirzam (2.0), Eta or Aludra (2.4) and Zeta or Phurad (3.0). The name for Beta, Mirzam (also seen spelt Murzim), means the 'announcer', and this is thought to relate to the fact that Mirzam rises shortly before Sirius, thereby 'announcing' the brightest star's imminent arrival. Wezen is very luminous, and could match 50,000 Suns; it is 1,800 light-years away. On the other hand Sirius, at 8.6 light-years, one of our nearest stellar neighbours, is only 23 times as powerful as the Sun, so that appearances are highly deceptive. Even more deceptive is Tau Canis Majoris, close to Wezen. It is of visual magnitude 4.4, but is even more luminous than Wezen. Tau is about 3,200 light-years away, and is of spectral type O9.

Of the fifty apparently brightest stars in the sky, much the most powerful is Deneb, in Cygnus, the Swan – about 270,000 times as luminous as the Sun. It too is about 3,200 light-years away. If it was close as Sirius, it would cast strong shadows, and would be easily visible with the naked eye in broad daylight.

James Clerk Maxwell and the Rings of Saturn. When the rings of Saturn were first discovered, nobody knew quite what to make of them. They looked solid – but could a solid or even a liquid ring exist in such a position? The strong gravitational pull of the planet would disrupt it, even if it could form in the first place.

Another suggestion was that the rings might be made up of tiny particles, all moving around Saturn in the manner of dwarf moons. Proof was finally obtained 150 years ago, in 1857, by the great Scottish mathematician James Clerk Maxwell. He found out that the inner ring had a revolution period shorter than that of the outer ring – which could not possibly happen with a solid structure. The particles at the inner edge of the visible rings (the Crêpe Ring) have a period of 5.6 hours; the period at the outer edge of ring A is 14.2 hours.

Spacecraft have shown that the rings are amazingly complex; there are thousands of ringlets and minor divisions (Figure 2). They are surprisingly thin, so that when presented edgewise-on to us they

Figure 2. View from the Cassini spacecraft revealing the enormous complexity of Saturn's rings. The dark Cassini Division, running top to bottom across the centre, contains a great deal of structure. The sharp inner boundary of the division (left of centre) is the outer edge of the B ring. The Cassini Division, similar to the C ring, contains more contaminated ice than do the B and A rings on either side. (Image courtesy of NASA/JPL/Space Science Institute.)

appear only as a slender line of light; in small telescopes they cannot be seen at all. The last edgewise presentations were in 1980 and 1995; the next will be in 2009. During the present opposition (2007) the rings are still reasonably 'open', and many people regard Saturn as the most beautiful object in the entire sky.

Non-Existent Satellites. Saturn has a wealth of satellites – about 50 in all – and more are being discovered every year, though these are very small. Before the end of the last century nine were known: Mimas, Enceladus, Tethys, Dione, Rhea, Titan, Hyperion, Iapetus and Phœbe. Some books listed two more: Chiron and Themis, but these were never confirmed.

The first of these was announced in 1861 by a well-known observer, Hermann Goldschmidt (1802–1866). He was born in Frankfurt and was trained for a commercial career, but soon abandoned it and settled in Paris. He observed through the attic window of his art studio, and between 1852 and 1861 discovered no less than fourteen asteroids. In 1857 alone, 150 years ago, he found four – 44 Nysa, 45 Eugenia, 48 Doris and 49 Pales. He also announced the detection of a new satellite of Saturn, moving between the orbits of Hyperion and Iapetus. He named it Chiron, but it was never seen again, and must have been either a faint star or else a telescopic 'ghost'. (The name Chiron was later given to the first of the Centaur asteroids, No. 2060, discovered in 1977 by Charles Kowal; it spends most of its time between the orbits of Saturn and Uranus.)

In 1904, an even more famous observer, William Henry Pickering, announced the discovery of a satellite moving between the orbits of Titan (which had been known since 1655) and Hyperion (discovered in 1848). Pickering named it Themis, but it too remained unconfirmed, and was almost certainly an ordinary star which was mistaken for a satellite. However, in 1898 Pickering did discover Phœbe, which has been imaged in detail by the Cassini probe. Phœbe is 214 km (133 miles) in diameter, and is generally believed to be an escapee from the Kuiper Belt; its orbital period is 550.5 days, and its motion is retrograde.

This Month's Centenary. Eric Lindsay was born 100 years ago, on 26 January 1907, at Portadown in County Armagh, Northern Ireland. He was educated at King's Hospital School, Dublin, then Queen's

University, Belfast, and Harvard University, from where he obtained his Ph.D. in 1934. After three years in South Africa, he returned to Ireland in 1937 to become Director of the Armagh Observatory. At that time, Irish astronomy was in a sorry state, and Lindsay was determined to revive its fortunes. He successfully negotiated a reopening of the Dunsink Observatory as part of the Dublin Institute for Advanced Studies, re-equipped both Irish observatories with modern facilities, and obtained funding for a new telescope (the Armagh/Dunsink/Harvard Telescope) to be erected at Boyden in South Africa to chart the southern skies. In 1954, he persuaded Sweden, Belgium and Germany to join Ireland and the USA in an international observatory at Boyden, the first joint venture of this kind. He also founded the Armagh Planetarium in 1966, the first in Ireland and one of only two in the United Kingdom at that time. Although he made no great astronomical discoveries, Lindsay's work – in particular his ability to persuade the politicians of the time to adopt his imaginative schemes – was crucial to the revival of Irish astronomy. He received the O.B.E. in 1963 in recognition of his services to astronomy. Eric Lindsay remained Director of the Armagh Observatory until his death at Armagh on 27 July 1974.

February

New Moon: 17 February *Full Moon:* 2 February

MERCURY is visible as an evening object during the first half of the month for observers in tropical and northern latitudes, where it may be detected low above the western horizon around the end of evening civil twilight. During this period the magnitude of Mercury fades from −0.9 to +1.4 , so it is at its brightest before it reaches greatest eastern elongation (18°) on the 7th.

VENUS, magnitude −3.9, continues to be visible as a brilliant object in the evenings. Because of its rapid motion northwards in declination, observers in the latitudes of the British Isles will see it for a little longer each night and by the end of the month it is still visible low in the western sky for over two hours after sunset.

MARS continues to be visible in the eastern sky in the early mornings, magnitude +1.3, though not to observers in the latitudes of the British Isles. During the month Mars moves from Sagittarius into Capricornus.

JUPITER continues to be visible as a brilliant object in the eastern sky for several hours before dawn. Its magnitude is −2.0.

SATURN reaches opposition on 10 February and is therefore visible all night long. Saturn continues to retrograde slowly in the constellation of Leo. Its magnitude is 0.0. Figure 3 shows the path of Saturn against the background constellations during the year. The rings of Saturn present a beautiful spectacle to the observer armed with a small telescope. The diameter of the minor axis is now only 11 arcseconds, as compared with the polar diameter of the planet itself of 18 arcseconds. The rings were last at their maximum opening in 2002 and will next appear edge-on in 2009.

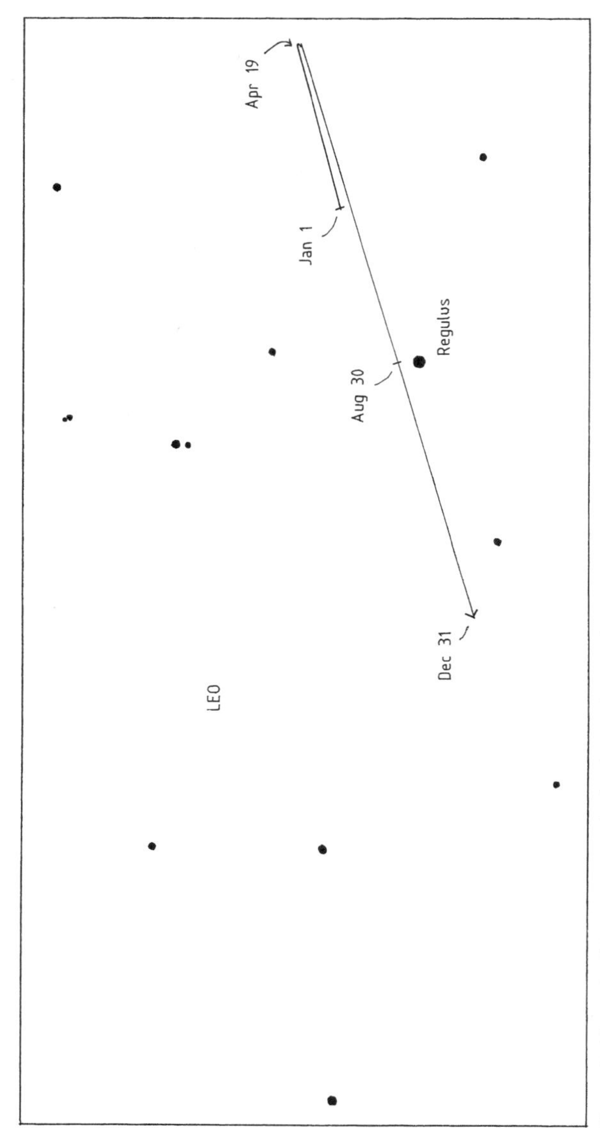

Figure 3. The path of Saturn against the background stars of Leo during 2007.

The Little Dog and Procyon B. Orion's second canine companion is comparatively small, covering no more than 183 square degrees of the sky. There are two bright stars, Alpha (Procyon) magnitude 0.38, and Beta (Gomeisa) magnitude 2.9. The name Procyon comes from the Greek word meaning 'before the dog', since it appeared to rise before the Dog Star, Sirius, as the Earth rotated. In fact, Procyon lies further east in the sky than Sirius, but it has a more northerly declination, and this means that it will rise above the horizon earlier than Sirius from northern temperate latitudes.

Procyon has an 11th magnitude white dwarf companion, Procyon B; the orbital period is 40.8 years. It is by no means easy to observe, because it is so drowned by the glare of the primary. Although the eighth brightest star in the sky, Procyon is in no way a cosmic searchlight; it is just 11.4 light-years away, and only 7 times as luminous as the Sun, so that of the fifty apparently brightest stars in the sky only Alpha Centauri is less powerful. The spectrum is F5, so that Procyon should in theory be slightly yellowish, though most people would see it as white. The red Mira-type variable star S Canis Minoris lies close to Gomeisa; the magnitude range is 6.6 to 13.2, in a period of 333 days.

The story of the discovery of Procyon's white dwarf companion is both interesting and unusual. Because Procyon is relatively close to us on the cosmic scale, it has a relatively large proper motion. It was found that it was not moving in a direct line, but was 'weaving' its way along, and so was probably being influenced by the pull of a companion star. The same had been true of Sirius, and calculations by the German astronomer Friedrich Wilhelm Bessel indicated where the invisible companion might be. In 1862 it was found, exactly where Bessel had expected it to be.

Another German astronomer, Georg Friedrich Julius Arthur von Auwers, made similar calculations for Procyon. Searches were made at several major observatories, but the expected companion refused to show up. At Washington, the Director of the observatory there, Simon Newcomb, was awaiting the completion of a new telescope, a 26-inch refractor made by Alvan Clark, whose reputation as an optical worker was second to none. He intended to hunt for Procyon's companion, and corresponded with Otto Struve, Director of the Pulkovo Observatory in Russia, suggesting that a new search would be worthwhile. Struve obliged, using the Pulkovo 15-inch refractor. He wrote back, saying that he had found the companion. The magnitude was given as 13. Struve's observation had been confirmed by his assistants, E. E. Lindemann and A. Wagner.

By this time the Washington telescope was ready; Newcomb lost no time in turning it towards Procyon. The companion should have been easy to see – but there was absolutely no sign of it. He made many attempts, with a total lack of success; the companion simply wasn't there – yet the Washington refractor was more powerful than Struve's. Had the companion disappeared? In 1874, Struve visited London, gave an address to the Royal Astronomical Society, and again reported his discovery of the companion. It was all very mysterious.

At last Struve found the answer. He turned his telescope towards Regulus, Capella and Arcturus in turn, and, to his chagrin, found that all three showed faint companions similar to Procyon's. He realized that he had been deceived by a telescopic 'ghost', a tiny fault in the optics of his telescope, brought out by the light of any brilliant star.

The real companion was discovered in 1896 by the American astronomer John Martin Schaeberle, using the 36-inch refractor at the Lick Observatory. Even Newcomb's telescope had not been sufficiently powerful to show it. Its real distance from Procyon is about 2230 million km (just under 1,400 million miles), rather less than the distance between our Sun and the planet Uranus.

The First Mission to Venus. The first interplanetary probe, Venera 1, was launched by the Soviet Union forty-six years ago, on 12 February 1961. The craft was launched in two stages: first, the main Molniya rocket launcher placed Venera 1 into a parking orbit around the Earth, and then a fourth stage Zond rocket engine was fired to place the craft on a trajectory towards Venus. This was the first demonstration of the technique of launching from Earth orbit.

The probe (Figure 4) was equipped with several instruments including a magnetometer attached to the antenna boom, devices to measure the solar wind and cosmic radiation, and micrometeorite detectors. Venera 1 successfully gathered data in near-Earth space, and seemed to be well on its way – but in those early days of space research the Russians were having trouble with long-range communications. On 19 February, just seven days after launch, at a distance of about 2 million km (1.25 million miles) from Earth, contact with the spacecraft was lost. On 19 and 20 May 1961, Venera 1 probably passed within about 100,000 km (60,000 miles) of Venus and presumably it

Figure 4. Photograph of a model of the first interplanetary spacecraft, Venera 1, at the Polytechnical Museum in Russia. (Image courtesy of Alexander Chernov and the Virtual Space Museum.)

is still in solar orbit. The first successful fly-by of Venus was achieved by NASA's Mariner 2, in December 1962.

Despite its failure, Venera 1 marked the beginning of what was to become a highly successful Russian Venus exploration programme. In later years, Venera spacecraft would be built and launched in identical pairs. This redundancy acted as insurance against technology failures.

For information on the work of later Venera probes, see the chapter by David Harland, Probing the Atmosphere of Venus, elsewhere in this *Yearbook*.

March

New Moon: **19 March** *Full Moon:* **3 March**

Equinox: 21 March

Summer Time in the United Kingdom commences on 25 March.

MERCURY, after the first week of the month, becomes visible as a morning object to those in tropical and southern latitudes. During the month its magnitude brightens from +1.2 to +0.1. For observers in southern latitudes this will be the most favourable morning apparition of the year. Figure 5 shows, for observers in latitude 35°S, the changes in azimuth (true bearing from the north through east, south and west) and altitude of Mercury on successive mornings when the Sun is 6° below the horizon. This condition is known as the beginning of morning civil twilight and in this latitude and at this time of year occurs about 25 minutes before sunrise. The changes in the brightness of the planet are indicated by the relative sizes of the circles marking Mercury's position at five-day intervals. It will be noticed that Mercury is at its brightest after it reaches greatest western elongation (28°) on 22 March. The diagram gives positions for a time at the beginning of morning civil twilight on the Greenwich meridian, on the stated date. Observers in different longitudes should note that the actual positions of Mercury in azimuth and altitude will differ slightly from those shown in the diagram, due to the motion of the planet. This change will be much greater still for the Moon, if it is shown, as its motion is about 0.5° per hour.

VENUS continues to be visible as a brilliant object in the western sky in the evenings and, for observers in the latitudes of the British Isles, is visible for nearly three hours after sunset. Those in the Southern Hemisphere will be restricted to only about half this time.

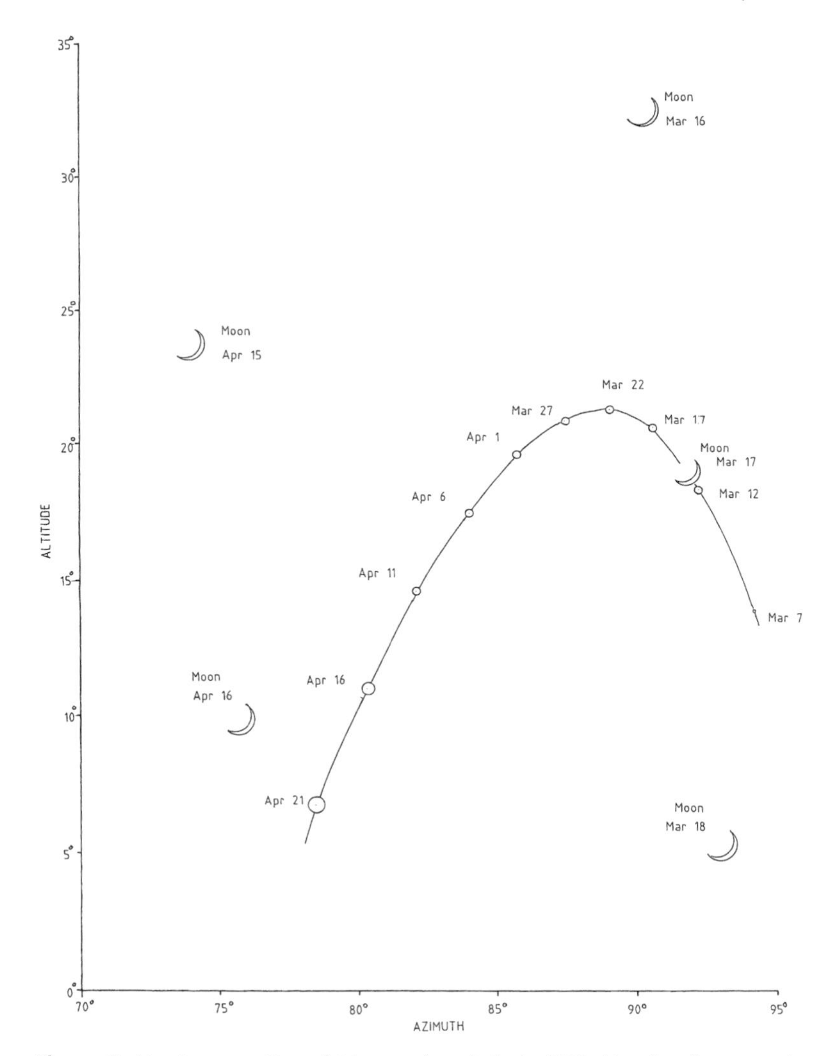

Figure 5. Morning apparition of Mercury, from latitude 35°S. (Angular diameters of Mercury and the crescent Moon not to scale.)

MARS, magnitude +1.2, continues to be visible in the eastern skies in the mornings for observers in more southerly latitudes, and is now visible by about 03h local time. Keen early-morning observers should note that Mars could be a useful guide to locating Neptune on 25–26 March, as it passes within a degree south of that planet on 25 March (see Figure 15 – the diagram for locating Neptune – given with the notes for August). Unfortunately for observers in the latitudes of the British Isles, Mars is still unobservable.

JUPITER, magnitude −2.1, continues to be visible as a brilliant morning object in the eastern sky long before sunrise. Observers in the Southern Hemisphere will be able to see the planet rising before midnight and being high in the sky before dawn.

SATURN is only just past opposition and therefore is still available for observation during the greater part of the night, becoming visible in the east as soon as the sky is dark enough. Saturn's magnitude is +0.2.

Linné and the Lunar Eclipse. The total eclipse of the Moon this month (on 3–4 March) will be well worth watching – and photographing. Totality lasts for 1 hour 14 minutes, so that there is no frantic rush, as there is with a total eclipse of the Sun. It cannot be said that a lunar eclipse is astronomically important, but the colours depend upon conditions in the Earth's upper atmosphere – through which all the light reaching the eclipsed Moon has to pass.

When the Earth's shadow sweeps across the Moon, the temperature on the lunar surface drops sharply; remember that there is no air to trap heat from the Sun. Can this 'wave of cold' be detected in any way? One astronomer who believed so was William Henry Pickering, who drew up a good photographic atlas of the Moon a century ago, and was a leading observer of the planets (as we have mentioned in the notes for January, it was he who discovered Saturn's satellite Phœbe). In particular, Pickering looked carefully at a small formation named Linné, on the Mare Serenitatis.

There are a few prominent craters on Serenitatis; the largest is the well-formed Bessel, 17 km (11 miles) across. In 1838 the first really good lunar map was drawn by two German observers, Beer and Mädler; they gave detailed descriptions of the surface, and described Linné as a deep, prominent crater. Subsequently, it was seen that Linné appears only as a small craterlet surrounded by a bright nimbus. Any real change seems most unlikely, because – like so many features – Linné looks different under different conditions of lighting, but Pickering was convinced that there had been an alteration, and that the white patch round Linné was icy. Therefore, he reasoned, it might well increase in size when a lunar eclipse caused an abrupt drop in temperature.

Working together with other observers – Andrew Ellicott Douglass in America and Samuel Arthur Saunder in England – he made measurements during several eclipses, and announced that the effects on Linné were real. However, they have never been confirmed, and certainly the Linné nimbus is not due to ice. Watch Linné by all means, but do not expect to see any change in it.

The Danjon Scale. The French astronomer André-Louis Danjon drew up a lunar eclipse brightness scale for measuring the appearance and luminosity of the Moon during a lunar eclipse.

There were five grades on the Danjon Scale:

0. very dark eclipsed Moon, almost invisible.
1. Dark grey or brownish; details difficult to identify.
2. Dark or rusty red, with a dark patch in the middle of the shadow; bright edges.
3. Brick red, sometimes with a bright or yellowish border to the shadow.
4. Coppery or orange-red; very bright, often with a bluish cast and varied hues.

On 18 May 1761, the Swedish astronomer Per Wargentin (after whom the famous lunar plateau is named) reported that during mid-totality the Moon disappeared so completely that it could not be found even with a telescope. The lunar eclipse of 10 June 1816 was also extremely dark, with the totally-eclipsed Moon again completely invisible to the naked eye. By contrast, the lunar eclipse of 19 March 1848 was so 'bright' that some lay observers refused to believe that an eclipse was happening at all. It will be interesting to see what happens at this month's lunar eclipse. The Moon enters the umbral shadow at 21h 30m UT on 3 March, totality lasts from 22h 44m until 23h 58m, and the Moon exits the umbra at 01h 12m on 4 March.

Olbers and the Fourth Asteroid. Two hundred years ago, on 29 March 1807, the asteroid 4 Vesta was discovered by the German amateur astronomer Heinrich Wilhelm Matthias Olbers (1758–1840). The discovery was not due to pure luck. Olbers was one of a team searching systematically for asteroids; up to that time three had been found, Ceres in 1801, Pallas in 1802 (by Olbers) and Juno in 1804. Vesta is the brightest of the asteroids, though smaller than Ceres and Pallas; it can just be seen with the naked eye when at its best. It has been surveyed by the Hubble Space Telescope (Figure 6), and is very interesting indeed; there are ancient lava-flows, and a gigantic impact crater about 460 km (285 miles) across that is so deep it exposes the asteroid's subsurface layer, or mantle – remember that the average diameter of Vesta itself is no more than 525 km (326 miles). The rotation period of Vesta is 5.34 hours.

Figure 6. This elevation map of the asteroid 4 Vesta clearly shows the giant impact basin and 'bull's-eye' central peak. The map was constructed from seventy-eight Hubble Space Telescope images. Surface topography was estimated by noting irregularities along the limb and at the terminator (day/night boundary) where shadows are enhanced by the low Sun angle. (Image courtesy of Ben Zellner (Georgia Southern University), Peter Thomas (Cornell University) and NASA/STScI.)

Olbers was born at Arbergen, near Bremen, on 11 October 1758. He studied medicine at Gottingen and Vienna, and set up a medical practice in Bremen in 1881. An enthusiastic amateur astronomer, he built an observatory on the roof of his house; from there he discovered Pallas and then Vesta. He devised a new method of calculating the orbits of comets, and in 1811 formed the theory that comets' tails are streams of minute particles driven out of the head by a 'repulsive force due to the Sun'; he was of course quite correct. In March 1815, he discovered the periodical comet which now bears his name (13P/Olbers); it has a period of 69.6 years, and is next due to return to perihelion in June 2024.

Olbers was very popular, and was known to be an exceptionally pleasant person, always ready to help and encourage others. He died at Bremen on 2 March 1840.

April

New Moon: 17 April *Full Moon:* 2 April

MERCURY continues to be visible as a morning object for the first three weeks of the month, though only to observers in tropical and southern latitudes. During this period its magnitude brightens from 0.0 to −0.9. Observers should refer to the diagram given with the notes for March (Figure 5).

VENUS continues to be visible as a magnificent object in the evening sky, magnitude −4.1. Conditions vary quite noticeably as the observer's latitude changes. Those in the latitudes of the British Isles will be able to see it for around four hours after sunset, by the end of the month, while those in temperate southern latitudes will enjoy only about two hours. Interestingly, similar conditions will prevail with the morning apparition of Venus six months later. Venus passes 7° north of Aldebaran, in Taurus, on 21 April.

MARS continues to be visible in the eastern sky in the mornings, for observers further south than the latitudes of the British Isles. The magnitude of Mars is +1.1. At the beginning of April, Mars moves from Capricornus into Aquarius. Mars can be a useful guide to locating Uranus on the early morning of 29 April when it passes only 0.7° south of that planet (see Figure 18 – the diagram for locating Uranus – given with the notes for September). Figure 7 shows the path of Mars against the background stars during the first five months of the year.

JUPITER, magnitude −2.4, is still in the constellation of Ophiuchus and reaches its first stationary point on 6 April, when it commences its retrograde motion. Jupiter is now a conspicuous object in the skies and is rising as evening astronomical twilight ends. Although never very high in the sky for observers in the latitudes of the British Isles, those in tropical and southern latitudes will have a much better view.

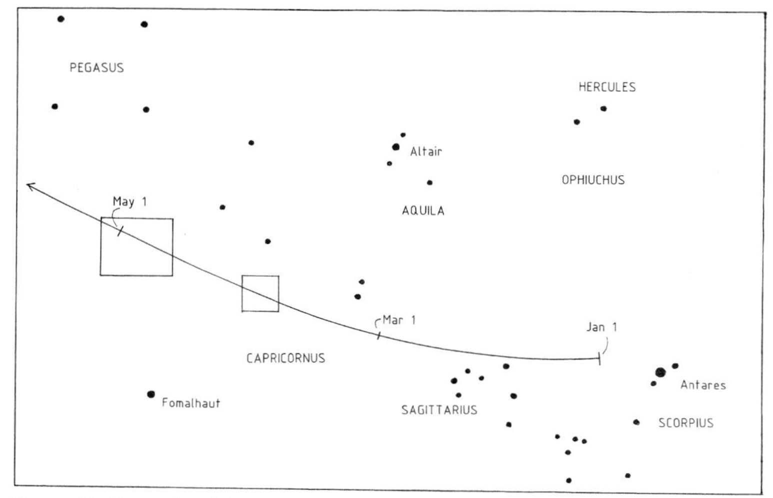

Figure 7. The path of Mars against the background stars of Ophiuchus, Sagittarius, Capricornus, Aquarius and Pisces during the first five months of 2007. The two rectangular boxes on the diagram show the locations of the two finder charts for Neptune (smaller rectangle left of centre) and for Uranus (larger rectangle to the far left), which are included with the notes for August and September, respectively.

SATURN continues to be visible as an evening object in the constellation of Leo, and crosses the meridian in the early evening. Long before dawn it sets over the western horizon. Its magnitude is +0.4. Saturn reaches its second stationary point and resumes its direct motion on 19 April.

The Herdsman and the Northern Crown. Boötes, the Herdsman, which is well placed, high in the south-east during April evenings, is one of the most prominent of the Northern Hemisphere constellations. No definite legends seem to be attached to it, but it was suggested that he invented the plough drawn by two oxen – for which flash of intellectual brilliance he was given a place in the sky! Corona Borealis, the Northern Crown, may represent a crown given by the god Bacchus to Ariadne, daughter of King Minos of Crete.

Of course the area is dominated by Arcturus, fourth brightest star in the night sky, and the brightest star in the Northern Hemisphere of the sky. Arcturus is a giant, with a diameter 24 times that of our Sun, that is to say, about 33 million km (20 million miles) across. Its declination is 19°N., so that it is visible from all the densely populated parts of the world. The leading stars of Boötes (Figure 8) are:

Star	Name	Mag.	Spectrum	Luminosity Sun = 1	Distance light-yrs
Alpha	Arcturus	−0.05	K2	115	37
Epsilon	Izar	2.35	A0	410	210
Eta	–	2.68	G0	9	37
Gamma	Seginus	3.04	A7	36	85
Delta	–	3.46	G8	46	117
Beta	Nekkar	3.49	G8	157	219
Rho	–	3.57	K3	67	149
Zeta	–	3.78	A3	81	180

The now discarded constellation of Quadrans Muralis (the Mural Quadrant) was made up from a few faint stars near Nekkar. At least it has given its name to the Quadrantid meteors of early January.

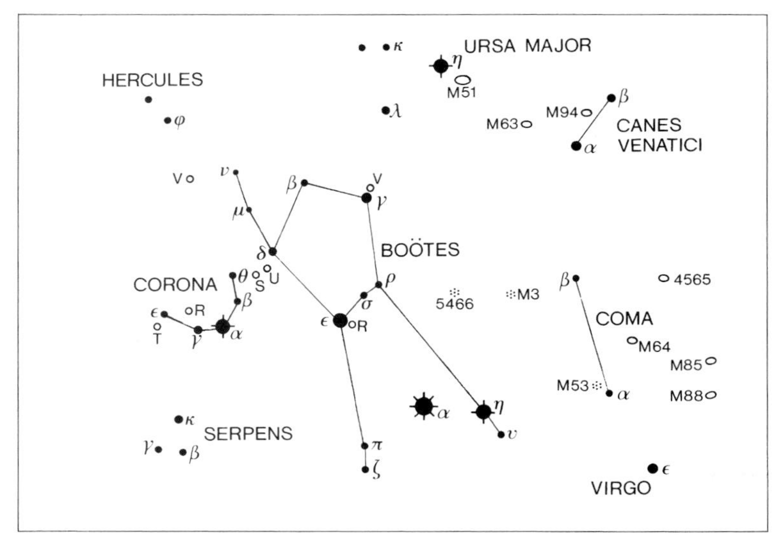

Figure 8. The principal stars of Boötes, the Herdsman. The brilliant Arcturus is below centre, with the semicirclet of stars comprising Corona Borealis, the Northern Crown, towards the left.

Zeta Boötis is a binary with equal components; magnitudes 4.5, 4.6; separation 0.7 arcsecond; period 123 years. Tau Boötis (magnitude 4.5) is known to be attended by a planet; it is an F7-type star, 51 light-years away, with three times the luminosity of the Sun. The planet, which has a mass at least four times that of Jupiter, has one of the shortest known periods, only 3.31 days. It follows a nearly circular orbit at a very close distance of 0.046 AU from the parent star, equivalent to 6.9 million kilometres, that is to say, just 12 per cent of Mercury's distance from the Sun, making it one of the many 'hot Jupiters' known. Mu Boötis (magnitude 4.3) has the unusual proper name of Alkalurops.

Corona Borealis is a conspicuous little group. Its main stars are:

Star	Name	Mag.	Spectrum	Luminosity Sun = 1	Distance light-yrs
Alpha	Alphekka	2.22	A0	59	75
Beta	Nusakan	3.66	F0p	36	114
Gamma	–	3.81	A1	51	145

The other stars in the semicirclet making up the shape of the crown are Theta (4.1) and Epsilon (4.2).

The interesting variable star R Coronæ is usually on the fringe of naked-eye visibility, but there are unpredictable minima – due to vast clouds of soot in the star's atmosphere – which make it fall to below magnitude 15. T Coronæ, the 'Blaze Star, is a recurrent nova. It is usually of around magnitude 10, but rose to naked-eye visibility (magnitude 2) in 1866; there was another outburst in 1946. Will there be another in 2026? Watch this space!

The Problem of T Boötis. On 9 April 1860, a well-known Manchester variable star observer, Joseph Baxendell, recorded a 9.75 magnitude star close to Arcturus. On 11 April, it was again seen and estimated to be of magnitude 10, but by 22 April it had faded to magnitude 12.8, and on the following night it was invisible with a 13-inch reflector in a sky which permitted stars of magnitude 14 to be seen. It has frequently been looked for since, but has never been observed.

The star has been catalogued as T Boötis; it was probably a nova, but just in case it is recurrent, regular monitoring of the field is worthwhile. Baxendell gave the position as 1m 45s preceding Arcturus and 11′ 30″ further south, but you cannot use these offsets today without making an allowance for the significant proper motion of Arcturus. Moreover, in his brief report on page 68 of volume 21 of the *Monthly Notices of the Royal Astronomical Society* for 1861, Baxendell gives no information as to how he determined these offsets or to their likely accuracy. There is a print from the Palomar Observatory's Sky Survey which most probably shows the post-nova, a star at (2000) 14h 14m 01.92s, +19° 04′ 04.0″, and this is probably the most positive identification one can give at the present time. The visual magnitude is given as 17.1.

This Month's Anniversary. Joseph Jérôme Lefrançais de Lalande was born at Bourg-en-Bresse in France on 11 July 1732. Although originally destined to study law, he was drawn to astronomy. On completion of his legal studies, instead of returning to Bourg to practise as an advocate, he went to Berlin to make observations of the lunar parallax. Having successfully completed this task, he was admitted to the Academy of Berlin and in February 1753 to the Académie des Sciences in Paris, a great achievement for so young a man; he was not yet 21 years of age.

Lalande devoted his time to the improvement of planetary theory, and in 1759, he published revised tables for Halley's Comet, which had returned earlier that year – the first predicted return and the first since Edmond Halley's death. Three years later, Lalande became Professor of Astronomy at the Collège de France, a post he held for forty-six years. His publications in connection with the 1769 transit of Venus won him great respect, and his planetary tables were the best available up to the end of the eighteenth century. In 1801 he published his *Histoire Celeste* giving the places of 47,390 stars, and which included many faint, nearby stars of low mass. He was also an energetic populariser of astronomy. A crater on the Moon, Lalande, is named for him. He died two hundred years ago this month, on 4 April 1807.

The Sky at Night After Fifty Years. This month marks the fiftieth anniversary of the beginning of the BBC television programme *The Sky at Night*, and I have been ordered by my co-editor to say something about how it all began. So here is the story.

In 1957, Paul Johnstone, a senior BBC producer, was anxious to start a monthly programme about astronomy in a new way. He had come across a book of mine – *Suns, Myths and Men* – and thought that it might be useful. He asked me to go and see him. I did. We talked; he put in a proposal; and the BBC agreed to put the programme on the air every month for four months, just to see how it was received. The first programme went out in April 1957, and we were extremely fortunate in having a bright comet, Arend-Roland, discovered by two Belgian astronomers, as the subject of our first programme. Well – we are still there. I have missed only one programme, when I was rushed into hospital with salmonella.

It has been an exciting period. I have seen the beginnings of the Space Age; the electronic revolution; eclipses; comets – including Halley's – and of course the first men on the Moon. I think that most of our leading astronomers have joined me on the programme at one time or another, and of course some of these are no longer with us, such as Bart Bok, Harlow Shapley, Clyde Tombaugh . . . We have been to major observatories all over the world; we have flown in the Kuiper Airborne Observatory; we have gone down into Homestake Mine to study neutrinos – it has been an amazing time.

We have tried to 'bring astronomy down to earth', and I like to think that we have helped many people along the way. Whether I have succeeded in this must be for others to judge.

Sadly, at the age of 83, I am no longer able to do what I once could. What next? Well, I hope that *The Sky at Night* will continue long after my time. So here's to the next fifty years.

May

New Moon: **16 May** *Full Moon:* **2 May**

MERCURY is not suitably placed for observation at first, but by the middle of the month becomes visible as an evening object, except for those in southern latitudes where the visibility period does not start until the third week of the month. For observers in northern temperate latitudes this will be the most favourable evening apparition of the year. Figure 9 shows, for observers in latitude 52°N, the changes in azimuth (true bearing from the north through east, south and west)

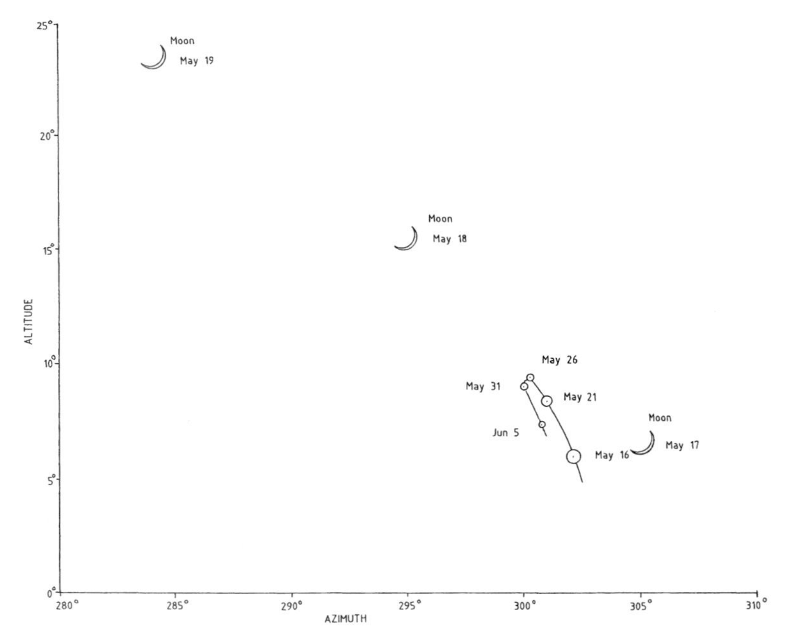

Figure 9. Evening apparition of Mercury, from latitude 52°N. The positions of the crescent Moon are shown for 17, 18 and 19 May as an aid to locating the planet. (Angular diameters of Mercury and the crescent Moon not to scale.)

and altitude of Mercury on successive evenings when the Sun is 6° below the horizon. This condition is known as the end of evening civil twilight and in this latitude and at this time of year occurs about 35 minutes after sunset. The changes in the brightness of the planet are indicated by the relative sizes of the circles marking Mercury's position at five-day intervals. It will be noticed that Mercury is at its brightest before it reaches greatest eastern elongation (23°) on 2 June. During the second half of the month Mercury's magnitude fades from −1.0 to +0.4. The diagram gives positions for a time at the beginning of evening civil twilight on the Greenwich meridian, on the stated date. Observers in different longitudes should note that the actual positions of Mercury in azimuth and altitude will differ slightly from those shown in the diagram due to the motion of the planet. This change will be much greater still for the Moon, if it is shown, as its motion is about 0.5° per hour.

VENUS, magnitude −4.2, continues to be visible as a magnificent object dominating the western sky in the evenings. Venus will be seen passing south of the Heavenly Twins, Castor and Pollux, in Gemini, at the end of the month.

MARS is becoming visible to observers in the latitudes of the British Isles for the first time this year, though only at the very end of this month, when they may be able to detect the planet low above the eastern horizon in the early mornings for a short while before the lengthening twilight inhibits observation. Further south, observers will have no difficulty in locating the planet as it moves north-eastwards through Pisces. The magnitude of Mars is +0.9.

JUPITER is now observable for most of the hours of darkness as it moves towards opposition early in June. Its magnitude is −2.5.

SATURN continues to be visible in the western sky in the evenings. Observers in the latitudes of the British Isles will still be able to see it up to midnight, even at the end of the month, though those in southern latitudes will lose it a couple of hours earlier. Saturn's magnitude is +0.5. Saturn continues its eastward motion towards Regulus, in the constellation of Leo.

The Ancient Mercury. The planet Mercury is at its best this month, at least as far as the Northern Hemisphere observers are concerned, with the planet visible in the evening twilight sky after sunset. Though Mariner 10 mapped an appreciable part of its surface (Figure 10), and we know much more about it than we did thirty years ago, in some ways Mercury is still an enigma. It is the smallest of the planets (now that Pluto has been demoted, by most people), but it is very dense, and – unlike Venus – it has a definite magnetic field. Presumably it has an iron-rich core which may be larger than the whole globe of the Moon.

One theory, supported by a team led by Dr. Jonathan Horner of the Theoretical Astrophysics and Planetary Science group at the University of Bern in Switzerland, suggests that Mercury was formed from a collision between a large proto-planet – about 2.25 times Mercury's current size – and a planetesimal about half Mercury's current size around four and a half thousand million years ago. Computer simulations showed what might have happened, leaving a dense, Mercury-like body with a large swathe of rapidly escaping débris. Though most of the débris would have fallen back on to the main mass, some of it might have been spread around – even as far as the Earth, in which case it is not impossible that we might have handled some fragments of proto-Mercury! At least the theory would explain why Mercury is the densest planet in the Solar System apart from the Earth.

Venus Near the Twins. This month Venus is not far from the heavenly twins of Gemini, Castor and Pollux. The twins are not alike, and have no actual connection with each other. It is interesting to compare their colours. Pollux (magnitude 1.16), 34 light-years away and 32 times as luminous as the Sun, is an ordinary K-type star, clearly orange. Castor (fainter at magnitude 1.58), 52 light-years from us and 50 times as luminous as the Sun, is a contrasting white.

Castor is a fine binary, with unequal components, Castor A and Castor B (magnitudes 1.9 and 2.9, respectively), orbital period about 420 years and a separation at present of 4.3 arcseconds. Both Castor A and Castor B have been shown to be spectroscopic binaries, consisting of almost identical pairs of white stars, with periods of 9.2 and 2.9 days, respectively. There is also a much fainter, distant member of the system, Castor C (magnitude 9.1), which is 72 arcseconds away and visible in any small telescope. It is probably orbiting the main pair in a period of around 10,000 years, and this too is a spectroscopic binary

Figure 10. After passing on the darkside of the planet, Mariner 10 photographed the other, somewhat more illuminated hemisphere of Mercury. The north pole is at the top, two-thirds down from which is the planet's equator. The Mariner 10 spacecraft had three encounters with Mercury in March and September 1974 and March 1975. (Image courtesy of NASA Jet Propulsion Laboratory.)

(period 0.8 days), made up of a pair of red dwarfs. Interestingly, the orbit of the two components of Castor C is more or less edge-on as viewed from Earth, so we see both primary and secondary eclipses of one star by the other; the amplitude of the eclipses is about half a magnitude, so they are detectable visually. Since it varies in brightness, Castor C is also given the designation YY Geminorum.

Castor is a truly remarkable, multiple star system, with six separate components – four comparatively bright and white, and two dim and red.

The Eta Aquarids. The Eta Aquarid meteor shower is active from about 24 April to 20 May, with its maximum on 4 May. The associated comet is none other than Halley's, and the shower occurs as the Earth encounters the meteoroid swarm distributed around the parent comet's orbit near the comet's descending node (Figure 11). At maximum, the radiant of the shower is located at (2000) 22h 20m, −01°, close to the naked eye star Gamma Aquarii.

The Eta Aquarids are not especially rich, but the ZHR has been known to rise to 40 at maximum. The ZHR – Zenithal Hourly Rate –

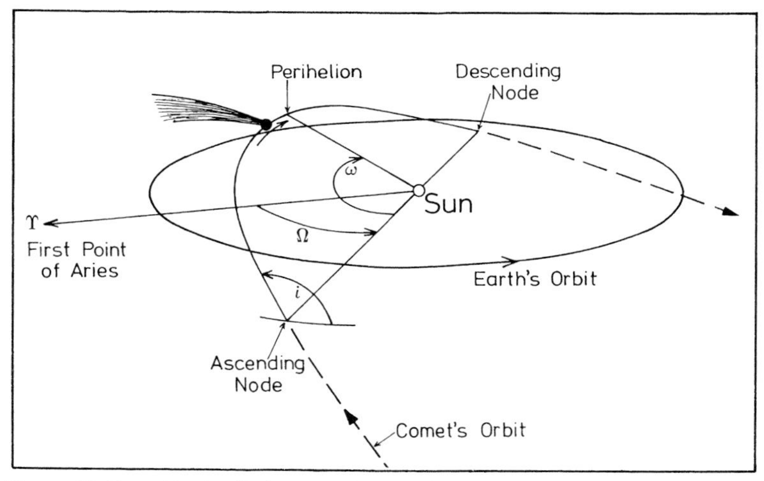

Figure 11. The orbit of Halley's Comet shortly before and after perihelion, relative to the plane of Earth's orbit around the Sun. The Eta Aquarid meteor shower occurs when the Earth passes near the comet's descending node in early May each year.

denotes the number of naked-eye meteors which would be seen by an observer under ideal sky conditions (limiting magnitude 6.5) with the shower radiant at the zenith, i.e. directly overhead. In practice these conditions are never fulfilled, so that the actual number of observed meteors is usually considerably less than the theoretical ZHR.

From the United Kingdom, the Eta Aquarid shower is never easy to observe because the radiant is fairly low in the south-eastern sky as morning twilight interferes. However, from locations further south, conditions are considerably more favourable, and from a site in the Tropics it is possible to make useful observations in the pre-dawn hours, with a dark sky.

Wiliamina Fleming. This month is the 150th anniversary of the birth of a great woman astronomer, Wiliamina (Mina) Paton Stevens Fleming. She was Scottish, born in Dundee on 15 May 1857. She attended public school, and in May 1877 married James Fleming; the young couple emigrated to America, and settled in Boston. Unfortunately the marriage soon broke up, and in 1879 Mina became a housekeeper in the home of Edward C. Pickering, Director of the Harvard College Observatory.

She showed a lively interest in astronomy, and Pickering hired her to do some clerical work at the Observatory. By 1881 she had become a permanent member of the Observatory research staff, concentrating upon the photography of spectra. Fleming examined the spectra of more than 10,000 stars and devised a classification system containing 22 classes. She was also put in charge of staff hired to do mathematical work and she edited the Observatory's publications. By 1898 she was curator of the astronomical photographs at Harvard, and in 1906 she was elected to the Royal Astronomical Society in London, the first American woman to be so elected. She made many contributions to research, discovering over 300 variable stars, plus 10 novæ and 59 gaseous nebulæ. She died in Boston of pneumonia on 21 May 1911.

It is an interesting aside that both she and the other great woman astronomer of the period, Annie Jump Cannon (who continued Fleming's work on the classification of stellar spectra), suffered from deafness – though they did not allow this to interfere with their lives or their research.

June

New Moon: **15 June** *Full Moon:* **1 and 30 June**

Solstice: 21 June

MERCURY attains its greatest eastern elongation (23°) on 2 June and therefore continues to be visible in the evenings for the first week of the month, its magnitude fading from +0.5 to +1.2. For observers in higher temperate latitudes like those of the British Isles it will be difficult to observe in the long evening twilight. For further guidance, readers should refer to the diagram given with the notes for May (Figure 9).

VENUS continues to be visible as a magnificent object in the western sky in the evenings, magnitude −4.3.

MARS, magnitude +0.8, continues to be visible as a morning object in the eastern sky. Mars moves from Pisces into Aries towards the end of the month.

JUPITER is visible throughout the hours of darkness as it reaches opposition on 5 June. It is now a very conspicuous object in the night sky with a magnitude of −2.6. Jupiter is moving slowly retrograde in the constellation of Ophiuchus, and Figure 12 shows the path of the planet against the background stars during the year. The four Galilean satellites are readily observable with a small telescope, or even a good pair of binoculars provided that they are held rigidly.

SATURN is still visible in the western sky during the early part of the evening, before disappearing over the western horizon. Observers in the latitudes of the British Isles will be handicapped by the long evening twilight. Its magnitude is +0.6.

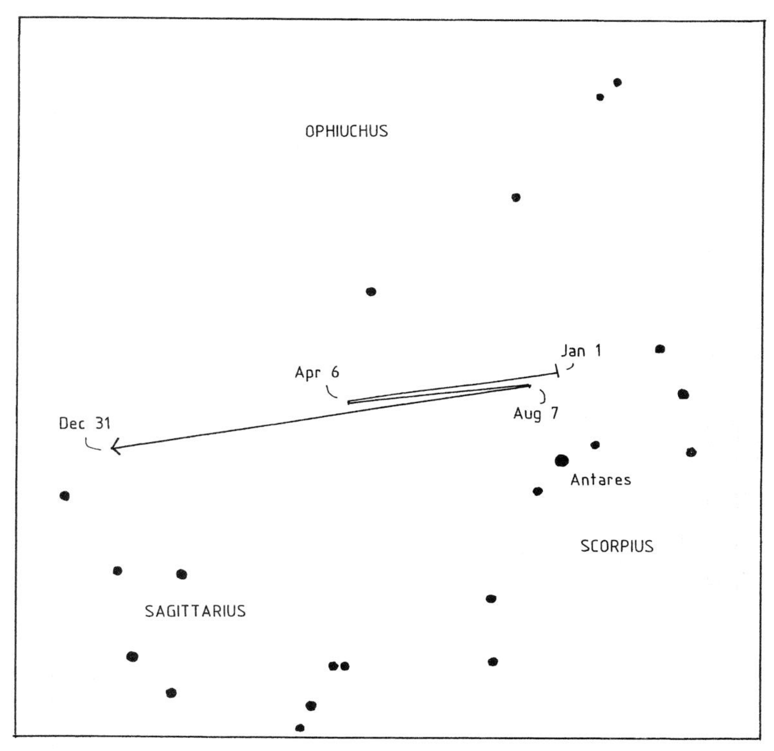

Figure 12. The path of Jupiter against the background stars of Scorpius, Ophiuchus and Sagittarius during 2007.

Pluto at Opposition. Pluto reaches opposition on 19 June, in the constellation of Serpens, at a distance of 4,530 million kilometres (2,820 miles) from the Earth. It is only visible with a moderate-sized telescope, since its magnitude is +14. Since 1999, Pluto has been further out than Neptune, and was said to have become once more 'the outermost planet', but it now seems that Pluto must be regarded simply as a large Kuiper Belt object (KBO) rather than a true planet.

Pluto, with a diameter of just 2,320 kilometres (1,442 miles) is considerably smaller than our Moon (and much less massive), and several other planetary satellites. More significantly, it is smaller than at least one of the recently discovered KBOs. If Pluto is ranked as a planet, then so must they be – and where does one draw the line?

A possible definition proposed by one of the Editors of this *Yearbook* (PM) is as follows. 'A planet of the Solar System is an independent body, moving round the Sun; it is spherical (or very nearly so), with a diameter of over 3,000 miles (4,830 kilometres).' This includes Mercury, but no known KBO. If a KBO above this limit is found, then we shall have to think again!

The Fishes. Mars begins this month in the constellation of Pisces, the Fishes. Pisces is usually called the last constellation of the Zodiac, though since it now contains the vernal equinox it really ought to be first. The naked-eye star closest to the equinox is Omega Piscium (Figure 13).

No firm legends are attached to Pisces, but the constellation may possibly represent the two fishes into which Venus and her son, Cupid, once changed themselves, when they plunged into the dark waters of the River Euphrates to escape from the fire-breathing monster Typhon – whose intentions were anything but honourable.

Pisces is a large but dim constellation. Its leading stars are:

Star	Name	Mag.	Spectrum	Luminosity Sun = 1	Distance light-yrs
Eta	Alpherg	3.62	G8	250	294
Gamma	–	3.69	G7	47	131
Alpha	Al Rischa	3.82	A2	47	139
Omega	–	4.03	F4	22	106

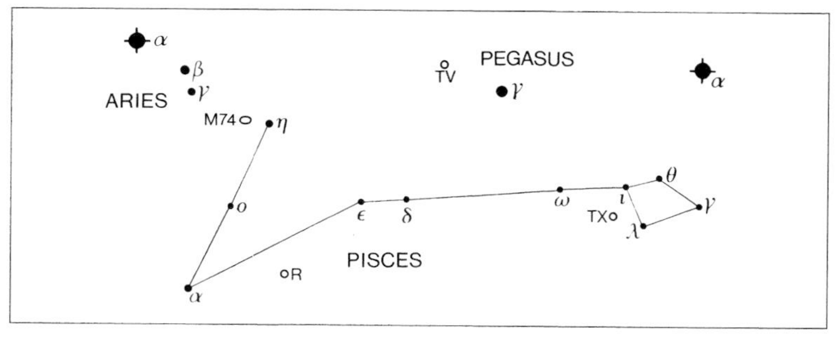

Figure 13. The principal stars of Pisces, the Fishes. The position of the vernal equinox (the so-called First Point of Aries) is slightly below the star Omega Piscium, which is to the right of centre on the map.

Alpha Piscium has several proper names; Kaitain and Okda are other alternatives. It is a binary; magnitudes 4.2 and 5.1; separation 1″.8, period 933 years.

R Piscium is a Mira-type variable star, with a range from magnitude 7.1 and 14.8, and a period of 344 days. However, the most interesting object in Pisces is probably the N-type irregular TX Piscium, which varies between magnitudes 6.9 and 7.7. It is easy to find, and looks almost like a glowing coal. M74 (RA 1h 36.7m, Dec. +15° 47′), near Eta, is an Sc-type spiral galaxy; though the integrated magnitude is given as 9.4, it can be decidedly elusive. It was discovered by Pierre Méchain in 1780.

This Month's Centenary. Alexander Stewart Herschel was born in February 1836, the second son of Sir John Herschel and therefore the grandson of Sir William Herschel, discoverer of Uranus. Alexander was actually born at Feldhausen, near Cape Town, during his father's spell in South Africa – where he had gone to extend Sir William's survey of the sky to the far south.

The Herschels returned to England in 1838, and Alexander spent the rest of his life there. He graduated from Trinity College, Cambridge, and entered the Royal School of Mines in London in 1861, where he initiated a programme of meteorological observations. Alexander was an enthusiastic teacher, but his main research was in connection with meteors. He made important observations of many of the now familiar annual meteor showers, and he initiated a programme to study the chemical constituents of meteors by observing their spectra. To this end, he developed an efficient binocular direct-vision spectroscope, fitted with prisms of his own design.

In 1866, Alexander was appointed Professor of Mechanical and Experimental Physics at the Andersonian University in Glasgow (now Strathclyde University), and it was from Glasgow that he observed the brief, but intense Leonid meteor shower in November of that year. He moved to become Professor of Physics at Newcastle upon Tyne in 1871. Alexander was admittedly eccentric; it is said that he never walked, but ran everywhere. Moreover he was so concerned with meteor watching that he neglected his health. He retired in 1886, and went to live at the Herschel home, Observatory House in Slough, where he died, at the age of seventy-one, on 18 June 1907, one hundred years ago this month.

July

New Moon: **14 July** *Full Moon:* **30 July**

EARTH is at aphelion (furthest from the Sun) on 7 July at a distance of 152 million kilometres (94 million miles).

MERCURY attains its greatest elongation west of the Sun (20°) on 20 July and is therefore a morning object. For observers in the latitudes of the British Isles it is a very difficult object to detect because of the long duration of twilight, but may possibly be seen within a few days of 26 July, low above the east-north-eastern horizon about 40–50 minutes after sunset. Conditions are better for observers further south, as Mercury will be slightly higher in the sky and considerably brighter towards the end of the month. On 15 July its magnitude is +1.2, though by the end of July it has brightened to −0.9.

VENUS continues to be visible as a magnificent object in the western sky in the evenings, magnitude −4.5. However, for those in the latitudes of the British Isles the period available for observation is shortening noticeably, and a few days before the end of the month the planet is lost to view in the glare of sunset. Further south the planet is visible right through to the end of the month. Venus attains its greatest brilliancy on 12 July, with a magnitude of −4.5. Venus passes 0.7° south of Saturn on 1 July, though Venus is then 100 times brighter than Saturn!

MARS continues to be visible as a morning object, magnitude +0.6. For observers in the latitudes of the British Isles the planet can be seen rising before midnight at the end of the month, over two hours earlier than for those in the Southern Hemisphere. Mars moves from Aries into Taurus towards the end of July. Figure 23, given with the notes for December, shows the path of Mars against the background stars during the last seven months of the year.

JUPITER, magnitude −2.5, continues to be visible as a brilliant object in the western sky in the evenings. As the planet is well south of the equator at a June opposition observers in northern temperate latitudes will not see it at any great altitude above the horizon; for them it has disappeared below the south-western horizon before midnight, while at the same time remaining high in the sky for observers in tropical and southern latitudes.

SATURN, magnitude +0.6, becomes a more difficult object to detect in the early evening sky as the month progresses, low above the western horizon. Although observers in the Southern Hemisphere should be able to detect it until the end of the month, those in the latitudes of the British Isles are unlikely to see it after the first few days of the month.

The Surprising Delta Scorpii. Scorpius, the Scorpion, is one of the most magnificent constellations in the sky. It is led by Antares (magnitude 1.06), the so-called 'Rival of Ares (Mars)' and the reddest of all the brilliant stars, 604 light-years away and more than 11,000 times as luminous as the Sun. Scorpius really does conjure up the impression of the creature it represents. From Britain it is always low down, and the extreme southern part never rises, but when high in the sky, as seen from countries such as Australia, it is superb.

The middle star in the line of three stars which make up the Scorpion's head is Delta Scorpii, which has a proper name – Dschubba; it has also been called Iclarkrav or Iclarkrau. It was regarded as a normal white giant star, about 1,600 times as luminous as the Sun (14,000 times as luminous if you include the invisible ultraviolet radiation), with five times the diameter of the Sun, and 402 light-years away according to the Hipparcos measurements; its spectrum was of type B0, and the apparent visual magnitude was 2.29. The main star has a slightly cooler B-type companion, over ten times fainter, which has an orbital period of 20 days, and is just 60 million kilometres (37 million miles) from the primary. A third member of this multiple system lies at a distance of around 1,500 million kilometres (over 900 million miles), taking over ten years to complete an orbit, and at probably double that distance lies yet a fourth, fainter star. So, Dschubba is a remarkably complex system.

In June 2000, an Argentine variable star observer, Sebastián Otero, found that Delta Scorpii was much brighter than it should have been.

Evidently there had been an outburst. Over the next months the magnitude fluctuated between 1.7 and 2, completely altering the whole look of the Scorpion's head; by 19 April 2002 the magnitude had climbed to 1.67 according to the astronomers in Buenos Aires.

Other stars have been known to show similar outbursts; the most famous example is Gamma Cassiopeiæ in the familiar 'W' pattern, which brightened from visual magnitude 2.25 to 1.6 in 1937. Delta Scorpii is now listed as a variable of the Gamma Cassiopeiæ (GCAS) type. It will repay attention from amateur observers; suitable comparison stars are Beta Scorpii (magnitude 2.56), Eta Ophiuchi (2.43), Beta Libræ (2.61) and, for southern observers. Theta Centauri (2.06).

T Scorpii and M80. Also in the Scorpion is a variable star of very different type, T Scorpii. On 21 May 1860, it flared up in the globular cluster M80 (NGC 6093), completely changing the appearance of the cluster for some days. According to George Auwers in Berlin, the star attained magnitude 7.0 on 21 and 22 May, but had faded to magnitude 10.5 by 16 June. This outburst was also witnessed by Norman Pogson, who made an independent discovery of it. Although Pogson reported that he had seen a re-brightening in early 1864, this is improbable as no other observer was able to confirm it, and it seems most likely that the star was a nova. In any event, it has not been seen since. At maximum, T Scorpii appeared considerably brighter than the entire M80 cluster, and if the star was a member of that cluster its absolute magnitude must have been around −8.5. If it were an ordinary nova it will not be seen again, but there is always a chance that it may be a recurrent object.

The globular cluster M80 (RA 16h 17m, Dec −22° 59′), also known as NGC 6093, has an integrated magnitude of 7.3, and is easy to locate because it lies midway between Antares and Beta Scorpii. It was discovered by Charles Messier on 4 January 1781, who described it as a 'Nebula without a star, resembling the nucleus of a comet.' Its distance is 28,000 light-years according to recent measurements, and is said by some observers to look like a tailless comet. It is unusually dense – one of the densest of the globular clusters in the Milky Way galaxy – and contains several hundred thousand stars packed into a volume about 90 light years across (Figure 14). If our Sun were a star within the M80 globular cluster, the night sky would glow like a jewel box with brilliant stars. Most of the stars in M80 are older and redder than our Sun, but

Figure 14. Hubble Space Telescope image of the globular cluster M80, one of the densest of the approximately 150 known globular star clusters in a halo surrounding the Milky Way. Globular clusters are particularly useful for studying stellar evolution, since all of the stars in the cluster have the same age (about 14 billion years), but cover a range of stellar masses. (Image courtesy of The Hubble Heritage Team (AURA/ STScI/ NASA).)

there are also so-called 'Blue Stragglers' – hot stars which seem to be younger and bluer than would be expected inside a globular – which maybe due to stellar collisions or 'near encounters', so that their outer layers have been stripped off.

August

New Moon: **12 August** *Full Moon:* **28 August**

MERCURY passes through superior conjunction on 15 August and will not be visible to observers in the British Isles. Only for observers in tropical latitudes will it be possible to detect the planet during the first few days of the month low above the east-north-eastern horizon shortly before sunrise, magnitude −1.1. For the last few days in the month it becomes visible to observers in tropical and southern latitudes, as an evening object, magnitude −0.7, low above the western horizon shortly after sunset. Refer to the diagram given with the notes for September (Figure 17).

VENUS is still visible as a brilliant object low in the western sky after sunset in the early evenings, magnitude −4.2. Although it is then lost to view for observers in the latitudes of the British Isles, further south it may still be seen low above the western horizon after sunset, for the first 10–15 days of the month. Venus passes through inferior conjunction on 18 August and emerges from the glare of the rising Sun to be visible above the eastern horizon before dawn for the last 10–15 days of the month (but only for the last 5 days for those in the latitudes of the British Isles). Again, its magnitude is −4.2.

MARS continues to be visible as a morning object in the eastern sky, magnitude +0.4. Observers in northern latitudes should be able to view the planet above the east-north-eastern horizon before midnight. Mars remains in the constellation of Taurus throughout the month, passing 5° north of Aldebaran on 24 August.

JUPITER continues to be visible as a brilliant object in the western skies in the evenings, with observers in the Southern Hemisphere still able to see the planet until well after midnight. Jupiter's magnitude is −2.3, and it reaches its second stationary point on 7 August when it resumes its direct motion eastwards.

SATURN is no longer available for observation as it passes through conjunction on 21 August.

NEPTUNE is not visible to the naked eye since its magnitude is +7.8, but it is fairly easy through binoculars, although rather low down for observers in the British Isles. Figure 15 shows the path of Neptune against the background stars during the year. The two brightest stars in the diagram are Gamma Capricorni, magnitude +3.8, shown in the lower left of the diagram, and Iota Capricorni, magnitude +4.3, shown in the lower right of the diagram. To assist observers in locating this area it is shown as the smaller rectangular box on the Mars diagram (Figure 7) given with the notes for April. At opposition on 13 August, Neptune is 4,343 million kilometres (2,699 million miles) from the Earth.

Out of Order. In Bayer's system, still in use after four centuries, the stars in each constellation are given Greek letters; the brightest star is Alpha, the second brightest Beta, the third brightest Gamma, and so on. Sometimes, however, things become chaotic. Thus in Sagittarius the three brightest stars are Epsilon, Sigma and Zeta; Epsilon outshines Alpha and Beta by more than two magnitudes. In the south polar constellation, Octans, the brightest stars are Nu, Beta and Delta. In Puppis, the brightest star is Zeta – but Puppis is part of the large and now-dismembered constellation, Argo Navis, and the brightest stars were given to other parts, Carina and Vela. (Canopus, now Alpha Carinæ, used to be Alpha Argûs.) In Leo Minor the brightest star is 46 Leonis; the only star with a Greek letter is Beta – there is no Alpha Leonis Minoris. Two star clusters were also given Greek letters: Epsilon Cancri (Præsepe) and Omega Centauri. Not that it really matters!

William Lassell and the Ring of Neptune. William Lassell was one of the leading amateur astronomers of the nineteenth century. Born in Bolton in 1799, he became a brewer, and was so successful that he was able to devote much of his time to astronomy. He made his own mirrors, and in 1844 built a fine 24-inch reflector. (He had the help of James Nasmyth, another amateur astronomer, who was also the inventor of the steam hammer.)

The planet Neptune was discovered in 1846 (see the monthly notes for August in the 2006 *Yearbook*). Soon afterwards Lassell found the main satellite, Triton, and also suspected a ring. Indeed, after one

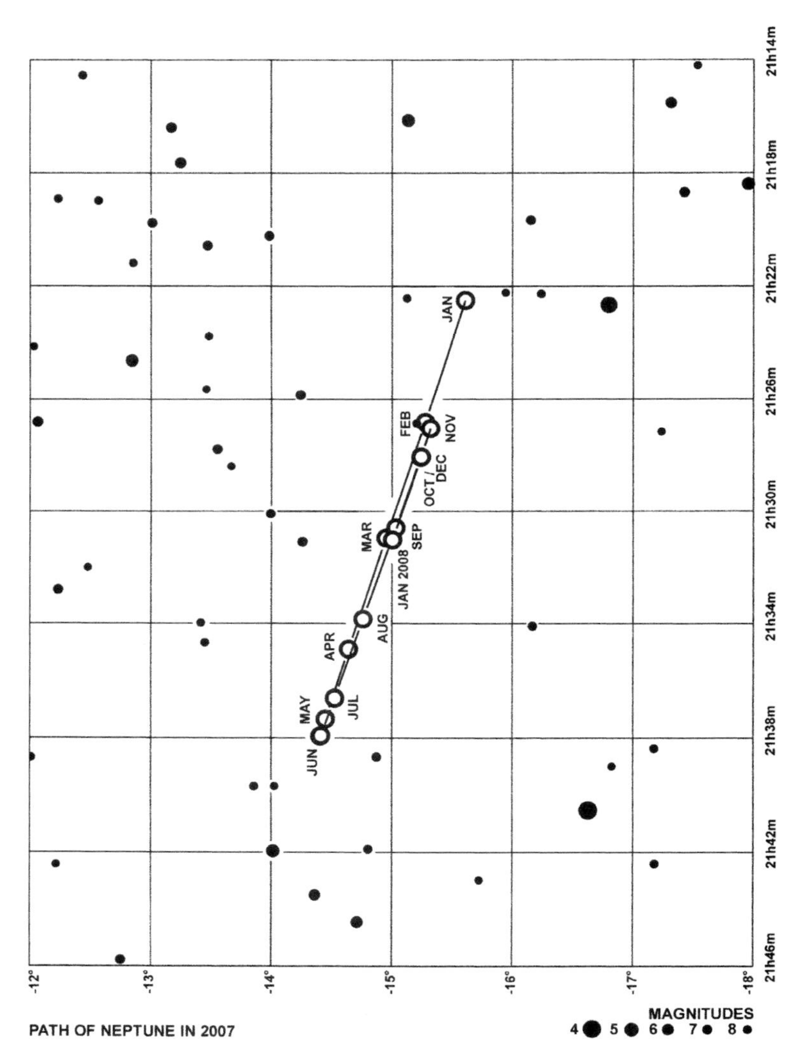

Figure 15. The path of Neptune against the stars of Capricornus during 2007. The two brightest stars on the chart are Gamma Capricorni, magnitude 3.8, shown in the lower left of the diagram, and Iota Capricorni, magnitude +4.3, shown in the lower right of the diagram.

observation he wrote: 'The planet was very like Saturn as seen with a small telescope and low power, but much fainter.' And later: 'With regard to the existence of the ring, I am not able absolutely to declare it, but I received so many impressions of it, always in the same form and direction, and with all the different magnifying powers, that I feel a very strong persuasion that nothing but a finer state of atmosphere is necessary to enable me to verify the discovery.'

He reported the observations at a meeting of the Royal Astronomical Society in 1846. One of those present was John Russell Hind, a well-known observer, who used a 7-inch refractor at George Bishop's observatory in Regent's Park. (Nothing now remains of this observatory – and today, Regent's Park would hardly be an ideal site.) Hind looked at Neptune, and wrote that the existence of a ring was 'most probable'.

James Challis, who had failed to identify Neptune even when all the information had been put into his hands, observed the planet with the Northumberland telescope at Cambridge. On 12 January 1847 he wrote: 'I had for the first time a distinct impression that the planet was surrounded by a ring like that of Saturn.' He informed Lassell, who was naturally pleased, and replied: 'I cannot refuse to believe that your observation puts beyond reasonable doubt the reality of mine.'

Yet doubts soon crept in. Other observers failed to see the ring, and Lassell himself was equally unsuccessful in 1849 and 1850. Slowly he began to doubt the existence of the ring. Then he took his powerful telescope to Malta, where the skies were very clear, and while observing the planet on 15 December 1852 he realized that the supposed ring changed its position when he rotated the tube of the telescope. The ring did not exist. Hind and Challis had simply 'seen' what they expected to see.

Of course Neptune does have a ring system (Figure 16); it has been clearly shown by the Voyager 2 spacecraft, which flew past the planet in August 1989, but the real ring was quite beyond the range of any telescope of the nineteenth century, and Lassell's ring was as unreal as the canals of Mars.

Herman Carl Vogel. Vogel was born in Leipzig (Germany) on 3 April 1841, and educated at the University there. He was appointed as an assistant at the Leipzig Observatory, where he became interested in astrophysics, helping Johann Zöllner in his work on solar prominences.

Figure 16. These two exposures of the rings of Neptune were taken by the Voyager 2 spacecraft on 26 August 1989. The two main rings are clearly visible and appear complete over the region imaged. Also visible in this image is an inner faint ring at about 42,000 kilometres (25,000 miles) from the centre of Neptune, and a faint band which extends smoothly from the 53,000 kilometre (33,000 miles) ring to roughly halfway between the two bright rings. (Image courtesy of NASA Jet Propulsion Laboratory.)

In 1870, Vogel became Director of the Bothkamp Observatory, near Kiel, before moving to the Potsdam Observatory in 1874, becoming its Director in 1882, and continuing in that post until his death in 1907.

Vogel carried out pioneering work on the spectra of the major planets, comets, the Sun and stars. He was the first to demonstrate the solar rotation by measuring the Doppler shift at its receding and approaching limbs. He made detailed tables of the solar spectrum and attempted the spectral classification of stars. Vogel's most important work was photographic measurement of Doppler shifts to determine the radial velocities of stars. In 1890, Vogel detected the double nature of the star Spica, thus establishing the existence of spectroscopic binaries – double-star systems that are too close for the individual stars to be discerned by any telescope but, through the analysis of their spectra, are revealed to be two stars revolving around one another. In 1883, he published the first spectroscopic star catalogue. He died in Potsdam, one hundred years ago, on 13 August 1907.

September

New Moon: 11 September *Full Moon:* 26 September

Equinox: 23 September

MERCURY attains its greatest eastern elongation (26°) on 29 September and is therefore an evening object, though not for observers as far north as the British Isles. For observers in southern latitudes this will be the most favourable evening apparition of the year. Figure 17 shows, for observers in latitude 35°S, the changes in azimuth (true bearing from the north through east, south and west) and altitude of Mercury

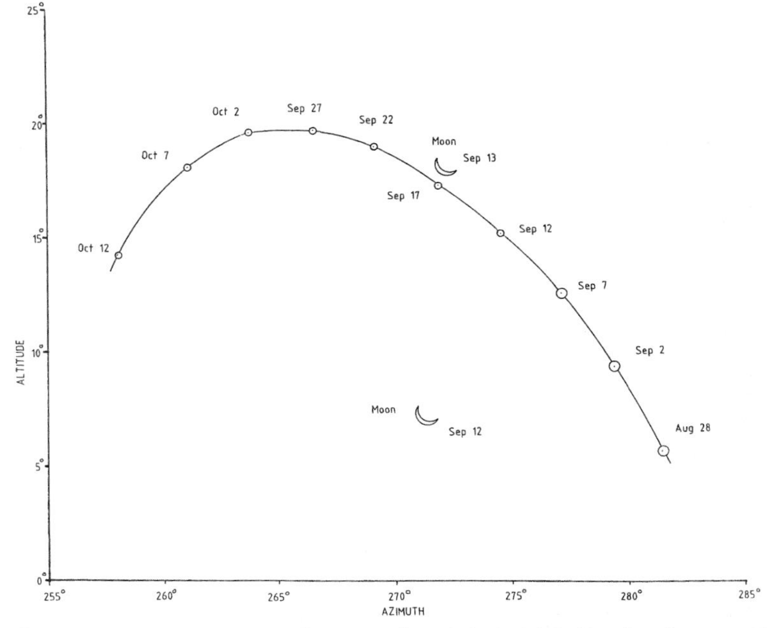

Figure 17. Evening apparition of Mercury, from latitude 35°S. (Angular diameters of Mercury and the crescent Moon not to scale.)

on successive evenings when the Sun is 6° below the horizon. This condition is known as the end of evening civil twilight, and in this latitude and at this time of year occurs about 25 minutes after sunset. The changes in the brightness of the planet are indicated by the relative sizes of the circles marking Mercury's position at five-day intervals. There is little variation in Mercury's magnitude throughout September, being −0.5 at the beginning and +0.1 at the end. Mercury passes very close to Spica in Virgo on 22 September, Spica being almost one magnitude fainter than the planet. Mercury is moving eastwards at the rate of about 2° a day, and the time of closest approach is around 09–10h GMT, when Mercury will be only 10 arcminutes north of the star. Only observers in Australia and in the area of the eastern Indian Ocean are likely to see the instant of the closest approach. The diagram gives positions for a time at the beginning of evening civil twilight on the Greenwich meridian, on the stated date. Observers in different longitudes should note that the actual positions of Mercury in azimuth and altitude will differ slightly from those shown in the diagram, due to the motion of the planet. This change will be much greater still for the Moon, if it is shown, as its motion is about 0.5° per hour.

VENUS, magnitude −4.6, becomes a magnificent object completely dominating the eastern sky before dawn. It attains its greatest brilliancy on 24 September with a magnitude of −4.6.

MARS continues to be visible as a morning object in the eastern sky, though for observers in northern temperate latitudes it is now rising before midnight. During September its magnitude brightens from +0.3 to −0.1. Towards the end of the month Mars moves from Taurus into Gemini.

JUPITER, magnitude −2.1, continues to be visible in the early evenings in the western sky for observers in the latitudes of the British Isles. The length of time for which the planet remains visible increases as one moves further south, and for those south of the tropics Jupiter is still visible after midnight.

SATURN, magnitude +0.6, slowly becomes visible as a difficult morning object in the sky, very gradually pulling away from the Sun and so getting more easily detectable. Observers in northern temperate latitudes may be able to see it after about the first ten days of the month, but those in southern latitudes will have to wait until the last week of the month. As will be seen from the diagram given with the notes for February (Figure 3), Saturn is moving slowly, just east of Regulus.

URANUS, magnitude +5.7, is barely visible to the naked eye, though it is readily located with only modest optical aid. Figure 18 shows the path of Uranus against the background stars during the year. The brightest star in the diagram is Lambda Aquarii, magnitude 3.8, shown in the right-hand part of the diagram. To assist observers in locating this area it is shown as the larger rectangular box on the Mars diagram (Figure 7) given with the notes for April. At opposition on 9 September, Uranus is 2,855 million kilometres (1,774 million miles) from the Earth.

The Bowling-Pin Comet. After the highly successful spacecraft encounters with Halley's Comet in 1986, scientists had to wait over 15 years for their next close-up views of a cometary nucleus. These came, six years ago this month, courtesy of a spacecraft called Deep Space 1. Launched from Cape Canaveral on 24 October 1998, the objectives of the spacecraft's primary mission were the testing of 12 advanced technologies with the potential to lower the costs and risks of future space missions. Having succeeded in these tasks, Deep Space 1 embarked on an extended mission, which took it first past the asteroid 9969 Braille on 29 July 1999, although because of a software crash shortly before closest approach the pictures were disappointingly fuzzy.

Deep Space 1 then went on to make a flyby of comet 19P/Borrelly on 22 September 2001, passing just 2,200 kilometres from the nucleus, and returning detailed images along with other science data. Borrelly's nucleus (Figure 19a) turned out to be roughly half the size of Halley, and even more elongated, measuring 8.0 × 3.2 × 3.2 kilometres (5 × 2 × 2 miles). Its shape was reminiscent of a tenpin bowling pin. Borrelly was less active than Halley with only one main dust and gas jet visible (Figure 19b), although this may have been produced from three discrete active areas on the nucleus. Once again only a small percentage of the surface area of the nucleus was active. Fortunately, the main jet did not appear to point towards the spacecraft, because it had no dust shields yet it survived its passage through the comet's dusty coma intact. Deep Space 1 was retired on 18 December 2001.

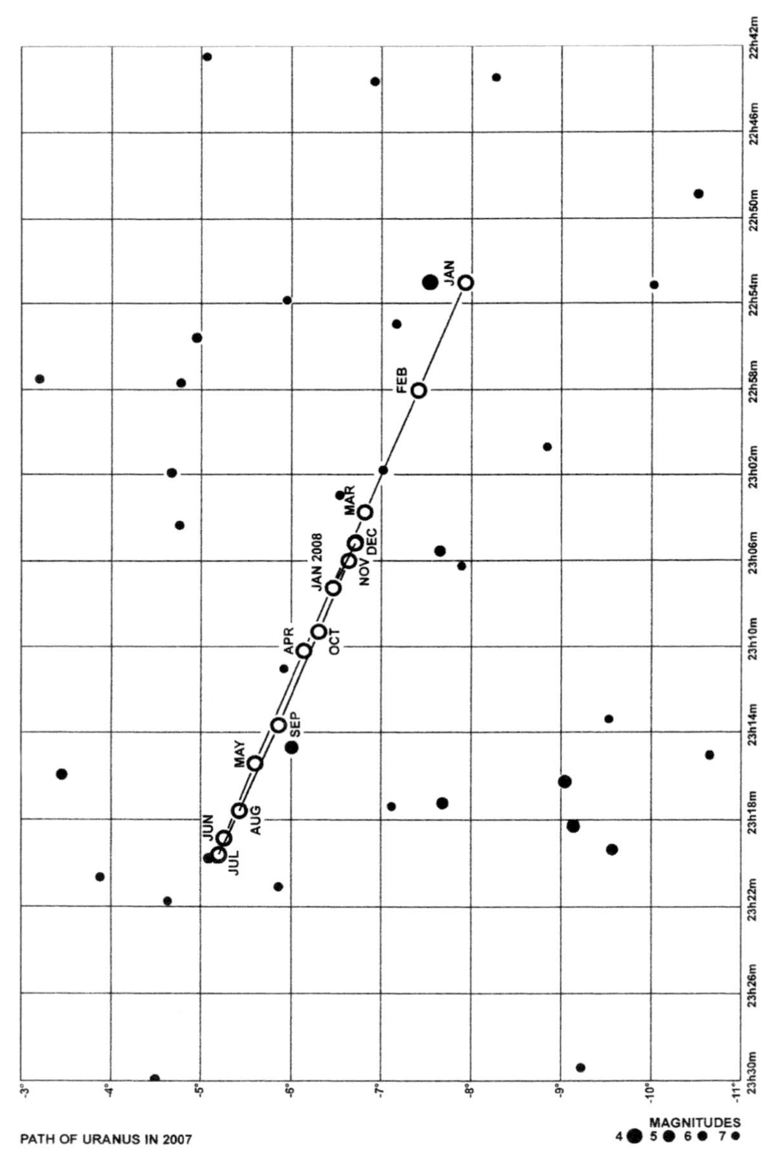

Figure 18. The path of Uranus against the stars of Aquarius during 2007. The brightest star on the chart is Lambda Aquarii, magnitude 3.8, shown in the right-hand part of the diagram.

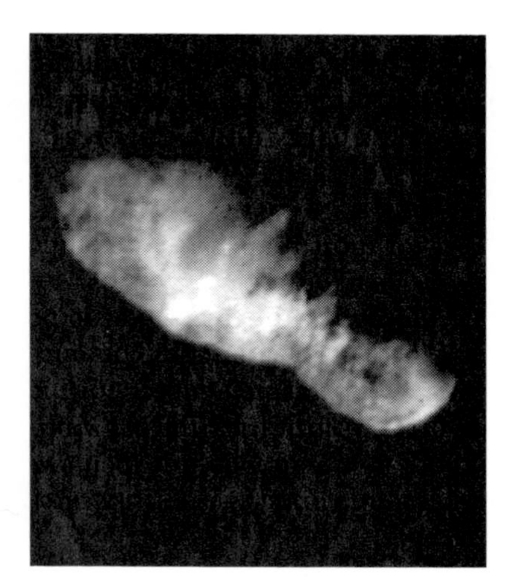

Figure 19 (a). An enlarged view of the elongated, bowling-pin-shaped nucleus of comet 19P/Borrelly, imaged by NASA's Deep Space 1 spacecraft on 22 September 2001. (Image courtesy of NASA Jet Propulsion Laboratory.)

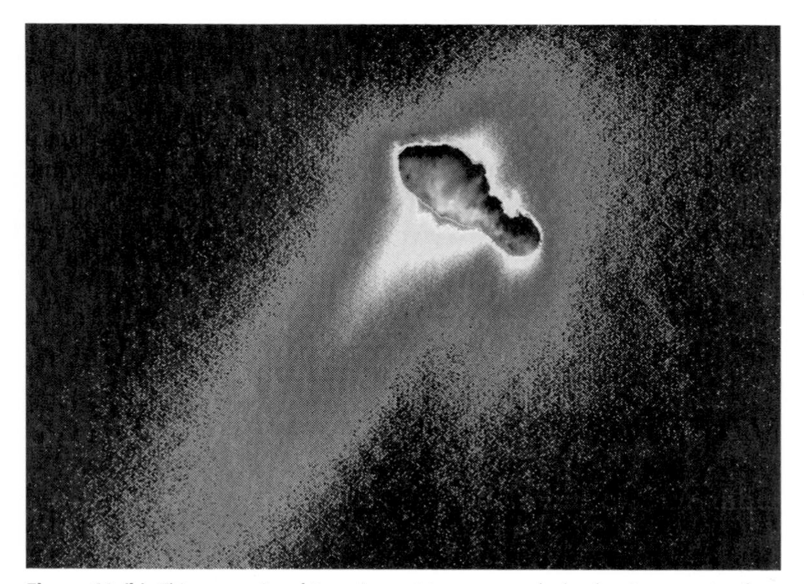

Figure 19 (b). This composite of Deep Space 1 images reveals the dust jets escaping from comet Borrelly's nucleus and the cloud-like coma of dust and gases surrounding it. The Sun shines from the bottom of the image. Near the nucleus, the jet resolves into three distinct, narrow jets, which probably come from discrete sources on the surface. (Image courtesy of NASA Jet Propulsion Laboratory.)

Pallas. Asteroid no. 2, Pallas, is at opposition on 3 September, when it will be 337 million kilometres (209 million miles) from Earth. This is not a particularly favourable opposition, and consequently the magnitude will be no better than 8.8. During the month, Pallas moves from Pegasus into Aquarius, and will be located in the region between Alpha Aquarii and the distinctive grouping of four stars comprising Pi, Gamma, Zeta and Eta Aquarii. Its high orbital inclination (nearly 35 degrees) means that at times it can wander well away from the Zodiac. Apart from Ceres, Pallas is the largest of the main belt asteroids; it is slightly triaxial in shape, measuring 570 × 525 × 500 kilometres (354 × 326 × 310 miles). At a favourable opposition, it can reach the eighth magnitude.

Pallas has been observed occulting a star on several occasions, including the best observed of all asteroid occultation events on 29 May 1983, when careful occultation timing measurements were taken by observers at 130 different locations. The combination of solutions from this and previous occultations showed the triaxial shape of Pallas to be elongated, but not severely so, with the ratio of the largest to the smallest axes being less than 1.15. The absence of any confirmed secondary occultations showed that any satellites of Pallas must be rare or very small. The photometric observations seemed to rule out a substantial cloud of dust surrounding Pallas, as had been thought previously.

Pallas was discovered on 28 March 1802 by Heinrich Wilhelm Olbers. The name honours the Greek goddess Pallas Athene, the goddess of wisdom and the arts – analogous to the Roman Minerva. Important data for Pallas are as follows:

Distance from the Sun,	max. 3.4117 AU (510.4 million kilometres)
	mean 2.7723 AU (414.7 million kilometres)
	min. 2.1328 AU (319.1 million kilometres)
Orbital period:	4.62 years
Orbital eccentricity:	0.2306
Orbital inclination, degrees:	34.840.
Rotational period:	7.81 hours
Diameter, Miles:	570 × 525 × 500 kilometres
Mean Density:	2.8 g/cm^3
Albedo:	0.159
Maximum magnitude:	8.0

Pallas has yet to be surveyed from close range by a spacecraft, but a mission to do so is being planned. The first four asteroids to be found – Ceres, Pallas, Juno and Vesta – are known popularly as the 'Big Four', though in fact Juno comes only fourteenth in the list of the largest main-belt asteroids. The largest ten are, in order, 1 Ceres, 2 Pallas, 4 Vesta, 10 Hygeia, 511 Davida, 704 Interamnia, 52 Europa, 15 Eunomia, 87 Sylvia and 16 Psyche.

Of the first hundred asteroids to be discovered, Pallas has the highest orbital inclination. Next comes 31 Euphrosyne (26.4 degrees), which was discovered by James Ferguson on 1 September 1854, and was the first asteroid found from North America.

October

New Moon: **11 October** *Full Moon:* **26 October**

Summer Time in the United Kingdom ends on 28 October.

MERCURY is unsuitably placed for observation from northern temperate latitudes throughout the month. However, for observers in tropical and southern latitudes it continues to be visible as an evening object for the first half of the month and observers should refer to the diagram given with the notes for September (Figure 17). During its period of visibility its magnitude fades from +0.1 to +1.2. Mercury passes through inferior conjunction on 23 October.

VENUS continues to be visible as a magnificent morning object, visible in the eastern sky for several hours before sunrise. Its magnitude is −4.5. On 9 October Venus passes 3° south of Regulus in Leo and five days later passes 3° south of Saturn.

MARS becomes noticeably brighter during the month, its magnitude changing from −0.1 to −0.6. It is still visible as a morning object in the eastern sky. Mars is in the constellation of Gemini.

JUPITER is still visible as a brilliant evening object in the western skies, magnitude −1.9. Observers in the southern hemisphere will continue to be able to see the planet until nearly midnight, while for those in the latitudes of the British Isles it will only be visible for about an hour after sunset.

SATURN, magnitude +0.7, is slowly moving away from the Sun, and is visible as a morning object low in the eastern sky for a short while before the morning twilight inhibits observation.

The Dawn of the Space Age. The Space Age began on 4 October 1957 – exactly half a century ago – when the Soviet Union launched Sputnik 1, the world's first artificial satellite. At the time, it was an open secret that the Russians were preparing something spectacular, but few had appreciated that they were so near to success. This was particularly so in the United States where the satellite programme, which had been announced almost two years earlier, had been beset with problems, and delay had followed delay. The reasons were partly technical, but also partly political, with a good deal of service rivalry between the army and the air force – and the Russians had wasted no time.

Sputnik 1 was the size of a beachball, and carried little except a radio transmitter which sent out the never-to-be-forgotten 'bleep! bleep!' signals. The satellite was launched by a multi-stage R-7 rocket, and it orbited the Earth at a height of between 215 and 940 kilometres (135 and 580 miles), completing one orbit every 96 minutes. The satellite itself was a 58 centimetre-diameter aluminum sphere, weighing 83 kilogrammes (184 pounds), which carried four whip-like antennae that were 2.4–2.9 metres long. The four antennae looked like long 'whiskers' pointing out to one side.

Reaction to news of the Sputnik was mixed; some people claimed to have seen strange lights in the sky, and others to have heard the strains of 'The Red Flag' wafting down from above. But the most popular question was: could the Sputnik be seen – and if so, where? In fact, Sputnik 1 itself was never visible to the naked eye, because it was just too small and faint, but the upper stage of the launch rocket was much larger, so that it looked like a bright star moving slowly and steadily across the sky against the starry background, and there was no real difficulty in locating it.

Every time Sputnik 1 orbited the Earth, it passed into the extremely tenuous layers of Earth's upper atmosphere when at the lowest point in its orbit, and this atmospheric drag caused the satellite's orbit to decay gradually. It couldn't stay up indefinitely and Sputnik 1 came to the end of its career on 3 January 1958, when it re-entered the atmosphere and was incinerated. Sputnik 1 had been in orbit for only three months, but in that time it had made 1,400 orbits of the Earth, travelling a cumulative distance of about 70 million kilometres (43 million miles).

The success of Sputnik 1 galvanized the Americans into swift action. They set up a rocket testing ground at White Sands in New Mexico, and carried out a long series of tests with the intention of launching an artificial satellite of their own before the end of 1958. One of their leading technicians was the German rocket pioneer Wernher von Braun, who had masterminded the V2 rocket campaign against England during the closing stages of World War 2. By the end of January 1958, von Braun's team had successfully launched America's first satellite, Explorer 1. It was a mere 15 centimetres (6 inches) in diameter, but it proved to be far more valuable scientifically than Sputnik 1 had been.

The primary science instrument on Explorer 1 was a cosmic ray detector designed to measure the radiation environment in Earth orbit. Once in space this experiment, provided by the late Dr. James Van Allen of the State University of Iowa, made the first great discovery of the Space Age – the detection of Earth's two main radiation belts (now called the Van Allen belts), arranged in a doughnut form around the Earth. They are due chiefly to electrically-charged particles emitted by the Sun (the solar wind), which are then trapped within Earth's powerful magnetic field. Sputnik and Explorer showed that satellites had come to stay, and in the fifty years since then satellites have made an enormous contribution to our knowledge of the universe around us.

First Close-up View of an Asteroid. Our first close-up views of asteroids were mere snapshots obtained by a spacecraft while *en route* to somewhere else. NASA's Galileo mission to Jupiter, due for launch using the Space Shuttle in May 1986, had been planned to include a flyby of the Main Belt asteroid 29 Amphitrite on 6 December 1986 – the first close-range inspection of such a body, and a great scientific bonus for the Galileo project. But it was not to be. The Challenger disaster of January 1986 necessitated a radical redesign of the Galileo mission. This was because the Centaur liquid-fuelled upper stage, which was to send the spacecraft direct to the giant planet, and had been adapted for use with the Shuttle, was now deemed too dangerous to be flown to low-Earth orbit in the Shuttle's payload bay. Instead, the much less effective IUS solid-fuelled rocket had to be used.

The revised plan meant that Jupiter could only be reached if the Galileo spacecraft followed a highly circuitous route involving flybys (and associated gravity assists) from Venus once and the Earth twice – the so-called Venus-Earth-Earth Gravity Assist (VEEGA) trajectory. Eventually launched in October 1989, the Venus flyby lifted the aphelion (furthest point from the Sun) of the spacecraft's orbit out beyond Earth's orbit, the first Earth flyby moved it out to the asteroid belt, and the second Earth flyby extended it to Jupiter's orbit. Arrival at the giant planet finally took place in December 1995. Now flybys of two asteroids were planned while Galileo was *en route* to Jupiter.

The first close-up pictures of an asteroid were obtained by the Galileo spacecraft sixteen years ago this month, on 29 October 1991. The target was 951 Gaspra (Figure 20), a typical Main Belt asteroid, measuring 20 × 12 × 11 km. Its surface reflects about 20 per cent of the sunlight striking it. Gaspra is classified as an S-type asteroid. Such bodies are of a silicaceous (stony) composition and are likely composed of nickel-iron metal mixed with iron- and magnesium silicates. S-type asteroids are most common in the inner part of the Main Belt, but become rarer further out. Gaspra is a member of the Flora family, and its irregular, tapered shape is consistent with it being a fragment produced by the break-up of a somewhat larger body, a few hundred kilometres across, sometime in the past. Galileo made a second successful asteroid flyby – of the Main Belt asteroid 243 Ida – on 28 August 1993.

Figure 20. A mosaic of two images of the asteroid 951 Gaspra acquired by the Galileo spacecraft from a range of 5,300 km on 29 October 1991. More than 600 craters, 100–500 metres in diameter, are visible. (Image courtesy of NASA Jet Propulsion Laboratory.)

November

New Moon: **9 November** *Full Moon:* **24 November**

MERCURY reaches greatest western elongation (19°) on 8 November. For observers in northern temperate latitudes this will be the most favourable morning apparition of the year. Figure 21 shows, for observers in latitude 52°N, the changes in azimuth (true bearing from the north through east, south and west) and altitude of Mercury on successive mornings when the Sun is 6° below the horizon. This condition is known as the beginning of morning civil twilight, and in this latitude and at this time of year occurs about 35 minutes before sunrise. The changes in the brightness of the planet are indicated by the relative sizes of the circles marking Mercury's position at five-day intervals.

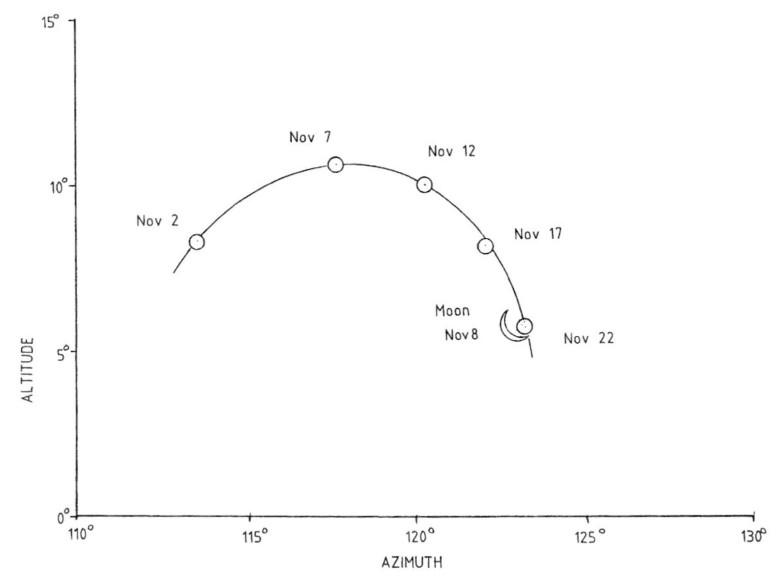

Figure 21. Morning apparition of Mercury, from latitude 52°N. (Angular diameters of Mercury and the crescent Moon not to scale.)

It will be noticed that Mercury is at its brightest after it reaches greatest western elongation. During its period of visibility its magnitude brightens from +0.8 to −1.0. The diagram gives positions for a time at the beginning of morning civil twilight on the Greenwich meridian, on the stated date. Observers in different longitudes should note that the actual positions of Mercury in azimuth and altitude will differ slightly from those shown in the diagram, due to the motion of the planet. This change will be much greater still for the Moon, if it is shown, as its motion is about 0.5° per hour. Mercury is unsuitably placed for observation by those in the Southern Hemisphere.

VENUS, magnitude −4.3, continues to be visible as a magnificent object, completely dominating the eastern sky for several hours before dawn. Shortly before the end of the month Venus passes nearly 5° south of Spica in Virgo.

MARS is now visible from the late evening onwards through the night, its magnitude brightening from −0.6 to −1.3. Mars' eastward motion in Gemini is slowing rapidly, and it reaches its first stationary point on 15 November before moving retrograde.

JUPITER continues to be visible as an evening object in the western skies, magnitude −1.8. Although observers in the Southern Hemisphere will be able to see the planet for a while after sunset, it will be much more difficult to observe by those in northern temperate latitudes; by the end of the month it will be lost to view over the southwestern horizon for those in the latitudes of the British Isles.

SATURN, magnitude +0.7, continues to be visible as a morning object in the eastern sky, in the constellation of Leo.

Asaph Hall and the Satellites of Mars. This month is the centenary of the death of Asaph Hall, a leading astronomer of the nineteenth century. He was born at Goshen, Connecticut, on 15 October 1829, and during boyhood was apprenticed to a carpenter. Hall was largely self-taught, although he did study briefly at Central College, McGrawville, New York, and at the University of Michigan at Ann Arbor. In 1856, he went to Harvard College Observatory in Cambridge, Massachusetts, and proved himself an expert computer of orbits. He became assistant astronomer at the US Naval Observatory in Washington DC in 1862, but within a year was made Professor. In 1875, he was put in charge of the 26-inch refractor there, the largest refracting telescope in the world at that time. The following year he noticed a white spot on Saturn and used it as a marker to make a very accurate determination of the planet's rotation period. In 1877, using the same 26-inch telescope, he discovered the two satellites of Mars. He retired from Washington in 1891, and in 1896 became a Professor at Harvard. He died in Annapolis, Maryland on 22 November 1907.

Possible satellites of Mars were first mentioned by Jonathan Swift, in Part III of *Gulliver's Travels: A Voyage to Laputa*, written in 1727. Laputa was a flying island – the first flying saucer in fiction! The Laputan astronomers were so keen-sighted that they had discovered two moons of Mars, one of which had an orbital period of less than a Martian day. In 1750 another novelist, Voltaire, also gave Mars two moons. He pointed out that Jupiter had four moons and the Earth one – so how could Mars possibly manage with less than two?

The first systematic search for a Martian satellite was made in 1783, by William Herschel. He had no success; neither did D'Arrest, in 1862 and 1864. The general idea was that the poet Tennyson was justified in writing about the 'snowy poles of moonless Mars'.

In 1877 Mars was well placed, and Hall decided to search with the large refractor. He had no luck, and was about to give up when his wife persuaded him to make one last attempt. He did so – and on the morning of 11 August detected a faint starlike object, which proved to be the outer satellite. The next few nights were cloudy, but on 16 August the sky cleared; Hall recovered the first satellite, and also found a second. Both were tiny; the inner moon did indeed move around Mars in less than a Martian day, just as Swift had predicted. The two satellites were named Phobos and Deimos, after the two attendants of the mythological God of War.

The satellites are not particularly faint (Phobos is of magnitude 11.6 when Mars is at mean opposition, Deimos 12.8), but they are so close to Mars that they are not easy to see. Both are irregular in shape; Phobos has a longest diameter of less than 30 kilometres (20 miles), and Deimos less than 15 kilometres (10 miles). Phobos moves less than 6,000 kilometres (3,700 miles) above the Martian surface – about the same distance as that between New York and Amsterdam. To an observer on Mars, Phobos would rise in the west, cross the sky in only

4½ hours and set in the east, with the interval between successive risings being just over 11 hours; Deimos would move from east to west, but would remain above the horizon for 60 hours continuously. Neither would be very effective at lighting up the Martian nights.

Both have been mapped by spacecraft; they are cratered, with dusty surfaces. The largest crater on Phobos, 10 kilometres (6 miles) across, has been named Stickney; this was the maiden name of Asaph Hall's wife, Angeline, who persuaded him not to abandon the hunt. The two largest craters on Deimos have been named Swift and Voltaire.

Searches for new small moons have been unsuccessful, and we may be sure that Phobos and Deimos are the only natural satellites. Almost certainly they are ex-asteroids, captured by Mars long ago.

The Most Massive Stars. A typical star begins life – as do all stars – inside a slowly spinning cloud of cool interstellar gas. This cloud gradually coalesces into lumps called protostars. At first, a protostar is a cool blob of gas several times larger than the Solar System. As the protostar collapses under its own gravity, its temperature rises, because gravitational energy is converted to heat energy. The protostar continues to shrink, until the temperature at its core reaches about 10 million °C, when nuclear fusion begins. The fusion of hydrogen to helium releases enormous amounts of energy and this creates conditions which finally halt the gravitational contraction. At that point, a stable star is born. A star at this stage of its life is known as a 'Main Sequence star'. It represents the most stable phase of a star's life, during which it will be slowly fusing hydrogen to helium at its core.

The most massive Main Sequence stars have masses about 150 times that of our Sun. Any more massive than that, and the collapsing cloud of gas probably fragments into a number of smaller, less massive protostars. It seems that stars can be born big, but only so big. Recent observations of a massive cluster of stars in the centre of our Galaxy have confirmed that this mass cutoff is about 150 times that of the Sun. Using the Hubble Space Telescope, astronomers measured the masses of stars in the Arches Cluster (Figure 22), which is 25,000 light-years away and ten times the size of typical clusters in our Galaxy. The Arches Cluster contains many more smaller mass stars than larger mass stars. This is typical for a cluster, but the best place to find the biggest stars is in the biggest clusters.

One problem in finding really massive stars is that they consume

Figure 22. Although hidden from our direct view, this artist's impression shows how the Arches star cluster might appear from deep inside the hub of our Galaxy. The illustration is based on infrared observations with the Hubble Space Telescope and with ground-based telescopes. (Image courtesy of NASA, ESA and A. Schaller (for STScI).)

their available nuclear fuel at such a prodigious rate. Stars of 100 solar masses will only live about 3 million years – compared with our Sun which has a Main Sequence lifetime of about 10,000 million years. Therefore, to catch a glimpse of a giant star, one has to look not only at a big cluster, but a young one as well. Fortunately, the Arches Cluster is between 2 and 2.5 million years old. The absence of any stars greater than about 150 solar masses in the Arches Cluster can only be explained by a physical barrier to more massive stars.

The most massive Main Sequence stars are also the most luminous. For example, a blue supergiant star known as LBV-1806–20, which resides in a giant cluster of freakishly massive stars, also tips the scales at about 150 times the mass of our Sun. It shines up to 40 million times brighter than the Sun. Despite its great luminosity, LBV-1806–20 is only visible in binoculars, because it lies 45,000 light-years away from us, on the far side of our Galaxy.

December

***New Moon:* 9 December** ***Full Moon:* 24 December**

Solstice: 22 December

MERCURY passes slowly through superior conjunction on 17 December and is unsuitably placed for observation throughout the month.

VENUS is still visible as a brilliant object in the eastern sky in the early mornings, magnitude −4.1. At the end of the year it rises above the east-south-eastern horizon over three hours before the Sun for observers in the latitudes of the British Isles (about half an hour less for those in temperate southern latitudes).

MARS is at opposition on 24 December and therefore visible throughout the hours of darkness, and by the end of the month it should be visible in the eastern sky by about 15–30 minutes after sunset. Its magnitude is then −1.6. Mars is moving retrograde in the constellation of Gemini, entering Taurus early in the New Year. Figure 23 shows the path of Mars against the background constellations during the last seven months of the year. Mars makes its closest approach to the Earth six days before opposition, on 18 December, when its distance from the Earth is then 88.2 million kilometres (55 million miles).

JUPITER remains too close to the Sun for observation throughout the month as it passes through conjunction on 23 December.

SATURN, although still a morning object, is now visible in the eastern sky well before midnight by the end of the month. Saturn's magnitude is +0.7. It reaches its first stationary point on 19 December and commences its retrograde motion.

Tuttle's Periodical Comet. This month is a good time to look at a very interesting periodical comet, 8P/Tuttle. It was originally seen by Pierre

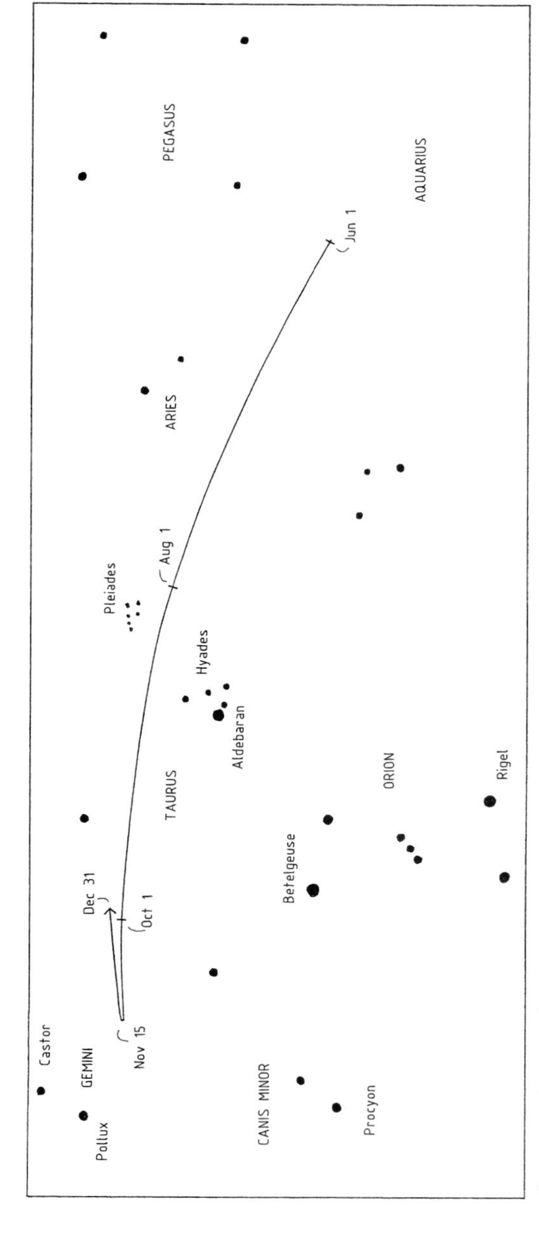

Figure 23. The path of Mars against the background stars of Pisces, Aries, Taurus and Gemini during the last seven months of 2007.

Méchain in January 1790; he computed an orbit, but because few observations had been made the comet was lost. It was picked up again by Horace Tuttle in January 1858, and was found to have a period of just under 14 years. It came back on schedule in 1871, and since then it has been seen at every return except that of 1953, when its position was particularly unfavourable. The current orbital period is 13.6 years.

At this return the comet is placed far north in the sky, and for most of December it will be circumpolar as seen from Britain. At the beginning of the month, the comet will be found on the border of Ursa Minor and Cepheus, only a few degrees from the North Celestial Pole. It then moves through the northern part of Cepheus, before entering Cassiopeia in the third week of December. By Christmas the comet will have passed into Andromeda, and by this time it should have attained naked-eye visibility. An ephemeris listing the positions of 8P/Tuttle during December will be found on page 148. The orbital eccentricity is 0.82, and the inclination 55 degrees. At its furthest from the Sun the comet moves out well beyond the orbit of Jupiter.

Horace Tuttle's name is attached to three periodical comets: 8P/Tuttle, 55P/Tempel-Tuttle, and 109P/Swift Tuttle; the latter two are the parent comets of the Leonid and the Perseid meteor showers, respectively, while 8P is associated with the Ursids, which peak on about 22 December each year, although rates are usually low. Tuttle was certainly a skilled and enthusiastic observer, but he had a decidedly chequered career. As a loyal Serviceman he fought against England in the American War of Independence, but also embezzled a large sum of money! This did not seem to affect his astronomical career, however.

The First Known Variable Stars. Variable star work has always played a major role in amateur astronomy; there are so many variables that professional observers cannot hope to keep a close watch on them all. Things were very different two hundred years ago. By 1807 only twelve variables had been identified. They were:

Star	Discoverer of Variability	Date	Type	Mag. Range
Omicron Ceti (Mira)	Phocylides Holwarda	1638	Mira	2.0–10.1
Beta Persei (Algol)	Geminiano Montanari	1667	Algol eclipsing binary	2.1–3.4
Chi Cygni	Gottfried Kirch	1686	Mira	3.3–14.2

Star	Discoverer of Variability	Date	Type	Mag. Range
R Hydrae	Giacomo Maraldi	1704	Mira	3.5–10.9
Mu Cephei	William Herschel	1782	Semi-regular	3.4–5.1
R Leonis	J.A. Koch	1782	Mira	4.4–11.3
Delta Cephei	John Goodricke	1784	Cepheid	3.5–4.4
Beta Lyræ	John Goodricke	1784	Beta Lyræ eclipsing binary	3.3–4.4
Eta Aquilæ	Edward Pigott	1784	Cepheid	3.5–4.4
Alpha Herculis (Rasalgethi)	William Herschel	1795	Semi-regular	2.7–4.0
R Scuti	Edward Pigott	1795	RV Tauri	4.2–8.6
R Coronæ Borealis	Edward Pigott	1795	R Coronæ	5.7–14.8

Although (Johann) Phocylides Holwarda was the first person to recognize the variability of Omicron Ceti (later called Mira, 'The Wonderful', by Johannes Hevelius of Danzig in 1642), it is now known that David Fabricius of East Friesland, Germany, discovered Omicron Ceti in 1596 while searching for the planet Mercury.

The variability of Algol was 'officially' discovered by Montanari in 1667, but it was almost certainly known long before that, and is perhaps the reason for the star's many nicknames. John Goodricke of England (who discovered the variability of Delta Cephei and Beta Lyrae in 1784) is credited with the detection of Algol's periodicity in 1782–83. It was apparently also independently discovered by the German amateur astronomer, Johann Palitzsch – who, incidentally, was the first person to see Halley's Comet at its first predicted return, on Christmas Night 1758.

Giacomo Maraldi discovered the variability of R Hydrae only after monitoring the area in which Geminiano Montanari was reported to have observed the star (in 1669), for a period of ten years between 1702 and 1712, noting maxima of the star in 1704 and 1708. Reports show that R Hydrae was actually seen as early as 1662 by Johannes Hevelius, when compiling his star catalogue. The star was noted as a sixth magnitude star, but was overlooked as a source of variability.

In 1783, when writing of his earlier discovery of the variability of Mu Cephei, Sir William Herschel (Figure 24) commented on its intense 'garnet' colour, an observation that led to the star's popular name 'Herschel's Garnet Star'. Alpha Herculis (Rasalgethi) is a fine

Figure 24. Portrait of Sir William Herschel, who discovered the variability of the two semi-regular stars Mu Cephei and Alpha Herculis. (Image courtesy of the Royal Astronomical Society, London.)

double star, with the brighter orange primary and rather fainter (magnitude 5.4) emerald or bluish-green secondary, having a separation of 4.6 arcseconds. Sir William Herschel did discover in 1795 that the primary was a semi-regular variable star, but it appears that the star was first shown to him by Nevil Maskelyne. On 29 August 1779, Herschel wrote: 'On May 2, 1781, Dr. Maskelyne very politely showed me the double star which he mentioned having discovered about four years ago.' Maskelyne had, in fact, discovered the duplicity of Alpha Herculis in 1777.

Eclipses in 2007

During 2007 there will be four eclipses, two of the Sun and two of the Moon.

1. *A total eclipse of the Moon* on 3–4 March. The beginning is visible from western Australia, Indonesia, the Indian Ocean, Asia (except the extreme east), Africa, Europe, the Atlantic Ocean, and the Americas (except for the extreme north-west). The end is visible from Asia (except the east), Africa, Europe, the Atlantic Ocean, South and Central America and North America (except for the western part), and the eastern part of the south Pacific Ocean. The partial eclipse begins at 21h 30m and ends at 01h 12m. Totality lasts from 22h 44m to 23h 58m.

2. *A partial eclipse of the Sun* on 19 March is visible from that part of Asia east of a longitude about 60–65° East (excepting south-eastern Japan). The eclipse begins at 00h 38m and ends at 04h 25m. At maximum, 87 per cent of the Sun is obscured.

3. *A total eclipse of the Moon* on 28 August. The beginning is visible from the western Atlantic Ocean, the Americas (except the extreme eastern part of Brazil), the Pacific Ocean, New Zealand and eastern Australia. The end is visible from western North America, the Pacific Ocean, Australasia, and eastern Asia. The partial phase begins at 08h 51m and ends at 12h 24m. Totality lasts from 09h 52m to 11h 23m.

4. *A partial eclipse of the Sun* on 11 September is visible from the central and southern parts of South America and part of Antarctica. The eclipse begins at 10h 26m and ends at 14h 36m. At maximum eclipse, 75 per cent of the Sun is obscured.

Occultations in 2007

In the course of its journey round the sky each month, the Moon passes in front of all the stars in its path, and the timing of these occultations is useful in fixing the position and motion of the Moon. The Moon's orbit is tilted at more than 5° to the ecliptic, but it is not fixed in space. It twists steadily westwards at a rate of about 20° a year, a complete revolution taking 18.6 years, during which time all the stars that lie within about 6.5° of the ecliptic will be occulted. The occultations of any one star continue month after month until the Moon's path has twisted away from the star, but only a few of these occultations will be visible from any one place during the hours of darkness.

There are eighteen occultations of bright planets in 2007: three of Mercury, two of Venus, two of Mars, and eleven of Saturn.

Only four first-magnitude stars are near enough to the ecliptic to be occulted by the Moon: these are Aldebaran, Regulus, Spica and Antares. Regulus, Spica, and Antares all undergo occultation in 2007.

Predictions of these occultations are made on a worldwide basis for all stars down to magnitude 7.5, and sometimes even fainter. The British Astronomical Association has produced a complete lunar occultation prediction package for personal-computer users.

Occultations of stars by planets (including minor planets) and satellites have aroused considerable attention.

The exact timing of such events gives valuable information about positions, sizes, orbits, atmospheres, and sometimes the presence of satellites. The discovery of the rings of Uranus in 1977 was the unexpected result of the observations made of a predicted occultation of a faint star by Uranus. The duration of an occultation by a satellite or minor planet is quite small (usually of the order of a minute or less). If observations are made from a number of stations it is possible to deduce the size of the planet.

The observations need to be made either photoelectrically or visually. The high accuracy of the method can readily be appreciated when one realizes that even a stopwatch timing accurate to a tenth of a second is, on average, equivalent to an accuracy of about 1 kilometre in the chord measured across the minor planet.

Comets in 2007

The appearance of a bright comet is a rare event which can never be predicted in advance, because this class of object travels round the Sun in enormous orbits with periods which may well be many thousands of years. There are therefore no records of the previous appearances of these bodies, and we are unable to follow their wanderings through space.

Comets of short period, on the other hand, return at regular intervals, and attract a good deal of attention from astronomers. Unfortunately they are all faint objects, and are recovered and followed by photographic methods using large telescopes. Most of these short-period comets travel in orbits of small inclination which reach out to the orbit of Jupiter, and it is this planet that is mainly responsible for the severe perturbations that many of these comets undergo. Unlike the planets, comets may be seen in any part of the sky, but since their distances from the Earth are similar to those of the planets their apparent movements in the sky are also somewhat similar, and some of them may be followed for long periods of time.

The following comets are expected to return to perihelion in 2007, and to be brighter than magnitude +15.

Comet	Year of Discovery	Period (years)	Predicted Date of Perihelion 2007
106P/Schuster	1977	7.3	Apr 2
96P/Machholz	1986	5.2	Apr 4
2P/Encke	1785	3.3	Apr 19
108P/Ciffreo	1985	7.3	Jul 18

Some ephemerides of comets which should be visible to observers with small telescopes in 2007 are given below:

Comet 2P/Encke

Date 2007	2000.0 RA		Dec.		Distance from Earth	Distance from Sun	Elong-ation from Sun	Mag.
0h	h	m	°	′	AU	AU	°	
Mar 21	1	22.5	+14	57	1.547	0.775	25.3	+9.8
26	1	38.3	+16	07	1.456	0.685	24.3	+8.8
31	1	55.5	+17	12	1.353	0.593	23.6	+7.8
Apr 5	2	14.2	+18	05	1.235	0.502	23.0	+6.5
10	2	33.3	+18	31	1.101	0.420	22.4	+5.1
15	2	50.0	+18	00	0.949	0.359	20.9	+3.7
20	2	58.0	+15	52	0.795	0.340	17.3	+3.0
25	2	51.5	+11	46	0.665	0.372	10.6	+3.2
30	2	32.7	+ 6	21	0.580	0.441	8.3	+4.0
May 5	2	08.5	+ 0	42	0.533	0.527	17.9	+5.0
10	1	44.2	− 4	24	0.513	0.618	29.6	+5.9
15	1	22.0	− 8	42	0.507	0.710	40.9	+6.8
20	1	02.1	−12	17	0.508	0.800	51.3	+7.6
25	0	44.0	−15	21	0.511	0.887	61.2	+8.3
30	0	26.8	−18	06	0.514	0.972	70.6	+8.9

Comet 8P/Tuttle

Date 2007	2000.0 RA		Dec.		Distance from Earth	Distance from Sun	Elong-ation from Sun	Mag.
0h	h	m	°	′	AU	AU	°	
Nov 21	17	57.7	+85	10	0.792	1.424	105.7	+9.1
26	19	17.1	+84	51	0.710	1.377	107.3	+8.6
Dec 1	20	48.2	+83	53	0.629	1.332	109.0	+8.2
6	22	13.3	+81	45	0.548	1.288	110.9	+7.6
11	23	20.0	+77	56	0.470	1.246	112.9	+7.1
16	0	08.8	+71	49	0.396	1.206	114.9	+6.5
21	0	44.8	+62	24	0.330	1.169	116.5	+5.9
26	1	12.2	+48	29	0.280	1.136	116.4	+5.4
31	1	33.7	+29	51	0.253	1.106	112.8	+5.0

Comet 96P/Machholz

Date 2007 0h		2000.0 RA h	m	Dec. °	′	Distance from Earth AU	Distance from Sun AU	Elongation from Sun °	Mag.
Mar	26	0	32.3	−13	51	1.243	0.400	16.2	+8.7
	31	1	02.3	− 4	10	1.137	0.239	10.4	+5.8
Apr	5	1	14.7	+11	02	0.999	0.126	7.2	+2.2
	10	0	37.0	+19	23	0.886	0.264	14.5	+5.8
	15	0	02.3	+21	33	0.832	0.422	24.4	+8.1
	20	23	34.0	+22	09	0.795	0.564	34.1	+9.5

Minor Planets in 2007

Although many thousands of minor planets (asteroids) are known to exist, only a few thousand of them have well-determined orbits and are listed in the catalogues. Most of these orbits lie entirely between the orbits of Mars and Jupiter. All these bodies are quite small, and even the largest, Ceres, is only 913 kilometres (567 miles) in diameter. Thus, they are necessarily faint objects, and although a number of them are within the reach of a small telescope few of them ever attain any considerable brightness. The first four that were discovered are named Ceres, Pallas, Juno and Vesta. Actually the largest four minor planets are Ceres, Pallas, Vesta and Hygeia. Vesta can occasionally be seen with the naked eye, and this is most likely to happen when an opposition occurs near June, since Vesta would then be at perihelion. Below are ephemerides for Ceres, Pallas and Vesta in 2007.

1 Ceres

Date		2000.0 RA		Dec.		Geo-centric Distance	Helio-centric Distance	Elong-ation	Visual Magni-tude
		h	m	°	′			°	
Aug	8	3	14.59	+ 8	53.9	2.765	2.884	86	+8.9
	18	3	22.42	+ 9	12.6	2.625	2.877	94	+8.8
	28	3	28.64	+ 9	23.5	2.487	2.870	102	+8.6
Sep	7	3	32.99	+ 9	27.0	2.352	2.863	110	+8.5
	17	3	35.16	+ 9	23.3	2.225	2.856	119	+8.3
	27	3	34.94	+ 9	13.6	2.109	2.849	129	+8.1
Oct	7	3	32.18	+ 8	58.9	2.007	2.841	139	+7.9
	17	3	26.95	+ 8	41.3	1.926	2.834	150	+7.7
	27	3	19.58	+ 8	23.3	1.868	2.826	161	+7.5
Nov	6	3	10.73	+ 8	8.1	1.837	2.818	170	+7.2
	16	3	01.27	+ 7	59.0	1.835	2.810	168	+7.3
	26	2	52.29	+ 7	59.2	1.861	2.802	158	+7.5
Dec	6	2	44.68	+ 8	10.5	1.914	2.794	147	+7.7
	16	2	39.17	+ 8	34.0	1.991	2.786	136	+7.9
	26	2	36.13	+ 9	09.3	2.087	2.778	126	+8.1

2 Pallas

Date		2000.0 RA		Dec.		Geo-centric Distance	Helio-centric Distance	Elong-ation	Visual Magni-tude
		h	m	°	′			°	
Aug	18	22	38.47	+ 7	12.5	2.319	3.269	156	+9.1
	28	22	31.18	+ 5	25.4	2.271	3.256	165	+8.9
Sep	7	22	23.64	+ 3	23.5	2.254	3.242	167	+8.8
	14	22	16.56	+ 1	13.9	2.267	3.228	160	+8.9
	27	22	10.64	− 0	55.1	2.310	3.214	149	+9.1

4 Vesta

Date		2000.0 RA		Dec.		Geo-centric Distance	Helio-centric Distance	Elong-ation	Visual Magni-tude
		h	m	°	′			°	
Jan	0	14	47.66	− 9	49.4	2.606	2.225	57	+7.8
	10	15	05.53	−10	55.8	2.495	2.217	62	+7.7
	20	15	22.94	−11	52.9	2.378	2.210	68	+7.7
	30	15	39.73	−12	40.1	2.258	2.202	74	+7.6
Feb	9	15	55.69	−13	17.5	2.136	2.196	80	+7.5
	19	16	10.59	−13	45.1	2.012	2.189	87	+7.3
Mar	1	16	24.11	−14	3.5	1.889	2.183	93	+7.2
	11	16	35.94	−14	13.7	1.767	2.178	100	+7.0
	21	16	45.72	−14	16.6	1.649	2.173	108	+6.9
	31	16	53.02	−14	14.0	1.537	2.168	116	+6.7
Apr	10	16	57.48	−14	07.7	1.433	2.164	125	+6.5
	20	16	58.74	−14	00.0	1.340	2.161	134	+6.2
	30	16	56.60	−13	53.2	1.261	2.158	144	+6.0
May	10	16	51.22	−13	49.9	1.200	2.155	154	+5.8
	20	16	43.10	−13	52.1	1.160	2.153	165	+5.5
	30	16	33.34	−14	1.9	1.143	2.152	172	+5.4
Jun	9	16	23.29	−14	20.4	1.151	2.151	167	+5.5
	19	16	14.42	−14	48.3	1.181	2.151	156	+5.7
	29	16	07.91	−15	25.5	1.234	2.151	146	+5.9
Jul	9	16	04.47	−16	10.9	1.304	2.152	136	+6.2
	19	16	04.33	−17	03.2	1.389	2.154	126	+6.4
	29	16	07.47	−18	00.4	1.486	2.156	118	+6.6
Aug	8	16	13.60	−19	00.3	1.591	2.158	110	+6.8

4 Vesta – *cont.*

Date		2000.0 RA		Dec.		Geo-centric Distance	Helio-centric Distance	Elong-ation	Visual Magni-tude
		h	m	°	′			°	
Aug	18	16	22.43	−20	00.9	1.702	2.162	103	+6.9
	28	16	33.61	−20	59.9	1.818	2.165	96	+7.1
Sep	7	16	46.83	−21	55.5	1.936	2.170	89	+7.2
	17	17	01.82	−22	45.9	2.055	2.174	83	+7.4
	27	17	18.32	−23	29.4	2.173	2.179	77	+7.5
Oct	7	17	36.09	−24	04.6	2.290	2.185	71	+7.6
	17	17	54.95	−24	30.3	2.404	2.191	66	+7.7
	27	18	14.68	−24	45.4	2.514	2.198	60	+7.7
Nov	6	18	35.09	−24	49.3	2.620	2.205	55	+7.8
	16	18	56.03	−24	41.5	2.721	2.212	50	+7.8
	26	19	17.31	−24	21.7	2.815	2.220	44	+7.9
Dec	6	19	38.78	−23	50.2	2.903	2.228	39	+7.9
	16	20	00.31	−23	07.2	2.983	2.236	34	+7.9
	26	20	21.79	−22	13.3	3.054	2.245	29	+7.9

Meteors in 2007

Meteors ('shooting stars') may be seen on any clear moonless night, but on certain nights of the year their number increases noticeably. This occurs when the Earth chances to intersect a concentration of meteoric dust moving in an orbit around the Sun. If the dust is well spread out in space, the resulting shower of meteors may last for several days. The word 'shower' must not be misinterpreted – only on very rare occasions have the meteors been so numerous as to resemble snowflakes falling.

If the meteor tracks are marked on a star map and traced backwards, a number of them will be found to intersect in a point (or a small area of the sky) which marks the radiant of the shower. This gives the direction from which the meteors have come.

The following table gives some of the more easily observed showers with their radiants; interference by moonlight is shown by the letter M.

Limiting Dates	**Shower**	**Maximum**	**RA**		**Dec.**	
			h	m	°	
Jan 1–6	Quadrantids	Jan 3	15	28	+50	M
April 19–25	Lyrids	Apr 22	18	08	+32	
May 1–8	Aquarids	May 4	22	20	−01	M
June 17–26	Ophiuchids	June 19	17	20	−20	
July 29–Aug 6	Delta Aquarids	July 29	22	36	−17	M
July 15–Aug 20	Piscid Australids	July 31	22	40	−30	M
July 15–Aug 20	Capricornids	Aug 2	20	36	−10	M
July 23–Aug 20	Perseids	Aug 13	3	04	+58	
Oct 16–27	Orionids	Oct 20	6	24	+15	
Oct 20–Nov 30	Taurids	Nov 3	3	44	+14	
Nov 15–20	Leonids	Nov 18	10	08	+22	
Nov 27–Jan	Puppids-Velids	Dec 9–26	9	00	−48	M
Dec 7–16	Geminids	Dec 14	7	32	+33	
Dec 17–25	Ursids	Dec 22	14	28	+78	M

Some Events in 2008

ECLIPSES

There will be four eclipses, two of the Sun and two of the Moon.

7 February:	Annular eclipse of the Sun – Antarctica, south-eastern Australia, New Zealand
21 February:	Total eclipse of the Moon – western Asia, Europe, Africa, the Americas
1 August:	Total eclipse of the Sun – north-east Canada, Europe, Asia
16 August:	Partial eclipse of the Moon – South America, Europe, Africa, Asia, Australia

THE PLANETS

Mercury may be seen more easily from northern latitudes in the evenings about the time of greatest eastern elongation (14 May) and in the mornings about the time of greatest western elongation (22 October). In the Southern Hemisphere the corresponding most favourable dates are around 11 September (evenings) and 3 March (mornings).

Venus is visible in the mornings until March for northern latitudes, and until May for southern latitudes. It is visible in the evenings from August to December for northern latitudes, and from July to December for southern latitudes.

Mars does not come to opposition in 2008.

Jupiter is at opposition on 9 July in Sagittarius.

Saturn is at opposition on 24 February in Leo.

Uranus is at opposition on 13 September in Aquarius.

Neptune is at opposition on 15 August in Capricornus.

Pluto is at opposition on 20 June in Sagittarius.

Part II

Article Section

Mars at Its Best

RICHARD McKIM

OPPOSITIONS OF MARS

The orbit of Mars is much more elliptical than that of the Earth, and so some oppositions – when the Red Planet is due south at midnight – are much closer and therefore more favourable than others. There is a 'cycle' of fifteen or seventeen years during which we experience a sequence of favourable oppositions (when Mars is near perihelion) and unfavourable oppositions (when Mars is near aphelion). Mars was very close to the Earth in 2003 and 2005, and the details were as follows:

Date of Opposition	Maximum Disk Diameter (arcseconds)	Declination (degrees)	Constellation
28 August 2003	25.1	−16	Capricornus
7 November 2005	20.2	+16	Aries

In fact, Mars came as close to us in 2003 as it ever can. It has been calculated that this was the closest opposition since the telescope was invented, and indeed for tens of thousands of years previously. Many amateur astronomers took every opportunity to view Mars telescopically, when it appeared as a brilliant red star, outshining everything else in the sky. In 2005 Mars was much higher in the skies of the Northern Hemisphere, even though the disc diameter was a little smaller. Of course, the Martian disc away from opposition is much smaller, and can even be less than 4 arcseconds when furthest away from us.

EQUIPMENT

These days, more observers use CCDs or webcams to image the planet than those traditionalists who – like myself – prefer sketching at the eyepiece. The most popular webcam costs less than £100, and together with free software from the Internet (such as Registax) one can record a short video of up to (say) 5,000 frames, and then 'stack' the best frames together to make some really amazing pictures. Such images, even with a modest 20-cm reflector, are often superior to the traditional 1950s photographs obtained at Mount Palomar or at the Lowell Observatory using giant telescopes. You do not need a huge telescope to view Mars. If you are thinking of imaging, a modest aperture reflector of 20 cm or larger, or perhaps one of the modern apochromatic refractors of 15 cm or above, will give you excellent results. For visual work a much cheaper achromatic refractor will be highly suitable.

I used a 22-cm (8.5-inch) reflector for many years, and now have a 41-cm (16-inch) Dall–Kirkham Cassegrain in a proper observatory (Figure 1). Figure 2 is a sequence of images by UK amateur astronomer Damian Peach, and shows what his camera could do at the eye end of the famous 15-inch reflector of Patrick Moore's observatory at Selsey during filming for the BBC *Sky at Night* programme. Figure 3 gives two of my best recent drawings: one from 2003 and one from 2005.

Figure 1. Richard McKim in his observatory with his 41-cm Dall–Kirkham Cassegrain reflector.

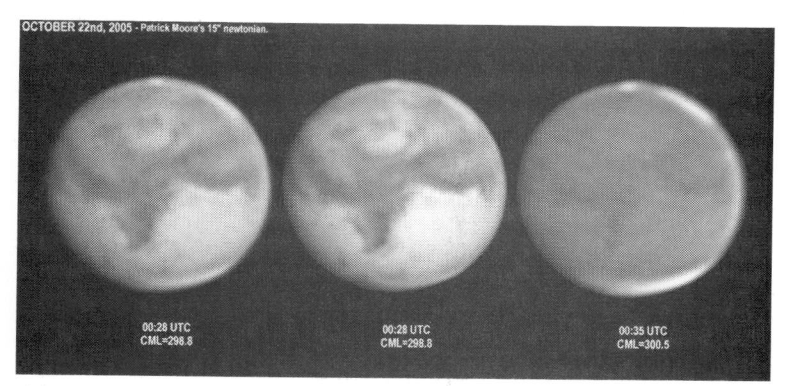

Figure 2. CCD images taken by Damian Peach on 22 October 2005 with Patrick Moore's 15-inch reflector at Selsey, West Sussex. Note the great amount of very fine detail in and around Syrtis Major, Hellas, Sinus Sabaeus, etc. The right-hand image is taken with a blue filter; the albedo markings are faint but the north polar hood (bottom) is large and bright.

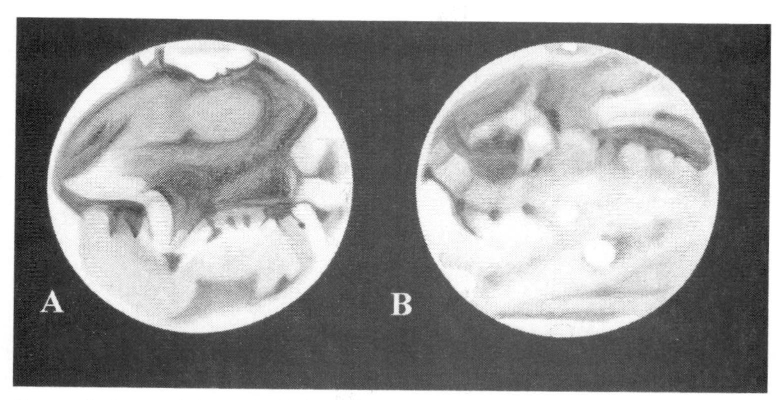

Figure 3. Some of the author's best Mars drawings (41-cm reflector, ×410). A (left), 20 August 2003. Note the Mitchell Mountains detached from the south polar cap (upper left). Sinus Sabaeus and Meridiani Sinus are well seen near the disc centre. B (right), 6 November 2005. Solis Lacus is to the upper left, and the bright spot below and right of the centre corresponds with the great volcano Olympus Mons. Very small summer SPC at top.

THE WORK OF THE AMATEUR ASTRONOMER

As Director of the British Astronomical Association (BAA) Mars Section, I received many thousands of observations from hundreds of observers all around the world during the 2003 and 2005 perihelic oppositions. In analysing them I try to produce a Martian 'meteorological report' as one of the most important final results. This consists of an analysis of which areas of the planet are subject to cloud on a monthly basis. This is not quite the cutting-edge research currently being done on the planet's surface by NASA's twin rovers Spirit and Opportunity, but nonetheless new telescopic phenomena are still being discovered and the historical record is being continued. In the last two decades amateurs have discovered evidence for a variable Martian Antarctic climate, measured the velocities of dust storms and charted their progress, found new initiation sites for such storms, shown that the Martian 'dust cycle' varies on a timescale of decades, reobserved dark markings not seen since the time of G.V. Schiaparelli in the nineteenth century, and mapped the seasonal growth and decay of the white equatorial cloud belts.

In this short article I shall only discuss the ground-based observations made in 2003 and 2005 by amateur astronomers. If you want to help with this research you can do so, but you should join an organization such as the BAA to get the most out of your observations.

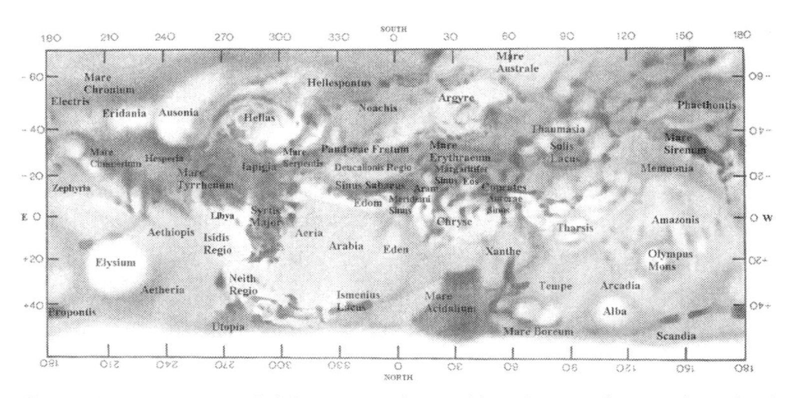

Figure 4. Mars map compiled from HST and ground-based images for 1990 by Richard McKim, with classical Martian names added. (Coprates is also known as Valles Marineris.)

For a map of the major features, using the classic telescopic names for convenience, see Figure 4.

MARTIAN DATE

Astronomers try to relate Martian phenomena to the calendar. At the start of the Martian year at the northern winter solstice, the areocentric longitude, or Ls, is 0°. Ls = 90° marks the start of spring, 180° the summer solstice and 270° the autumnal equinox, all for the Northern Hemisphere. The seasons are of unequal length. Northern winter, or southern summer, when Mars is moving fastest near perihelion, is the shortest.

POLAR CAPS

Telescopically, one of the most exciting things to watch is the seasonal decline of the Martian polar caps in spring and summer of their respective hemispheres. As the caps shrink they release volatiles, leading to a higher frequency of 'white' clouds. By measuring the size of the caps it is possible to see whether one Martian year is exactly the same as the one before. In practice, small differences are observed from year to year. When Mars was last at its best, in the decade of the 1980s, I produced the graphs of Figure 5, which show the south polar cap's slightly different behaviour in those years.

As the caps shrink, they become slightly asymmetric with respect to the poles. This is especially so for the southern cap. Rifts appear in the caps as some parts evaporate faster than others, and some areas get left behind in the general retreat. The most famous detached part is the so-called Mountains of Mitchell, which appears on a regular seasonal basis. It appears in Figure 3. In 2005 the observations extended to the end of southern summer where (in December of that year) a polar cloud hood began to veil the tiny remnant cap. A new cap grows under the hood and so the seasonal cycle repeats.

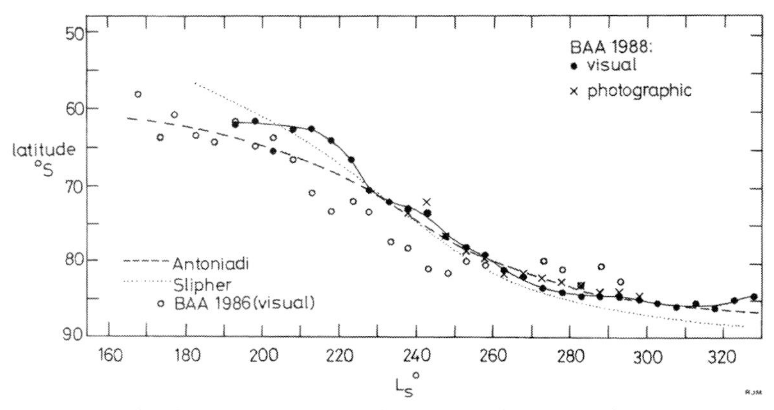

Figure 5. South polar cap recession curves (plotting latitude versus Ls) for the oppositions of 1986 and 1988 (BAA data). Note the slight differences from one year to the next, and when compared with the historical average results of E.M. Antoniadi and E.C. Slipher.

A DUSTY WORLD

Mars is a dusty world and dust storms can occur anywhere, but large events are limited to the warmest points of the Martian year when the winds are more energetic, namely the Southern Hemisphere in spring and summer. If conditions are right, surface dust (a fine silicate material pounded by aeons of meteoritic bombardment) can be stirred up, and the tiny micron-sized particles remain for weeks (or even months) in suspension in the air. Telescopically, these storms appear as yellow clouds, brighter in red light, obscuring the dark albedo markings. Their movements reveal the velocities of Martian winds. In 2005 the NASA twin Mars rovers took amazing videos of the many dust devils passing over the areas where they landed. All the changes ever observed in the patterns of the bright and dark markings on the Martian surface are caused by the shifting Martian dust. Storms can be local, regional, or planet-encircling, on an increasing scale.

The most significant events in 2003 began over Hellas and over Chryse-Valles Marineris (the Martian 'Grand Canyon', and often labelled 'Coprates' on telescopic maps). The first such event was quite typical of many past storms. (Refer again to Figure 4 for a map of Martian features.) Observations on 1 July revealed several small discrete dust clouds in the form of bright ochre spots rimming Hellas and obscuring Deltoton-Iapigia. Little detail was seen on the floor of Hellas. Over the next few days the dust storm expanded to the east over part of Mare Tyrrhenum and Ausonia and Eridania, with dust veiling Hesperia and part of Mare Cimmerium. Some dust obscured the southern part of Syrtis Major. The SPC was not affected. Dust also expanded to the west, into Noachis, and some dust cut across the eastern end of Sinus Sabaeus. After one week, the storm began to subside without spreading beyond the above limits. But as things returned to normal, an important new development on the surface could also be seen: Mare Serpentis was greatly broadened, and the eastern end of Deucalionis Regio was seen to have darkened, owing to dust removal from the surface. There were other changes, too. The aspect of the south-east part of Mare Tyrrhenum was altered somewhat, being invaded in several places by bright dust newly settled on the Martian surface.

The later event which began in Chryse-Valles Marineris was not so typical. On 13 December a significant dust storm arose over southern Chryse and the eastern part of Valles Marineris. Smaller, secondary dust cores were seen in northern Argyre and over Aram (or Thymiamata). By 13/14 December a band of dust had extended south-west from Argyre to higher latitudes and westward across Thaumasia to the south of Solis Lacus (with the latter somewhat obscured). There was a general expansion of the original cloud to veil Eos-Aurorae Sinus-Mare Erythraeum. On 15/16 December, further images showed a belt of dust crossing Noachis and Pandorae Fretum-Deucalionis Regio diagonally from Argyre, and impinging upon Sinus Sabaeus. (Indeed, the Meridiani Sinus area was later affected by dust for a time.) By 17/18 December, activity was observed in Hellas in the form of a secondary bright core in the vicinity of the deepest (north-western) part of the basin. However, the dust did not develop any further, probably having reached its maximum extent on this date. Observing visually on 17 and 18 December, I detected a small projection of part of the Noachis dust cloud beyond the morning terminator. (Before the Space Age, astronomers estimated the heights of clouds by such observations.) By 22 December little suspended dust remained over Noachis, and the north-western Hellas dust core was smaller and weaker. On the same date, images showed that the western end of the activity had significantly declined, with the very little remaining dust in eastern

Thaumasia connected to a bright persistent core in Argyre. Solis Lacus was again dark and well defined. In mid-January images continued to show small patches of dust around Aurorae Sinus and over Argyre. On 16 January 2004, the Hellas basin was again normal and free from dust.

There were several temporary albedo changes associated with the storm. For instance, the terrain about Depressiones Hellesponticae (which had marked the southern boundary of the Noachis dust) became much darker than before. Although I have studied every Martian dust storm since records began, I actually cannot recall any historical event beginning in the precise location of the present one (southern Chryse–eastern Valles Marineris) which showed such a considerable expansion in longitude, or which was of such long duration.

Interestingly, the major storm of the 2005 opposition followed a broadly similar pattern. It began as a small yellow cloud located just west of Margaritifer Sinus on the southern border of Chryse on 13 October 2005. After a few days activity seemed to cease, but on 18 October there was a strong resurgence, with dust moving north across Chryse, while a second bright core appeared further west near Aurorae Sinus. Dust then rapidly spread along Valles Marineris. I had a good view of all this in the pre-dawn hours on 20 October. Another dust disturbance occurred on 17 October, at the western border of south-east Tempe. Beginning at Ls = 306° (13 October), this dust storm – in terms of both Martian date and location – was similar to the large regional storm that had taken place at Ls = 315° (13 December 2003) at the previous opposition. Starting so late in the Martian year, and having not started in one of the classic locations, I predicted that it would not become planet-encircling. Fortunately for me, it didn't! (The seasonally latest planet-encircling storm ever observed commenced at Ls = 311°, back in 1924, but only storms that have begun in Hellas, Noachis or near Solis Lacus have ever achieved encircling status.)

Although few UK observers could witness the event, due to a combination of weather and circumstances, it was much better seen from the USA, and an excellent series of images by Clay Sherrod appears here as Figure 6. By 21 October, fingers of dust had spread into (or more likely, secondary dust cores had freshly arisen over) northern Argyre and southern Solis Lacus. The Argyre activity rapidly spread south-east into southern Noachis and began to impinge upon the south polar cap. On 28 October a spectacular resurgence of activity

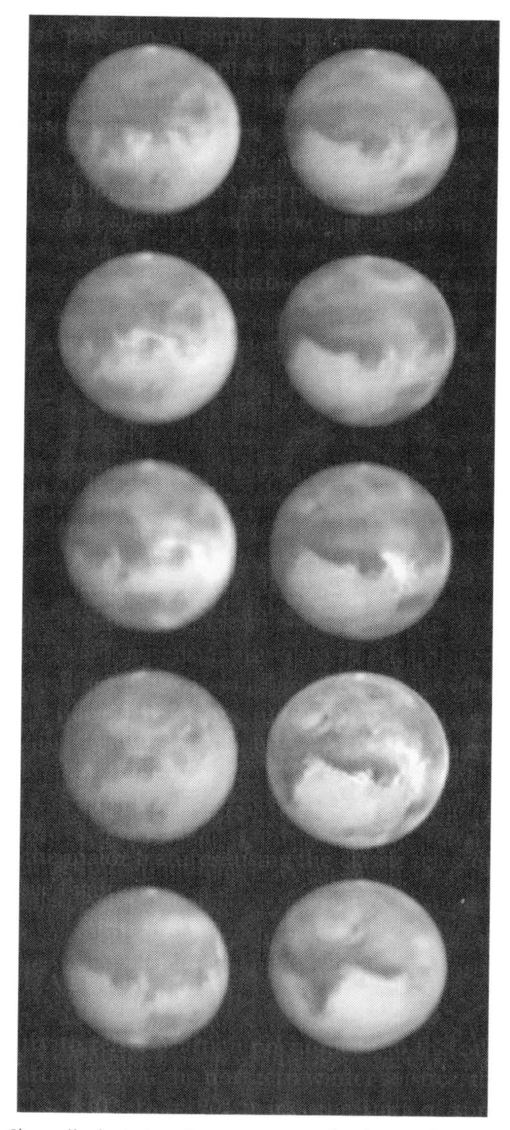

Figure 6. Clay Sherrod's dust-storm image sequence for the initial phases of the October 2005 event. Left column, top to bottom: 18, 19, 20, 21, 23 October 2005; right column, top to bottom: 26, 27, 28, 29, 30 October. (40-cm reflector, Arkansas, USA.)

occurred over Margaritifer Sinus–Aram (Thymiamata), as the original core of the storm was decaying. This latter activity (captured in detail by the HST) expanded to the south-east, and Meridiani Sinus was greatly obscured by 30 October. The small summer SPC was affected by the dust, becoming fainter and yellowish. Those who only observed the planet at opposition were therefore disappointed to find the cap unusually hard to see!

The international nature of the BAA's Mars patrol enabled the daily timecourse of the storm to be followed in detail. The dust reached and dimmed Hellespontus to the east, but no dust core arose in neighbouring Hellas, nor did the event penetrate beyond Solis Lacus to the west. The event did not last more than a few weeks, but a persistent dusty haze veiled some of the markings – especially around Noachis–Argyre–Margaritifer Sinus – for some time afterwards.

THE NEXT OPPOSITION

The next opposition of Mars is approaching: 24 December 2007 should be a date in your diary. If you are an active observer reading this, you will now know what to do. Don't forget that observations that are not shared with an organization such as the British Astronomical Association are lost to science, even if of great interest to you personally. So let me close by wishing you good luck with your views of the Red Planet!

BIBLIOGRAPHY

William K. Hartmann, *A Traveller's Guide to Mars*, Workman Publishing, 2003

Richard McKim, *Telescopic Martian Dust Storms*, BAA Memoirs, volume 44, 1999.

Patrick Moore, *Patrick Moore on Mars*, Cassell, London, 2006.

The Sky At Night magazine, No. 8, January 2006 (with CD-ROM of the November 2005 episode of the programme).

Recent Developments at the Keck Observatory

RICHARD ELLIS

THE EVOLVING NEEDS OF A LARGE TELESCOPE

The largest fully steerable reflectors, the twin 10-metre Keck telescopes atop Mauna Kea on the Big Island of Hawaii, have provided a rich legacy of discoveries ranging from the impressive tally of over 100 extrasolar planets to studies of the earliest galaxies seen when the Universe was barely 5 per cent of its present age. But an unchanging telescope is a stagnant one, so how is the Keck Observatory adapting to the presence of other, comparably powerful facilities such as the Japanese Subaru 8.4-metre reflector, the twin Gemini 8-metre telescopes and the impressive European Southern Observatory's Very Large Telescope – an array of four 8-metre telescopes in the Chilean Atacama desert?

The ultimate power of a telescope lies in the combination of its aperture – the size of the primary mirror used to gather light from distant sources – and the efficiency and suitability of its astronomical instruments, be they cameras or spectrographs. A modern instrument for an 8–10-metre telescope is often designed and constructed within a university group. However, even with economies possible in the academic environment, the cost of a modern instrument can lie in the $10–20m range. Only the most affluent observatories can afford a full range of instruments, given these kind of costs! It helps, therefore, to be selective, targeting instruments that are of the highest scientific utility.

Growth areas at Keck in the last five years include multi-object spectroscopy of stars in nearby galaxies, and faint-object spectroscopy of the most distant known sources in the infrared and high-resolution spectroscopy as a means for searching for planets around nearby stars. These achievements follow investment in wide-field optical spectrographs, efficient near-infrared spectrographs and improved detectors on a high-resolution spectrograph. A particularly exciting development is the rôle that adaptive optics is playing at Keck in providing extraordinarily sharp images of a full range of celestial objects. In this short article, I shall review some of the most recent news from this famous observatory.

RECENT SCIENCE HIGHLIGHTS

The Deep Imaging Multi-Object Spectrograph (DEIMOS) is a wide-field spectrograph developed at the University of California, Santa Cruz, capable of surveying regions of sky 16 arcminutes by 5 arcminutes in extent. As the full moon is 30 arcminutes across, it will be realized that this is a huge field for a large telescope. Scott Chapman at Caltech and his collaborators have used this instrument to undertake an impressive survey of the velocities of thousands of stars in the nearby Andromeda spiral, Messer 31 (Figure 1). Using special filters to select a narrow wavelength range where the stellar velocities can be measured, with DEIMOS they were able to record several hundred stars at a time. Their work has probed much further out in the edge of M31 than hitherto and revealed a rotating stellar disc fully three times larger than previously imagined. Their large sample of velocities also gives clear evidence of complex structures – tidal streams and subcomponents – in our closest large neighbour, indicative of the fact that it had an interesting history, merging frequently with now long-disrupted companions. This project is a very good example of how a new instrumental capability often leads to unforeseen science. DEIMOS was largely built to undertake a different kind of survey – 60,000 high redshift galaxies – one that has also been remarkably successful.

The most distant galaxies are not only seen when the Universe was very young – a consequence of the fact that their light has taken billions of years to reach us – but at these great cosmic distances, most of their energy is redshifted into the near-infrared spectral region. Astronomers at Caltech and the University of California, Los Angeles, are now developing an infrared survey instrument, equivalent to DEIMOS, called MosFire (a Multi-Object Spectrometer for Infrared Exploration). The potential of near-infrared spectroscopy has been evident for some time from work done at Keck with its current (single-object)

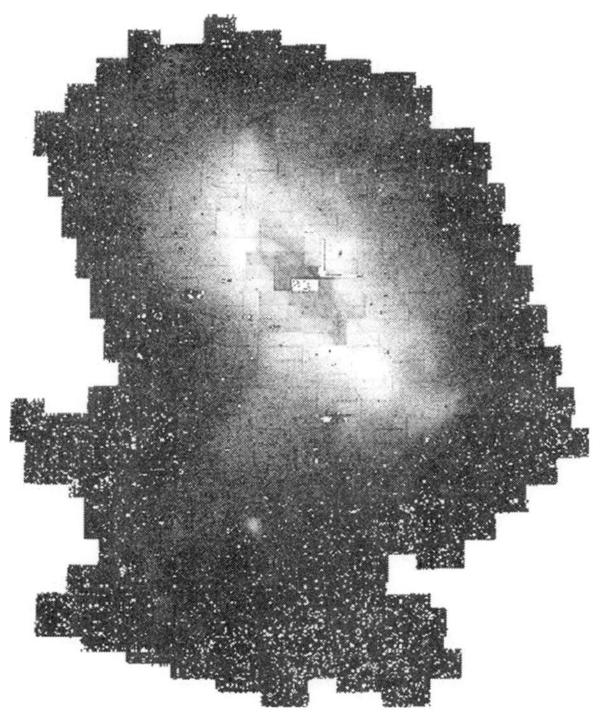

Figure 1. Panoramic view of the Andromeda Galaxy, Messier 31. The original image was colour-coded according to the velocities of stars measured using the DEIMOS optical multi-object spectrograph at the Keck Observatory. This unique study reveals a complex assembly history for our nearest spiral neighbour. 'Halo' stars loop around the rotating disc, which is far more extensive than previously thought. (Image courtesy of Scott Chapman, Caltech.)

spectrograph, NIRSPEC. The earliest known sources have been located through follow-up work undertaken at Keck based on deep Hubble and Spitzer Space Telescope imaging of foreground clusters of galaxies which act as strong gravitational lenses (Figure 2). The additional boost in magnification afforded by a natural gravitational lens, when combined with Keck's large aperture, has enabled Caltech astronomers not only to locate the earliest galaxies seen when the Universe was only 700 million years old, but also to study their detailed properties. A surprising recent discovery is the existence of a population of 'mature'

Figure 2. Using a gravitational lens to find the earliest systems. The gravitational field of the rich galaxy cluster Abell 2218 distorts and magnifies objects behind it, giving Caltech astronomers a natural 'magnifying glass'. The earliest known systems (marked) have been located and studied at Keck using this remarkable technique. (Image courtesy of Richard Ellis and Jean-Paul Kneib, Caltech.)

galaxies – some containing over 100 billion stars in an advanced state of evolution – at these early times. This suggests much of the 'action' in forming the first systems occurred yet earlier in cosmic history, perhaps as soon as 100 million years after the Big Bang!

BRINGING LASER-GUIDED ADAPTIVE OPTICS TO THE COMMUNITY

The most exciting development at Keck is the commencement, in October 2005, of the first 'common-user' laser guide star adaptive optics system for general use.

As an astronomical technique, adaptive optics has been around for over a decade and, at Keck and other observatories, has already achieved many significant science results. In its most basic application, the technique works by monitoring the light of a bright 'guide star' close to a celestial object of interest. Using a deformable mirror whose elements are corrected according to fluctuations in signal observed in the guide star, the blurring effects of the Earth's atmosphere can be largely removed. The resulting corrected image can be sharper than that observed by the Hubble Space Telescope and can be used to feed any suitable instrument such as an imaging camera or spectrograph. With a telescope of Keck's aperture (sixteen times the light-gathering power of Hubble) the potential is truly enormous. A recent Keck result from Mike Liu at the University of Hawaii is shown in Figure 3. Here we are imaging a region the size of the Solar System around a star thirty-three light years away!

As with all good things, adaptive optics has some restrictions. Firstly, the corrections are only currently practical at near-infrared wavelengths. Secondly, not all celestial objects of interest have a suitably bright guide star nearby; this is a particularly annoying restriction for those who wish to study distant galaxies, like myself. And thirdly, as the technique is fairly complex, only a small set of experienced 'black-belt' users have entered the game!

Much of this has now changed at Keck! A powerful 14-watt sodium laser is now routinely launched into the sky from Keck II (Figure 4). This beam excites a layer of sodium atoms 90 km up in the atmosphere whose reflecting signal acts like a tenth-magnitude guide star in any direction the observer wishes to look. With the aid of a local team of trained engineers, laser-guided adaptive optics is now being used routinely by non-experts and fantastic discoveries are being made.

First science highlights of Keck's new era of adaptive optics include imaging of globular star clusters in Andromeda which showed that many thought to be unusually young systems were in fact spurious and not star clusters at all! With the sharpened eye of Keck, even the Hubble Space Telescope had been misled! Improved images of the galactic centre can now trace the eccentric orbits of stars around the central black hole whose mass is 3–4 million times that of the Sun. The precession of these stellar orbits – all contained within 1 arcsecond of the black hole itself – may provide a valuable test of Einstein's General Theory of Relativity in a hitherto untested régime. Distant galaxies come sharply into view as well. Although faint galaxies have been imaged by Hubble for over a decade revealing their morphological forms, by sending the laser-corrected image into a spectrograph astronomers can use Keck to determine whether these early galaxies are

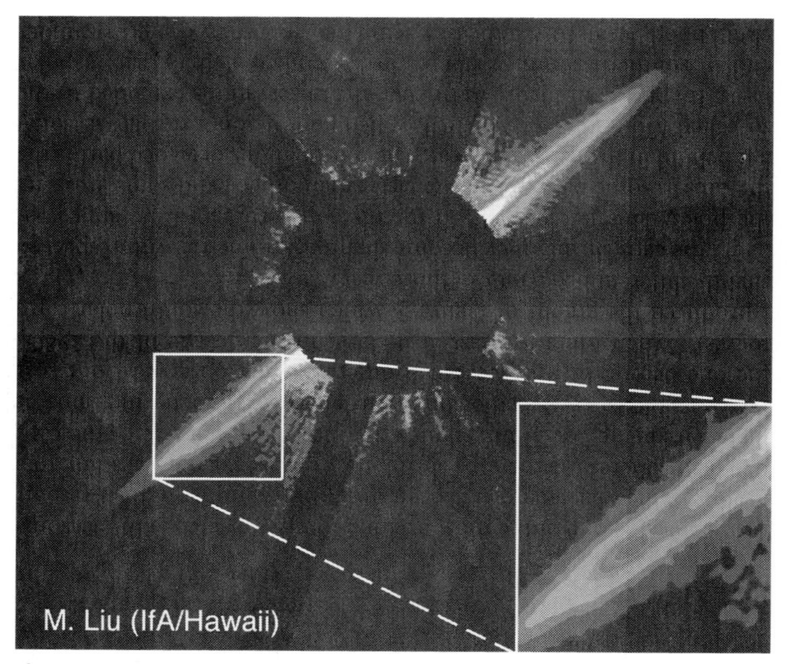

Figure 3. Keck adaptive optics imaging of the dust disc around the young star AU Microscopii. This system, thirty-three light years away, is one of the closest revealing such a disc, and this is the sharpest view of its internal structure. The inset shows that the disc has 'gaps' probably associated with young forming planets. The image is 100 Astronomical Units across – about the diameter of our Solar System. (Image courtesy of W.M. Keck Observatory and Dr Michael Liu, University of Hawaii.)

Figure 4. Launching the powerful sodium laser at the Keck Observatory. The 14-watt laser creates a tenth-magnitude artificial guide star in the sky which can be monitored and used to correct for atmospheric blurring. Image courtesy of W.M. Keck Observatory.

rotating like present-day spirals. The degree of rotation not only addresses whether such systems are fully formed, they can also be used to measure their total mass (including any components that contain dark matter). Finally, the recently discovered tenth 'planet' 2003 UB_{313} has a moon, the orbital period of which supports the claim that this object is more massive than Pluto (Figure 5).

The above results represent just a small fraction of the exciting new

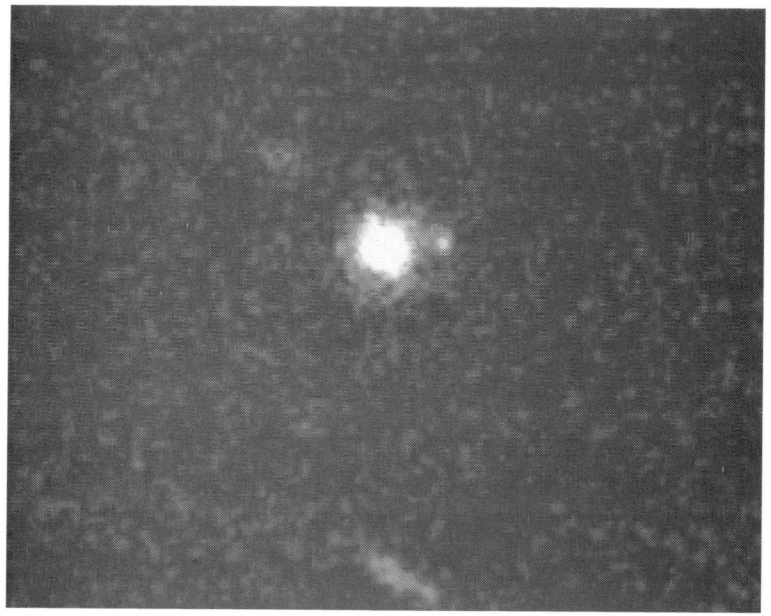

Figure 5. Image of the distant Kuiper Belt object 2003 UB_{313} (also known as Xena) observed with the Keck laser guide star system revealing its associated moon (Gabrielle). The separation is about 0.4 arcseconds. The orbital period of around fourteen days indicates that Xena is more massive than Pluto. Thus, if Pluto is considered to be a planet, it would seem that Xena should also be in that category. (Image courtesy of W.M. Keck Observatory and Dr Mike Brown, Caltech.)

results made possible by the Keck laser-guided adaptive optics system. Such a system was not foreseen when the Keck Observatory was planned in the 1980s, and none of the science above is currently possible with any other current facility. This is a very good example of how modern technology can rejuvenate an observatory, giving it a new lease of life. The sociology is also interesting. Astronomers not used to working with complex adaptive optics instruments have jumped into the deep end and learned to swim! Who says you can't teach an old dog new tricks?!

Twice a Fortnight: the Astronomical Origin of the Week

DUNCAN STEEL

The year, month and day all have clear astronomical origins. Our seven-day week, though, is not linked in any obvious way with a celestial cycle. If one were to divide the lunar month of twenty-nine and a half days by four, the nearest integer to the result is seven. But . . . So what? The division is nowhere near exact. Why not split a month into six blocks of five days, or three lots of ten? Each of those renders a closer approximation to the lunar month than the four lots of seven days.

Nor is there an even number of weeks in the year. A calendar year lasts fifty-two weeks plus an odd day – or two extra days in a leap year – meaning that the dates do not repeat on the same weekdays, except over a cycle lasting twenty-eight years (seven times the quadrennial leap cycle). If your birthday is on a Thursday this year, next time around it will be a Friday (or perhaps a Saturday).

So, why does a week contain seven days? This peculiar septenary cycle governs our lives, dictating what we must do on waking each morning – rush to catch the train, or breakfast in bed with the Sunday papers – and yet we seldom pay it much attention. It's one of life's givens. So how did it come about? And why are some days named after planets, and in that order?

The week is a human construct having a major influence upon our lives, and yet we seldom ponder its effects, yet alone its origins. For centuries, churches and universities have appointed *hebdomadaries* and convened *hebdomadal* meetings. Those words derive from the Greek *hebdomas*, meaning 'seven days', which in turn comes from *hepta*, 'seven' (as in the women's heptathlon at the Olympics). Shakespeare often wrote of the 'sennight' (seven nights), a term that has fallen into disuse although the double week of fourteen nights (a fortnight) persists.

Obviously, the week is of ancient invention. As we shall see, the seven-day round evolved in the Middle East during the first millennium BC, being derived from a mixture of astrological and religious beliefs, although there's much astronomy involved, too. Its later adoption in the West and eventual global spread came later.

DIFFERENT LENGTHS FOR THE WEEK

First of all we need to answer this apparently simple question: what is a week? That is, what is a week of *any* length, given that not all civilizations have used a seven-day period?

The answer is that a week is a cycle longer than a day but shorter than a month that fits in with various human necessities, such as shopping, a work/rest rhythm, the frequency with which the laundry needs to be done, and so on. Often local climate and food preservation considerations have controlled the week length, representing a market cycle, as did the ancient Roman eight-day weeks termed the *nundinae*.

The Mayans had a twenty-day reckoning period. The Incas used eight. In tropical Africa, a brief four-day cycle has been common. The Baha'i use nineteen days, and the ancient Chinese employed a ten-day week.

This convenient decimal length was used also by the Egyptians. Their 360-day civil year was divided into thirty-six *decans*, each associated with the appearance of a particular group of stars in the sky. It is from this that our 360 degrees in a circle derives (and the degree symbol as a small raised circle is a representation of the Sun). The extraneous five or six days in a year were not part of any week to the Egyptians, but rather an annual interval for special ceremonies and festivities.

Although the seven-day week has been in use for more than two millennia, some modern societies have tried to displace it. Following the Revolution in France, in 1793 a ten-day week was introduced along with other alterations of the calendar, although none lasted for long. An echo remains in French cuisine: the dish known as *Lobster Thermidor* gets its name from the title given to the hottest month of the year in the Revolutionary calendar.

The Soviet Union tried first a five- and then a six-day week in the initial decades of the communist regime, in an attempt to boost productivity. With a single day as a weekend, the comrades would work for 80 per cent of a five-day week or 83 per cent of a six-day week, compared with 72 per cent of a seven-day week with two days off. Reversion to the septenary cycle soon occurred, after mass protests. There seems to be something special about those seven days.

DISCORDANCY IN THE BEGINNING OF THE WEEK

The week is an oddity compared with the other units of time we employ. As the clock ticks to the end of 31 December, a new second, minute, hour, day, month and year (and maybe century and millennium) all begin at the same instant. Most often, though, it is not the start of a new week.

The beginning of the week is not the same for all cultures. Even the Bible is confusing on this score: in some passages Sunday is the *last* day of the week, in others it's the *first*. Similarly, some almanacs print the cycle as SMTWTFS, others as MTWTFSS.

Different religions use different days (and even times of day) to start their weeks. To a Jew, the Sabbath is Saturday, but it starts with sunset the evening before, on Friday. Similarly the Islamic holy day is Friday.

In passing we might note that the Islamic calendar is interesting in other astronomically connected ways. The months still follow the lunar phases, beginning with the sighting of the crescent new moon, whereas the calendar we have inherited in the West derives from a Roman tradition in which the calendar months became divorced from the phases of the Moon in the second century BC. Twelve lunar months, usually adding up to 354 or 355 days, comprise an Islamic year, which is why Ramadan slips backwards through the seasons by about eleven days per solar year.

Returning to the subject of the day that starts the week, the global standard (stipulated in 1988 as part of ISO 8601) has Monday as the first day. To verify that, check the numbering of the days in airline schedules.

THE WEEK BEGINS IN BABYLONIA

Clearly, then, the septenary week is ascendant. How did this come about? The answer is that it derives from a melding of different cultural traditions. The Book of Genesis account of the Creation, with God labouring for six days and resting on the seventh, will be familiar to most readers.

We associate this with the word *Sabbath*. That term stems originally from the Babylonian word *sabattu*, which referred to those days nearest full moon. Early in the first millennium BC in Mesopotamia this was considered to be an unlucky interval, when activity was best avoided. It was thought to be the time when the lunar goddess Ishtar was menstruating, emphasized by the fact that the Moon goes the colour of blood during a lunar eclipse, which can only occur at full moon.

A distinct Babylonian word was *sibutu*, meaning 'the seventh'. In each month, counted from the appearance of the new moon, the seventh day was regarded as being special, when rites of purification and expiation were performed. In that culture the number seven gradually became taboo, as did its multiples. The fourteenth day after new moon became regarded as the day of full moon (even though the fifteenth was often closer), and thus the meanings of *sibutu* and *sabattu* were mixed up.

The general meaning of the latter, however, was still in the context of an episode within a month, rather than an ongoing seven-day cycle divorced from the Moon. The idea of using such a continuing cycle – what we now regard as the seven-day week – was a Judaic invention. The word *sabattu* was gradually appropriated by the Jews during their exile and captivity in Babylonia from 587 to 538 BC, forming the Hebrew word *shabbat* and rendering the concept of the 'Sabbath' with the days in the week each being named for an archangel (such as Michael and Gabriel).

This, then, is how the seven-day cycle originated: during the Exile in the sixth century BC. When the Jews returned to the eastern shores of the Mediterranean, they took this custom with them.

But how did the seven-day week pervade the rest of the world? In particular, given that much of our timekeeping system derives from the Roman calendar, which evolved during the era of the Republic and was then formalized by Julius Caesar in 46 BC under Egyptian advice, how did the Jewish seven-day week usurp the eight-day *nundinae* that the Romans had been hitherto employing?

ENTER THE PLANETS

The major factor that led to the dominance of the seven-day week was the planetary gods. These deities belonged to a completely different belief system from that of the Jews.

In English the term 'planets' derives from the ancient Greek word *planetai*, meaning 'wanderers'. The planets in this sense originally included both the Sun and the Moon. In the cosmological models of the time, the planets were the seven familiar objects regularly meandering across the sky relative to the fixed stars; comets were regarded as being a different class entirely, causing great consternation with their sporadic appearances.

Until the introduction of the Copernican heliocentric model of the Solar System in the sixteenth century, people thought that all these heavenly bodies circuited the Earth as the centre of the universe. This is termed the *Ptolemaic system*, although it was invented long before Ptolemy's era, the second century AD.

If these celestial objects moved on spheres of increasing distance from the Earth, then logic dictated that those moving quickest across the sky (the planets) must be relatively close by, while the slower ones (the stars) must be further away. In terms of increasing distance and hence falling speed the planets were ordered by the ancients like this:

Moon, Mercury, Venus, Sun, Mars, Jupiter, Saturn.

These were taken to define seven celestial zones, beyond which were the so-called eighth and ninth heavens containing the firmament of stars, and eventually the *Primum Mobile* (the motor that kept everything going) and the *Empyrean*, the highest heaven (see Figure 1).

From this sequence of planets in the Ptolemaic system is derived what is known as the *planetary week*. This seems to have been a Hellenistic invention, following the conquest of western Asia by Alexander the Great in 336–323 BC. Because it grew in popularity in the following centuries around Alexandria, this week is often described as being of Egyptian origin, but it was fundamentally Greek, thriving with the Macedonian line that terminated with Cleopatra. (The situation is

Figure 1. The Ptolemaic theory of the heavens had seven 'planets' (including the Sun and the Moon) circling the Earth at distances based on their apparent speed of motion across the sky. The sequence of days in the week is derived from this ordering. (Image from the *Cosmographicus Liber* of Peter Apianus, 1524.)

further confused by the fact that this dynasty, the Ptolemies, is not directly connected with Claudius Ptolemaeus, the later astronomer/mathematician whose name is given to the Ptolemaic system.)

THE SEQUENCE OF THE DAYS

The day order in the planetary week stems from an astrological belief allocating each hour to a particular planet, said to be the *controller* of that hour. The controller of the first hour of each day is called the *regent*, for whom that day is named.

To decide which day was allocated to each regent, the planets were written down in terms of imagined decreasing distance from the Earth (the reverse of the sequence above), and allotted to each hour in turn. Then, as now, there were twenty-four hours counted in a day (and that *was* indeed an Egyptian invention). Because twenty-four is not a multiple of seven, this leads to jumps in the day-name sequence. Taking Saturday as an example, the planets were thought to control its hours as follows:

Saturn	1	8	15	22
Jupiter	2	9	16	23
Mars	3	10	17	24
Sun	4	11	18	
Venus	5	12	19	
Mercury	6	13	20	
Moon	7	14	21	

Continuing the hour count, the first hour of the *next* day has the Sun as its regent, two planets (Jupiter and Mars) having been skipped. Thus Sunday follows Saturday.

This same general rule applies throughout the week. From Sunday, skip two planets (Venus and Mercury) to get the controller of the following day (the Moon, hence Monday). Thus the ordering of the days derives from an hour-lore, which belief persisted into the Middle Ages (both Geoffrey Chaucer and Roger Bacon wrote about it). The word *horoscope* is testament to the significance of the hour in astrological belief systems.

On this basis, the final list of the planets is:

Sun, Moon, Mars, Mercury, Jupiter, Venus, and Saturn.

To get this sequence, just write in a circle the seven names previously tabulated, and then move clockwise around it, jumping two planets at a time, as in Figure 2.

Note that this does not correspond with any real physical ordering, such as brightness, or the times these celestial objects take to lap the Earth, or indeed the actual heliocentric sequence (Sun, Mercury, Venus, Moon, Mars, Jupiter, Saturn). It stems from an ancient cosmological theory, astrological beliefs, the twenty-four hours counted in a day, and the seven wandering stars or planets.

Our common week, then, seems to have gained ascendancy due to

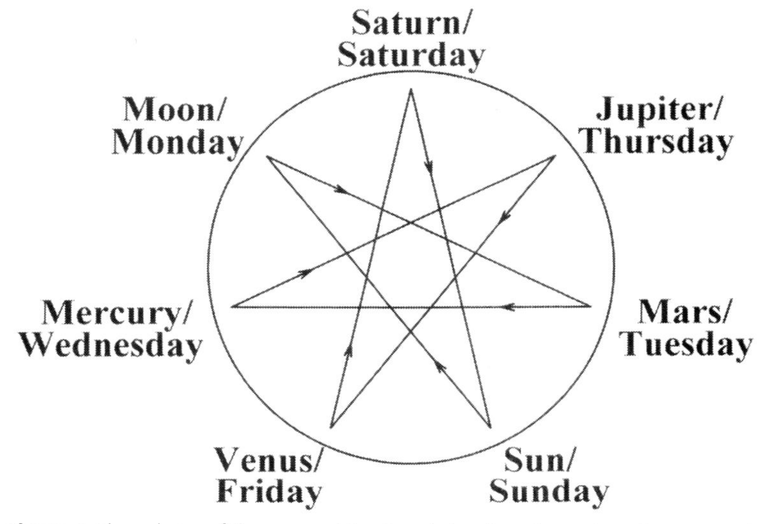

Figure 2. The ordering of the names of the days derives from the ancient planetary week. The planets were thought to circle the Earth with distances in descending order as in the clockwise sequence shown here, Saturn being the most remote. In each 24-hour day there would be three complete circuits of the seven planets, plus another three steps (or two 'jumped planets') as shown by the course of the arrows within the circle. Thus Saturn's day is followed by the Sun's day is followed by the Moon's day, and so on.

reinforcement between two quite independent seven-day cycles – the Jewish and the planetary weeks – during the last few centuries BC, in and around Egypt. But how did the days get their names?

NAMING THE DAYS

Following the conquest of Egypt by Pompey and Julius Caesar in the middle of the final century BC, the Roman legions took back to the Eternal City the seven-day cycle, and eventually it displaced their long-established eight-day system (as we shall see later). The days of the week, though, are not named directly after the Roman gods. Generally our day names have come from the Teutonic languages.

In Scandinavian mythology, the equivalent god to Jupiter is *Thor*, hence Thursday. Because he was the king of the gods, some peoples have held this to be the holiest day of the week: this was the case in Estonia even into the twentieth century.

Similarly, *Tyr* or *Tiu* was the divine equivalent of Mars, *Woden* or *Odin* that of Mercury, and *Frigga* (the origin of a vulgar term) or *Freya* that of Venus, the goddess of love. Those give us Tuesday, Wednesday and Friday respectively. Next time you see a job advertisement for a 'Man Friday', based of course on the character in Daniel Defoe's *Robinson Crusoe*, note that Friday is actually named after a female deity.

You may now have jumped to the understandable but incorrect conclusion that Saturday is just a concatenation of *Saturn's day*. Yes, the Romans called it *dies Saturni*, the day of Saturn, but our word *Saturday* comes directly from the god *Saeter* or *Seterne* of Norse legend. If you want to use the original deities for days, but don't want to learn Latin, speak Welsh. It's the only language that directly preserves the planets' names in its terms for the days.

Why the contrast of *Sunday* and *Monday* compared with the distinct Germanic names of the other five days? It seems that in northern Europe a five-day week was used by pagan tribes, and Sunday and Monday were only added later due to the influence of, first, the spreading Roman legions, and later the Christian missionaries who followed them.

SWAPPING SEVEN DAYS FOR EIGHT

Owing to the scarcity of written records from the time, it's not possible to give a specific date for when the seven-day week replaced the eight-day cycle in the Roman Empire. A single surviving manuscript almanac from around the turn of the era shows both the nundinal days labelled from *a* to *h*, and also a column of days marked *a* to *g* and hence a seven-day cycle. An inscription on a wall at Pompeii, which was destroyed and buried by the eruption of Mount Vesuvius in AD 79, shows the 'Days of the Gods' in week order, starting with Saturn and ending with Venus. Thus the picture we see is of a gradual rise in the use of a seven-day cycle from Julius Caesar's time (he was assassinated in 44 BC) through the following century or two.

Although it had been in use for some centuries the seven-day week, the hebdomad, did not become the legal week until AD 321. The first Roman emperor to accept Christianity was Constantine the Great, and in that year he legislated for unnecessary work to be forbidden on a Sunday, providing the civil basis in law for a seven- rather than an eight-day cycle to be used throughout the Empire.

We can also state which event in history was the first to be placed on a specific day of the week, albeit retrospectively, as follows.

In early August of 30 BC, the year after defeating Mark Antony and Cleopatra at the Battle of Actium, Augustus Caesar (then still named Octavian) entered Alexandria in triumph, the Egyptian queen famously killing herself by clutching an asp to her breast rather than adorn his parade. At that stage the month was still called Sextilis, not being retitled in honour of Augustus until later. The end of that Roman month coincided with the start of the Egyptian month of Thoth, the first in their year. This was later taken to mark the start of the Augustan era of the new expanded empire, and regarded to have been a Sunday. On that basis the first day of January in AD 1 was a Saturday.

The cycle has never been interrupted. Even when Britain reformed its calendar in 1752, deleting eleven dates such that 2 September was followed by the 14th, the septenary sequence of days was maintained. It was precisely the same when the Catholic Church changed in 1582 – the Gregorian reform of the calendar – the week being essentially sacrosanct. And long, no doubt, will it continue.

Editors' Note: As Duncan Steel explains, most Latin-based languages connect the days of the week with the names of the seven so-called 'planets' of ancient times – the Sun, Moon, Mercury, Venus, Mars, Jupiter and Saturn, although in English the original names have been retained only for Saturday, Sunday and Monday, with the names of Anglo-Saxon or Scandinavian gods replacing the Roman names for Tuesday (after *Tiu*), Wednesday (*Woden*), Thursday (*Thor*) and Friday (*Freya*).

However, the link is rather more apparent in French, where we have lundi (Moon), mardi (Mars), mercredi (Mercury), jeudi (Jupiter), vendredi (Venus) and samedi (Saturn). The link with the Sun appears to be broken in French, but the word dimanche (for Sunday) comes from the Latin *dies solis* (day of the Sun).

Quasar: Child of ULIRG?

CHRIS KITCHIN

There are uncountable numbers of galaxies of all shapes and sizes. Most of them we see because of the light coming from their constituent stars. However, for a small fraction of the galaxies, much of their energy comes from relativistic electrons spiralling around magnetic fields or from even more exotic sources. These strange objects are called 'active galaxies'. More frequently, because most of the real action occurs within their nuclei, they are called AGNs ('Active Galactic Nuclei'). The history of AGNs dates back nearly two centuries, though it is only within the last five decades that any real understanding of them has been achieved.

AN UNUSUAL GALAXY

Southern Hemisphere observers sweeping the skies with a pair of binoculars might be forgiven for not halting to gaze at an insignificant faint blur 20° north of the Southern Cross. A small telescope, however, will reveal it much as Sir John Herschel saw it from the Cape of Good Hope in the mid-1830s – 'a most wonderful object . . . two semi-ovals of elliptically formed nebula appearing to be cut asunder and separated by a broad obscure band parallel to the larger axis of the nebula'. The object had first been noted a decade earlier by James Dunlop, but it would be well over a century before it was recognized to be a galaxy.

From the start, it was obvious that this was no run-of-the-mill nebula, and better telescopes than those of Herschel and Dunlop revealed it to be a giant elliptical galaxy with a very broad and dense obscuring dust lane running across it (Figure 1). Listed as the 5,128th object in Johan Dreyer's *New General Catalogue of Nebulae and Clusters of Stars*, the galaxy became known as NGC 5128. It has long been theorized that the remarkable features of NGC 5128 arose from a merger or collision between two galaxies, and that has been confirmed

Figure 1. (See also the front cover photograph.) The unusual radio galaxy Centaurus A imaged by the ESO's 8-metre Kueyen telescope. (Image courtesy of the European Southern Observatory.)

recently by the detection of an arc of young blue stars within the galaxy (Figure 2). The arc is all that remains of a dwarf irregular galaxy that collided with the much larger elliptical galaxy around 300 million years ago. The elliptical galaxy itself probably also formed through a collision – but between two large galaxies and several thousand million years before the dwarf galaxy came upon the scene.

NGC 5128 really started to make the headlines when it became one of radio astronomy's early successes. In 1949, a single 24-metre radio antenna perched on a cliff in Australia detected the direct radio waves from a bright source in Centaurus as well as those that had bounced off the sea. The two beams acted as an interferometer, and the data led to a precise position for the source. The radio source had already been named Centaurus A (abbreviated to Cen A), and its position turned out to be that of NGC 5128. This was one of the first detections of radio waves from outside our own Milky Way galaxy and NGC 5128 was one

Figure 2. The arc of blue stars (arrowed) that are the remnants of a dwarf irregular galaxy cannibalized by Centaurus A around 300 million years ago. (Image courtesy of JHU/NOAO/AURA/NSF.)

of the first radio galaxies to be discovered. Now classed as one of the many types of AGN, at just 11 million light years away, NGC 5128 is the closest active galaxy to ourselves.

SEYFERT GALAXIES

Six years before the identification of Cen A, Carl Seyfert noticed a dozen galaxies with unusual properties that set them apart from classical galaxies, and went on to study six of the spectra in detail. The galaxies were almost all spirals, but the cores of their nuclei were very small and extremely intense (Figure 3). In fact, on short exposure images, only the cores show up, looking like stars. Furthermore, the galaxies' spectra contain strong emission lines, whose widths corresponded to speeds of hundreds or even thousands of kilometres per second. By contrast, classic galaxies' spectra, like those of stars, contain only absorption lines or at the most very feeble emission lines. Later work has shown

Figure 3. One of Carl Seyfert's original group of peculiar galaxies, M 77 (also known as NGC 1068). Note the small and intensely bright core. (Image courtesy of ING Archive and Nik Szymanek.)

that the characteristics of Seyfert's galaxies occur in up to 10 per cent of spirals, though often only weakly.

In the early 1970s Ed Khachikian and Dan Weedman divided the group into the Seyfert 1 and Seyfert 2 subtypes (and they have subsequently been even further divided within that classification). Seyfert 1s have very broad hydrogen and helium spectrum lines. If the widths of the lines are the result of the motions of the emitting material (Doppler broadening), as is almost universally accepted, then the velocities within that material must be up to 10,000 kilometres per second. The other lines in Seyfert 1s' spectra are narrower, corresponding to speeds of a few hundred to a thousand kilometres per second. Within Seyfert 2 spectra, all the lines are relatively narrow with velocity equivalents of around 500 kilometres per second. The most recent counts give 9,500*

* Thanks are due to Dr Mira Véron-Cetty of the Observatoire de Haute Provence for advance notice of the data being compiled for the twelfth *Catalogue of Quasars and Active Nuclei*.

Seyfert 1s and 4,500 Seyfert 2s, but there are nearly 7,000 further objects awaiting certain identification, most of which are probably Seyfert 1s.

SOLVING A PUZZLE

Two decades after Seyfert identified 'his' galaxies, a long-standing astronomical puzzle was cracked. Since the 1950s radio astronomers at Cambridge (UK) had been using their newly built radio telescopes to survey the sky repeatedly for radio sources. By the time of the third survey, radio telescopes had improved to the point where the resulting catalogue of sources was reliable (in the sense that the sources were mostly real and not artefacts produced by the instrumentation), but their positional accuracy was still poor. Identifying a radio source with a particular optical object was thus difficult. Eventually, in 1960, radio astronomers at Caltech, using an interferometer, managed to measure the position of the forty-eighth object in Cambridge's third survey (3C 48) to within 5 seconds of arc. Allan Sandage promptly employed the 5-metre Hale telescope to identify the radio source with a 16^{m} star-like object. When he examined the star's spectrum, however, it was most odd – it contained strong emission lines that did not match those of any known element.

For three years 3C 48 remained an enigma. The crucial clue to its true nature came when an accurate position for a second radio source, 3C 273, was obtained. Cyril Hazard used the 64-metre Parkes radio telescope (Figure 4) in Australia to observe lunar occultations of the radio source and so to deduce its position to within one second of arc. The corresponding optical image showed a star-like object (Figure 5) and a faint jet. An optical spectrum of the 'star' obtained by Maarten Schmidt at Mount Palomar contained strong, but again unidentifiable, emission lines.

By 1963 it was known that almost all galaxies were moving away from us, so that the lines in their spectra had longer wavelengths than would occur in the laboratory. The greater the distance of the galaxy, the greater was its recessional velocity and so the greater the redshift of its spectrum lines. With hindsight we now know that most of this redshift is not caused by a true velocity away from us. The redshift of the galaxies has, along with other evidence, led to the development of

Figure 4. The 64-metre Parkes radio telescope whose observations led to the identification of 3C 273. (Image courtesy CSIRO Australia.)

the Big Bang theory for the origin of the Universe. In this, all the contents of the Universe started off by being crammed into a very small volume indeed. Around 14,000 million years ago the contents of that volume started expanding in an explosion that dwarfs anything that has occurred since – including even the hypernovae that may power gamma-ray bursters. However, the explosion was not of the material of the Universe through pre-existing space but an explosion that included the expansion of space itself. Thus, for a while, the rate of expansion of the Universe exceeded the speed of light in a vacuum by many orders of magnitude, but without violating the constraints of relativity. The present cosmological redshift is a remnant of that expansion of space – the galaxies are not moving through space at enormous velocities, but moving with space at those velocities. On top of the cosmological redshift, the galaxies' intrinsic and genuine velocities are superimposed, but these are small compared with the cosmological effects except for nearby galaxies. For most practical purposes though, the cosmological redshift can be regarded as a velocity-induced Doppler shift without too many difficulties.

Returning to the problematic 3C 273 and 3C 48, the maximum redshifts that had been found for galaxies by the early 1960s were just a few per cent. Schmidt, puzzling over his spectrum, noticed that some of the lines formed a pattern with regularly decreasing intervals between their wavelengths. Now such a pattern is well known to spectroscopists – it is the Balmer series and is produced by the commonest element in the Universe, hydrogen. In the spectrum of 3C 273,

Figure 5. An optical image from the Hubble Space Telescope of the quasar 3C 273, the first to be identified as such in 1963. At thirteenth magnitude, 3C 273 is visible in many amateur astronomers' telescopes. Note the star-like appearance and the single jet. (Image courtesy of NASA/STScI and the late John Bahcall.)

however, the lines were well adrift of their normal positions – shifted towards the red by nearly 16 per cent. Schmidt soon found that if he assumed a redshift of 16 per cent (actually 15.8 per cent) then *all* the lines in the spectrum matched those from known elements, not just those of hydrogen. The result was irrefutable – 3C 273 was moving away from us at over 47,000 km/s. If its redshift were cosmological then not only would it be the most distant object then discovered, at some 2,000 million light years away from us, but its apparent magnitude of 13^{m} implied a true brightness that was two trillion times that of the Sun – twenty times brighter than the most luminous classical galaxy.

3C 273 did not retain its record as the furthest object for long. Its large redshift hinted at the answer to the 3C 48 conundrum, and the latter's spectrum lines were quickly identified with those produced by known elements, but shifted by a whopping 48 per cent. This corresponds to a recessional velocity over 110,000 km/s and a distance of 5,200 million light years. In other words, the photons that we receive today from 3C 48 were emitted some 700 million years before the Earth was born.

YET MORE DISCOVERIES

3C 273 and 3C 48 were soon found to be just two among many hundreds of similar objects, and from their star-like appearances they became called Quasi Stellar Radio Sources – though that was rapidly abbreviated to 'quasar'. It was also found that there were many objects similar to quasars that did not emit strongly at radio wavelengths, and these were dubbed Quasi Stellar Objects (QSOs). Nearly 85,000 QSOs and quasars have now been found, the majority having redshifts corresponding to recessional velocities near 250,000 km/s. We thus see them as they were about 12,000 million years ago, when the Universe was some 2,000 million years old.

The launch of the Infrared Astronomy Satellite (IRAS) in 1983 led to another spate of discoveries. IRAS found thousands of galaxies that emitted strongly in the infrared; the most luminous of these were the Ultra Luminous Infra-Red Galaxies (ULIRGs), which emit most of their energy in the infrared – and that energy seems to come from dust clouds heated by vast star-forming regions. Those star-forming regions in their turn probably arise through a collision between two large galaxies. All ULIRGs are extremely bright and one, IRAS 10214+4724 in Ursa Major, at 300 trillion solar luminosities, may be the brightest object in the visible Universe, although gravitational lensing could be intensifying its perceived brightness.

Can entities as diverse as radio galaxies, Seyferts, quasars, QSOs and ULIRGs possibly be related to each other? According to the latest ideas, the answer is 'Yes'. One link is that a sufficiently distant Seyfert galaxy would show only its bright, star-like core and so resemble a faint quasar. Conversely, very careful studies of quasars show that most of them occur inside 'host' galaxies that often also contain very active regions of star formation. Thus Seyferts seem to be less powerful versions of quasars.

As the resolution of radio telescopes improved it was soon found that the radio emission from Cen A and many other radio galaxies came from two regions on either side of the visible galaxy. In the case of Cen A the radio lobes were over 250,000 light years apart. Now, with 3C 273 and many other quasars, a single jet of very high-speed material can be found being ejected from the object. In most cases, in fact, two jets are probably emitted, but relativistic effects make the one moving away from us appear much fainter than the one coming towards us, so that often the second jet is not seen. The material in the jets is moving at nearly the speed of light and it will thrust its way out into intergalactic space. Even intergalactic space, however, contains a few atoms, and these eventually slow the jets down. As the material in the jets comes to a halt its energy is released and emitted in the form of radio waves – a quasar seen sideways-on would thus bear a strong resemblance to a very bright radio galaxy.

AT THE HEART OF IT

The phenomena found in radio galaxies, Seyferts, quasars and QSOs are all thought to originate from gargantuan black holes at their centres. The black holes have masses ranging from a million times that of the Sun for the fainter Seyferts to several thousand million solar masses in the largest quasars. Material is still falling into the black hole from the surrounding galaxy. It does not, however, fall straight into the black hole but goes initially into orbit, forming a dense, thick disc around the black hole. Energy released as the material falls inwards heats the disc to extremely high temperatures, and some of the material is flung out along the rotational axes of the black hole where the gas is thinnest. Precisely how the material eventually reaches speeds close to the velocity of light is still something of a mystery but, as it emerges from the region around the black hole, it becomes visible to us as the jets of quasars and eventually as the radio-emission regions of radio galaxies.

How do such super-massive black holes form in the first place? It is now thought that largish black holes exist at the centres of most galaxies, being produced by the collisions and mergers of stars near the galaxies' centres. The Milky Way, for example, contains a two-and-a-half- to four-million solar mass black hole that we observe as the radio source Sgr A* – and so our own galaxy may itself have been a faint Seyfert at some point in the past. When the earliest galaxies were born, their average separations were only 10 per cent or so of those today. Collisions must thus have been extremely common. Nowadays when galaxies collide, it is the gas and dust clouds that actually hit each other – the stars are so well separated that they mostly pass by each other at great distances. However, at the centres of the early galaxies, star densities may have been sufficiently large that individual stars did collide – such collisions might then produce enormous explosions similar to supernovae but, when all the fuss had died down, most of the material would collect together to form a new and larger star. The mass of the new star might be sufficient for it to collapse down to a black hole immediately, or to do so having proceeded through a fairly normal process of stellar evolution. These stellar-sized black holes might then mutually collide to build up to larger and larger masses, eventually reaching tens or hundreds of thousands of solar masses or more and residing close to the core of the galaxy.

During later collisions, the central black holes of the two galaxies could merge and the new and even larger black hole would then absorb many of the remaining central stars of the galaxies. The collision would also induce a frenetic period of star formation so that the galaxies resulting from such mergers would glow brightly from all the hot young stars within them. Further collisions would result in larger and larger galaxies and increasingly massive central black holes. Finally, some galaxies would become sufficiently large that their collisions are still visible to us today, some 12,000 million years later. The mightiest of galaxy collisions are the ULIRGs whose extreme infrared emissions are powered by the huge spate of star formation induced during the collision and merger of two massive galaxies.

As might be expected from this process, the larger the galaxy, the more massive tends to be its central black hole. Although there are relatively few measurements of both the mass of the galaxy and its black hole within the same galaxy, those that are available suggest that the black hole's mass will be between 0.2 per cent and 0.6 per cent of the mass of the galaxy – implying that the most massive black holes may have masses up to five billion times the mass of the Sun.

Although it can probably never be proved, it seems likely that as the star-forming activity in a ULIRG dies down, the now huge central black hole will start developing relativistic jets and it will gradually re-emerge as a quasar or QSO, or if we see it from the side, as a radio galaxy. Smaller galaxy mergers likewise probably result in the Seyfert galaxies and even in 'normal' galaxies such as the Andromeda Galaxy and the Milky Way. Quasars are thus in a very real sense the product of ULIRGs.

Widefield Astrophotography with Digital SLR Cameras

NICK JAMES

INTRODUCTION

Amateur astronomers have used digital cameras for many years but these have been specialized devices, designed to allow long exposures with high-quality read-out direct into a computer. These cameras are expensive and, generally, have small image sensors, but they have huge advantages over film in terms of sensitivity and ease of use. By the mid-1990s, with the exception of widefield imaging, specialized digital cameras had replaced film in all areas of astronomy. Film remained dominant in widefield work since it could provide a much larger imaging area than digital.

The standard camera used by amateur astronomers for many years was the 35-mm single-lens reflex camera. In an SLR camera the image from the lens is routed to the viewfinder by a mirror. When the picture is taken this mirror flips up out of the optical path for the duration of the exposure. This means that what you see in the viewfinder is exactly what you get on the film. SLRs have interchangeable lenses and the large size of 35-mm film (24 × 36 mm) meant that you could get a large field of view with a relatively large aperture lens. With the right film and a good lens they could produce spectacular results (Figure 1.)

All digital cameras are based on an imaging sensor which consists of an array of light-sensitive picture elements, or pixels (Figure 2), and which replaces the film used in conventional cameras. Each pixel is sensitive to light and during an exposure an electrical charge builds up which is proportional to the brightness of the image at that location. At the end of the exposure each pixel is read out and the resulting image is stored in a computer file. Until recently, the manufacturing cost of large image sensors was very high, so most high-street digital cameras had sensors much smaller than 35-mm film. To compensate

Figure 1. Scutum star clouds from the Sinai Desert. Five-minute exposure on hypersensitized Technical Pan film. Canon T70, 85-mm f/1.2L lens.

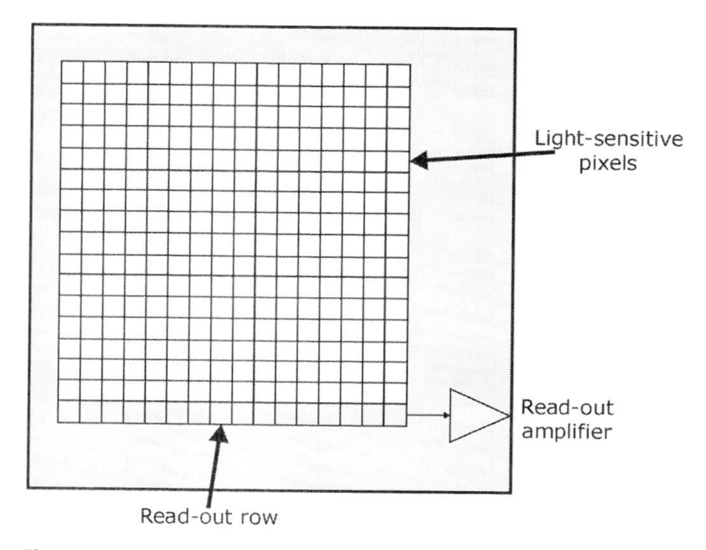

Figure 2. Diagram showing a typical image sensor.

Figure 3. Milky Way from the Sinai Desert. Stack of 6,299s exposures. 8-mm lens, Canon EOS 10D.

for the small sensor the common 'point-and-shoot' digital camera has a very short-focal-length lens with a correspondingly small aperture. This works fine for daytime photography but it does mean that the camera is not very sensitive at night. It is possible to get reasonably good images with this type of camera, but what was needed was an affordable version of the trusty 35-mm SLR.

Recent developments have made it possible to manufacture large, high-resolution image sensors at a reasonable price, and you can now buy a digital equivalent of the old 35-mm SLR in the high street. Digital SLRs (DSLRs) have everything that you would expect from an SLR: interchangeable lenses, full manual control, large image sensors and very high resolutions. They make it possible to obtain amazing widefield astro images (Figure 3) using normal SLR lenses, and even the most diehard film photographer can see that the days of film are numbered.

As with all digital imaging systems, DSLRs have made it possible to take very impressive astro images from light-polluted locations, but there are some important 'tricks of the trade' that you will need to use if you are going to get the best out of these cameras. I shall describe these later, but let's first look at what is available on the market and how it works.

WHAT'S AVAILABLE?

All of the major camera-body manufacturers produce DSLR cameras. Technology moves on rapidly, so any specific recommendations are likely to be out of date by the time you read this, but the two main competitors are Canon and Nikon, who both offer a range of cameras. The DSLR that I own is the Canon EOS 10D (Figure 4). This has a 6.3-megapixel camera with a 15.1 × 22.7-mm sensor. It has now been superseded by the EOS 20D which has 8.2 megapixels in the same area and which, in early 2006, costs around £700 for the body. The 10D and

Figure 4. A Canon EOS 10D DSLR with a 100-mm f/2 lens.

20D were accompanied by lower-priced 'consumer' DSLRs, the 300D and 350D respectively, and these are both very capable cameras for astrophotography. In fact the 300D, being an obsolete model, can be obtained for under £350 on the second-hand market. Nikon also offers a range of DSLRs with the D70s, with its 6-megapixel, 15.5 × 23.7-mm sensor, placed to compete with the 10D/20D. The performance of the Nikon cameras is very similar to the Canon ones but most amateur astrophotographers seem to be using Canon bodies.

Most camera lenses are designed to work best in the visible part of the spectrum, and they tend to have significantly different focus in the infrared. The sensors in DSLR cameras are actually very sensitive in the infrared and so the manufacturers include an infrared blocking filter in front of the sensor to ensure the best performance from the lens. Unfortunately, the filter used in these cameras also blocks most of the deep red hydrogen alpha light that is a major component of the light from many nebulae. Various brave people have dismantled their cameras to remove this filter (web ref. 1), but Canon have recently introduced a special version of the 20D (called the 20Da) which has the filter removed. This camera also includes a live focusing mode which is particularly useful to astrophotographers. The cost of this specialized body in early 2006 was around £1,400.

One very interesting recent addition is the Canon EOS 5D. This semi-professional DSLR has a full-sized 35-mm sensor (24 × 36 mm) containing over 12 million pixels. In early 2006 the 5D body cost around £2,000. A comparison of the 10D and 5D sensors is shown in Figure 5.

Figure 5. Comparison of the EOS 10D image sensor (left) and the EOS 5D sensor (right).

SOME TECHNICAL DETAILS

Historically, imaging sensors have been based on charge-coupled devices (CCDs), and these are the sensors used in the Nikon cameras. Canon use a different kind of technology called complementary metal oxide semiconductor (CMOS). Large CMOS sensors are relatively cheap to manufacture since they have a similar structure to other microelectronic components such as microprocessors and memory chips. CMOS has the further advantage that support functions, such as memory, image processor and read-out electronics, can be integrated on the same chip.

Whichever sensor is used the basic operation is the same. The shutter opens and the sensor is exposed to the image for a set duration. At the end of the exposure the shutter closes and the charge in each pixel is measured. The camera then generates a computer file which uses integer numbers to represent the charge measured for each pixel. The resolution of these numbers determines the camera's dynamic range or the number of grey shades from brightest to darkest that can be represented by the file. Some cheaper cameras use 8-bit integers which allows 2^8 or 256 grey levels. Better cameras use 12-bit (4,096 level) or 16-bit (65,536 level) numbers. If the charge is more than the maximum level allowed by the number the pixel is said to be saturated.

The array of numbers resulting from the sensor read-out is called the raw image. Depending on the file format selected this may be stored directly to the camera's memory for later processing in a PC; alternatively, further processing may be applied in the camera to produce a common image format, such as JPEG, which can be used directly on a computer.

Use a magnifier to look closely at a colour TV screen or monitor and you will see that the image is made up of red, green and blue light-emitting elements. All of the colours that you see in the image are represented by certain proportions of these three primary colours. Many computer-image file formats represent each pixel in a similar way, with three numbers representing the brightness of the red, green and blue components.

To enable the camera to produce a colour picture the image sensor has a set of primary colour filters deposited over each pixel site. Most

Figure 6. Bayer matrix.

cameras use an arrangement called a Bayer matrix, as shown in Figure 6. This consists of alternating green and red filters in odd rows and blue and green filters in even rows. These filters do not affect the raw image file, which is still an array of numbers representing the brightness of the image at each point, but they do change the response of each pixel in a way that allows software to extract colour information from the image. The Bayer matrix means that the colour resolution in the resulting image is less than the luminance (or black-and-white) resolution, but this is not normally a problem since it matches the characteristics of the human eye.

CAMERA FILE FORMATS FOR ASTROPHOTOGRAPHY

For general photography most people want to get a colour picture from the camera which can be displayed on a computer with no further processing. Practically all cameras have a JPEG image setting and in this mode the camera takes the raw sensor pixel values and processes the Bayer matrix to assign RGB colour values to each pixel in the resulting image. This processing is done using a mathematical function called interpolation so that each pixel in the image is made up of samples from several adjacent sensor pixels. In addition to the colour interpolation the camera also has to reduce the number of brightness levels so that the 4,096 levels from the sensor fit within the 256 levels permitted by the JPEG standard. This is done using a function which approximates to the way that the human eye perceives changes in brightness. The JPEG format also makes use of various techniques to remove redundant information from the image so that the resulting file is much smaller than the raw image.

Since the files are so compact JPEG is a great format to use for your final images, especially if you are going to be posting them to a website or sending them by email; however, it is not a good choice as the format to use for your original files. All the image-processing steps described later in this chapter depend on having access to the original raw image files captured by the sensor. There are a number of reasons why you should use raw format for your astro images. Firstly, the original measurement of pixel charge is retained whereas the JPEG format smears it over several pixels. This property is essential for dark-frame subtraction. Secondly, the inherent dynamic range of the camera is retained whereas the JPEG format applies a non-linear compression. It is only possible to perform a flat field correction if the pixel values have a linear relationship with the original image brightness. Finally, the processing required for the Bayer filter matrix can be performed on a PC with more sophisticated interpolation algorithms than are available in the camera.

For Canon cameras this means that you should select the raw file format (.CRW or .CR2 file types). A similar format is available from Nikon cameras (.NEF), though various people have reported that the Nikon raw format is actually slightly 'cooked' and so does not exactly represent the raw pixel samples. Some ways to overcome this problem with the Nikon cameras are listed in the references (see web ref. 2). With raw images, computer-based processing is used to extract the maximum amount of information from the original image. The processing performed on the raw image replaces the old-fashioned photographic darkroom so, instead of chemicals and photographic paper, a digital photographer uses special programs running on a PC. Details of the processing steps required are given later on, but first we should consider what lens to put in front of the sensor.

LENSES

A camera is only as good as its lens. The body manufacturers produce a wide variety of lenses using their standard lens mounts and many of these are suitable for night-time use. If you are looking for a new lens specifically to use for astrophotography, this section should help you make your selection. Otherwise, just pick the most appropriate lens from your current collection.

Camera lenses are defined by their focal length and their focal ratio (the ratio of the focal length to the aperture). Daytime photographers know that lenses with small (or fast) focal ratios give brighter images than lenses with large (or slow) focal ratios. This also applies to extended objects in the sky such as the Milky Way or nebulae. Stars are rather different since they are point sources, and in this case it is the aperture that matters, but for any given focal length a lower focal ratio implies a larger aperture; in all cases we are therefore better off with fast (small focal ratio) lenses.

The focal length of the lens defines the field of view and resolution that you will get with any given sensor. For a lens of focal length *FL* mm, each *d* micron-sized pixel will subtend an angle of

$$206 \times d \,/\, FL \text{ arcseconds}$$

on the sky. My Canon 10D has 7.4μm pixels, so each pixel subtends just over 15 arcseconds when I use the camera with a 100-mm focal length lens. The field of view is this angle multiplied by the number of pixels. For the 10D with 3072 × 2048 pixels this corresponds to approximately 13.0° × 8.7°.

Stars are a particularly hard test for lenses since they are point sources which we want to be imaged as small, round dots. Any optical aberrations are painfully visible when the image is examined at high magnification. Figure 7 shows an image of the region around the Pleiades in Taurus taken using a Canon EOS 5D and a Canon EF 100 mm, f/2 lens operating at f/2.5. The insets show full-resolution sections of the image taken from the centre, 60 per cent of the way to the corner and the corner. This is a very good lens but it is clearly not perfect over the full-frame field of the 5D. A camera with a smaller sensor, such as the 20D, would not have this problem since the corner

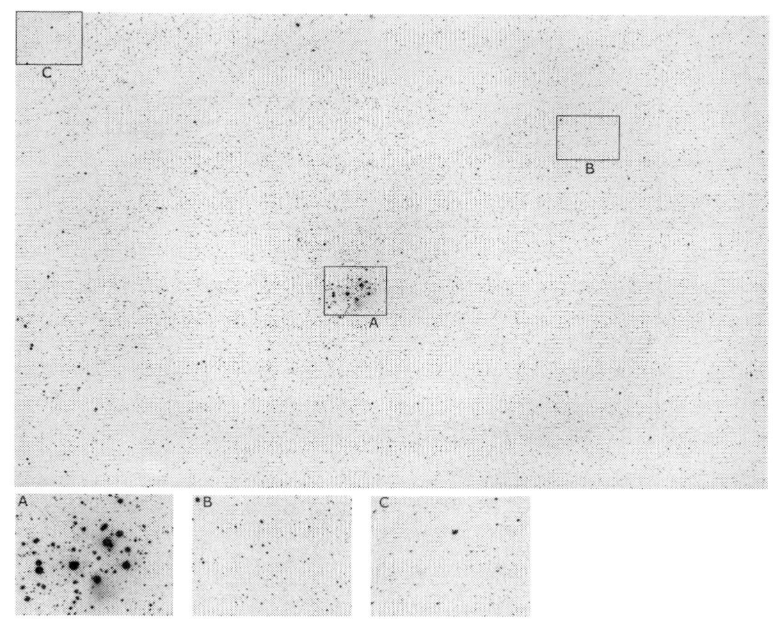

Figure 7. Canon EOS 5D full-frame image. Insets are full-resolution crops of various parts of the frame showing quality of lens images. 100-mm f/2 lens at f/2.5.

of the field is closer to the optical axis (around 62 per cent of the distance compared with the 5D sensor).

The best-performing lenses for astrophotography are often those that daytime photographers no longer want, and so it is possible to pick up some excellent bargains on the second-hand market. I prefer to use fixed focal length (sometimes called 'prime') lenses for astrophotography since they are generally faster than similarly priced zoom lenses. Their optical quality is usually better as well since they don't need as many lens groups as the zooms. One important thing to remember when you are looking at a lens is that it must be able to focus manually. All modern lenses are designed for autofocus cameras but autofocus will not work on the night sky! Most lenses do have a manual focusing option but in some cases the manual-focus action is so poor that it is pretty well useless. The fact that we only need manual focus can be used to advantage since some very high-quality lenses with broken autofocus mechanisms occasionally appear on the second-hand market. These can be picked up very cheaply. Alternatively, many of the excellent manual-focus lenses from the past can be pressed into service with suitable lens mount adaptors.

OBTAINING THE IMAGE

Once you have all the necessary equipment it is then a matter of waiting for a clear night so that you can take some images. There are a few camera settings to configure before you take the image. Firstly, exposures should be taken in full manual mode. You should manually select the lens aperture, and the exposure will usually be set to 'bulb'. This means that the exposure will continue for as long as the shutter release is pressed. DSLR cameras have an ISO setting which determines the sensitivity of the camera and you might think that higher ISO numbers (more sensitivity) would be good for faint astronomical subjects, but this is not necessarily the case. Thermal-noise effects are much more significant at high ISO values, and saturation due to noise or sky brightness occurs much sooner. The higher ISO values are actually wasting the dynamic range available in the 12-bit raw files, and I have found that a setting of ISO 200 is optimum on my 10D.

To get the best from the camera you will need to take calibration frames in addition to the object image. Two types of calibration frame are required. A flat field is a short exposure of an evenly illuminated field (often the bright twilight sky) taken with the lens that will be used to image the object set up with the same focal ratio. Since the lenses on a DSLR can be changed it is possible to get specks of dust on the imaging sensor. These specks appear as out-of-focus dark blobs in the final image. In addition, camera lenses do not uniformly illuminate the image sensor. With most lenses the image gets darker towards the edge of the frame. This effect is called vignetting. The flat field records the variations in pixel sensitivity due to these effects and it can be used later on to correct for them. Flat fields are useful when you are trying to detect very faint nebulosity or a comet's tail, and they are especially important if you live in an area where the light pollution is significant.

With the flat fields taken and stored during twilight the next task is to focus the camera accurately. This can be done as soon as stars become visible. The quality and limiting magnitude of the final image is critically dependent on focusing, but you will find that autofocus does not work under these circumstances, so the camera will need to be focused manually. Unfortunately, most DSLRs have small, faint viewfinders which have not been designed to assist focusing, so alternative techniques are required. Just to make life even more difficult, most modern lenses do not have a stop at infinity so you can't just turn the focus ring until it won't go any further.

The method I use for focusing is an iterative one. I take a short exposure with the lens wide open and focused as near as possible to infinity and then zoom the picture up on the display LCD so that I can judge the size of the star images. I then change the focus a small amount and try again. With practice good focus can be achieved quite quickly. There are some software tools available to help with focusing (web ref. 3), but all of them require you to have a laptop connected to the camera so this isn't practical in many cases.

Since astronomical objects are usually very faint we need the ability to take long-exposure images so that the charge from incoming photons can build up over a long time. In practice, the maximum length of exposure for digital image sensors is limited by thermal noise. This thermal charge adds to the wanted charge and appears as spurious bright dots in the resulting image. The warmer the sensor and the longer the exposure, the worse this problem becomes.

It used to be that the sensors used in astronomical cameras had to be cooled to a very low temperature (typically −20°C) so that the thermal noise on its own did not saturate the pixels during long exposures. Things are different now; modern image sensors have incredibly low noise levels so that it is possible to take exposures of ten minutes or more at room temperature without problems. This remarkable ability makes modern DSLRs ideal for astrophotography.

The small amount of thermal noise that is present can be reduced by processing the image with a dark frame. One of the features of the thermal noise is that for any given sensor and pixel it is highly reproducible. That is, if you take two frames with the same exposure and with the sensor at the same temperature the amount of thermal noise in any given pixel will be the same in both frames. We can use this fact to remove the thermal noise in our long-exposure images by taking a dark frame. This is just an image taken using an exposure length which is the same as the one used for the sky but with the lens cap on. The

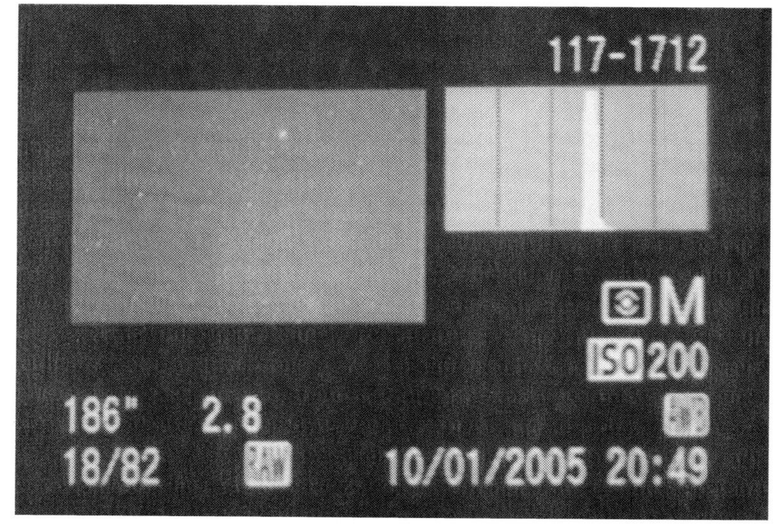

Figure 8. LCD information display on the Canon EOS 10D showing the histogram in the upper right.

charge in each pixel of the dark frame will be entirely due to thermal effects, since no light was reaching the sensor. Computer software can subtract the dark frame from the image frame pixel by pixel, so that we remove the thermal noise from the final image. This works very well as long as none of the pixels in either image is saturated. You can check this by looking at the image histogram which can be displayed on the LCD monitor. There should be no hump in the histogram at the extreme right-hand end of the graph (Figure 8).

BASIC IMAGE PROCESSING

In my opinion the best software for processing DSLR astro images is called IRIS. This program was written by Christian Buil and it can be downloaded for free from his website (web ref. 4) along with a very useful set of step-by-step tutorials. The program can read both Canon and Nikon raw file formats and is continuously updated. There are also a number of commercial programs such as MaxDSLR (web ref. 5) and imagesplus (web ref. 6) which do a similar job.

The following discussion of processing is written as generally as possible but it is illustrated with examples using IRIS. Similar routines should be available in other programs. I have tried to keep things as simple as possible consistent with getting excellent results. There are plenty of online tutorials that will take you through more complex procedures for special situations.

The first step is to transfer all the image files from your camera to your PC. At this stage the image files contain the raw pixel samples read from the sensor at the end of each exposure. In most cases this means that each pixel in the image is represented by a single 12-bit integer. With IRIS, subsequent processing is simplified if the raw image and dark files are converted to FITS format using 'Digital Photo>Decode Raw Files' with the target set to Colour Filter Array (CFA). The flat should be converted to FITS with the target set to Black and White (B&W). An example raw image is shown in Figure 9a. This image is noisy and has an uneven background.

The first processing step is to subtract the dark frame (Figure 9b) from the image frame. With IRIS this is achieved by loading the image FITS file and then selecting 'processing>subtract>file from disk'. The resulting image has had the thermal noise component removed but still has a varying sky background. You can now divide this result image by the monochrome flat field (Figure 9c) ('processing->divide' in IRIS) and save the result file under a new name.

Now that the image has been corrected for thermal noise and dust/vignetting you can perform the Bayer matrix interpolation to convert it into a colour image. In IRIS this is done by selecting 'Digital photo>Image CFA conversion'. If your sky is anything like mine the background will be an unpleasant green or yellow colour. IRIS has a very useful function to correct this which at the same time removes any gradient in the background. Select 'Processing>Remove gradient' and make sure the 'balance background colour' box is ticked. After running this you should find that the sky is a much more natural colour. Select suitable contrast stretch values and the full range of the image becomes visible (Figure 9d).

Careful use of the calibration steps allows us to take advantage of the large dynamic range of the image sensor. This means that it is possible to extract information even when the image is apparently washed out by light pollution. With the right processing it is possible to reveal objects which are only 1 per cent as bright as the sky background; this

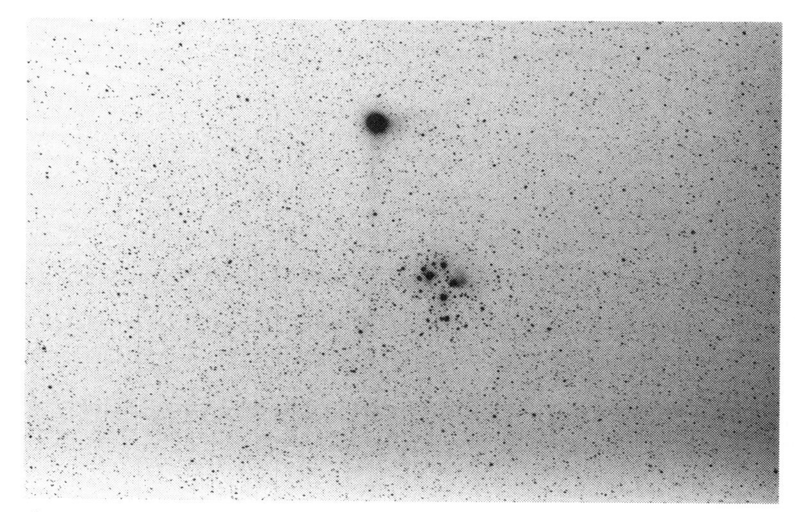

Figure 9a. Raw image (negative) of comet C/2004 Q2 (Machholz) passing near the Pleiades taken with a Canon EOS 10D and 100-mm, f/2 lens. Note the uneven background and noisy image.

Figure 9b. Example dark frame (in negative). This is a 929-second exposure at ISO 1600! The glow on the right is from the chip electronics.

Figure 9c. Example flat field in negative showing the variation in illumination across the chip and some dust shadows.

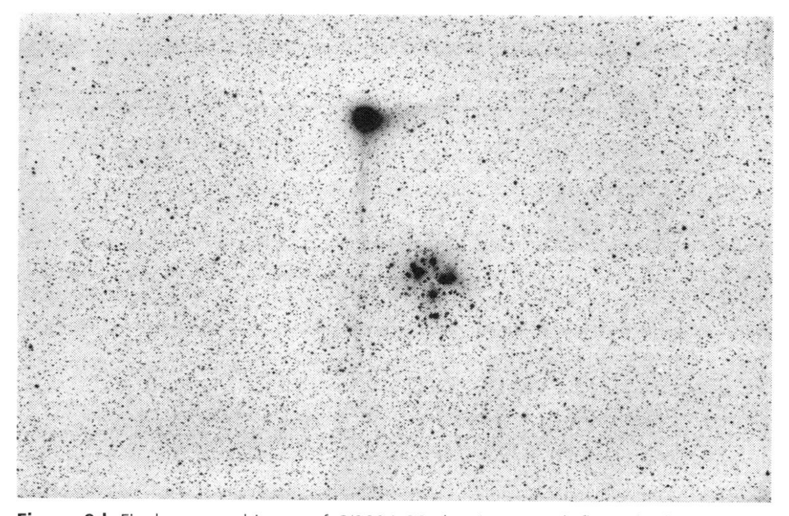

Figure 9d. Final processed image of C/2004 Q2 showing a much flatter background and more tail detail.

has huge implications for those of us who live in towns and cities, since it makes it possible to detect faint comet tails or nebulae when they would otherwise remain invisible.

Using film, I could never have taken the picture shown in Figure 9d from the site that I use, just outside a large town in south-east England. The advent of the DSLR has made this possible, and I am still amazed that so much technology is available in such a small package. We live in exciting times, and the next few years will be particularly exciting as imaging technology races ahead. This article has only had the space to give a rather superficial review of the techniques and technology involved in this area of astro-imaging, and the web references listed below will provide much more information.

WEBSITE REFERENCES

1. http://www.startrails.de/html/mod.html
2. http://astrosurf.com/buil/d70v10d/eval.htm
3. http://www.dslrfocus.com/
4. http://www.astrosurf.com/buil/us/iris/iris.htm
5. http://www.cyanogen.com/products/maxdslr_main.htm
6. http://www.mlunsold.com/

A Centenary of Some Gravity

FRED WATSON

There can't be too many articles in the *Yearbook of Astronomy* that come with a government health warning. This one does – but I'll try to deliver it as gently as I can. If you suffer from arachnophobia, it might not be a bad idea to skip the first few paragraphs. In fact, don't even peep.

Australia is famous for its spiders, of course – although in reality you don't see that many more here than you do in the UK. It's just that they tend to be a bit bigger, are often meaner-looking, and are occasionally vaguely poisonous. Very, very rarely, they are lethal. But in Australia, as elsewhere, you're far more likely to die in a road accident than from a spider bite.

What brought this excursion down the byways of Australian spider lore to mind in the context of a *Yearbook* article was an event this morning, when my 12-year-old son woke to find himself confronted with a large and extremely handsome huntsman spider on the wall opposite his bed. These sleek-looking creatures have a smallish body with what seems like dozens of long, hairy legs attached, and this one measured a healthy 100 mm (4 inches) across its widest span. They aren't venomous, although they can give you a painful nip if, for example, they've taken up residence inside one of your wellies and you innocently attempt a spot of double occupancy with your foot. Huntsmen spend most of their working lives spreadeagled flat against whatever surface they happen to be on, and feed by simply grabbing passing insects. When disturbed, they can move with astonishing speed on those long legs, but they do tend to ignore anything that's happening away from the surface on which they're sitting.

Given that James is decidedly arachnophobic, I have to give him great credit for not leaping out of bed shouting 'Aaarrrggh – there's a huge spider in my room', at his usual waking time of six in the morning. Instead, he waited until a more reasonable hour, and we then removed the spider by the time-honoured method of gently covering it with a large transparent kitchen bowl, sliding a sheet of thin card between it and the wall, and delivering it somewhere more distant than the bedroom – to wit, the farmer's field over the garden fence. But the spider looked decidedly miffed about this. In fact, it appeared to be shaken rigid – and that is when it occurred to me that I had just committed a horrendous crime against the natural order of spiderhood. Huntsmen normally inhabit the purely two-dimensional world of a surface – a comfortable bedroom wall, for example – and I had just propelled this one into a three-dimensional nightmare of coarse grass in Fred Swanson's back paddock. No wonder it was peeved. Suddenly having an extra dimension to deal with would be enough to give any spider a hefty dose of agoraphobia.

SPECIAL CIRCUMSTANCES

If it's any consolation to the spider, something very similar happened to humankind rather more than a century ago. For over two hundred years, we had been told by Isaac Newton that we occupied a Universe of three dimensions, and then along came a fellow called Albert Einstein who said no, there's actually another one. Einstein was not the first to suggest that time might behave like a fourth dimension, but the idea is so deeply ingrained in his Special Theory of Relativity of 1905 that we tend to associate it with him. It was, in fact, Hermann Minkowski (1864–1909) who gave us the full-blown four-dimensional Universe in elegant mathematical form some three years later.

The difference between Newton's Universe and Einstein's is that Newton thought of time as an absolute – something that was regularly meted out, and against which everything else was measured. There were no difficult questions about simultaneity, for example – if two events happened at the same time anywhere in the Universe, they were simultaneous. But Einstein asked what would happen when simultaneous events were seen by two observers, one of whom was moving with respect to the other. It turns out that because of the finite speed of light, the notion of simultaneity gets rather vague.

It's easier to visualize this paradox if you swap the notion of time for that of space – because another feature of this brave new world is that the four dimensions are subtly interchangeable. So there you are, sitting on the upper deck of your brand-new Qantas Airbus A-380, en route from Sydney to London. You have finished reading the latest issue of *Australasian Arachnid Fanciers Monthly*, and dinner is about to be served. Half an hour later, as you take your last sip of lukewarm coffee, you reflect on the fact that two events – the beginning and end of your meal – have occurred in exactly the same place, since you haven't moved from your seat. But to an observer on the ground, they are separated by nearly 500 kilometres. The occurrence of events in space and time is therefore relative rather than absolute – hence the name of Einstein's theory. And it's 'special' because it refers to the special case of things moving with respect to one another at constant speed, as in an airliner at its cruising altitude.

The discovery that we live in a four-dimensional Universe was nowhere near as traumatic for us as it is for a huntsman spider suddenly finding itself in a three-dimensional world. Our extra dimension is not populated with swooping magpies looking for a quick meal. But space–time did take some getting used to – especially when people saw what it could lead to.

The notion of space–time is one of three basic postulates of special relativity. The other two are that the laws of physics are the same whether you're moving or not (airline coffee stays in the cup – assuming there's no turbulence – even though you're moving at nearly 1,000 km/h over the ground), and that the speed of light in a vacuum is always the same, no matter how fast the source of light is moving. That surprising fact had been demonstrated in the 1880s. When Einstein worked his mathematical magic on these ideas, he got some unusual results about time and space that take on real significance for things moving at speeds close to the speed of light. But more dramatically – and entirely unexpectedly – he arrived at perhaps the most famous equation of all time, linking the mass of an object with its value in energy. You know the one I mean. It is this equation that allows us to understand the prodigious energy output of stars, and to predict the devastation associated with nuclear weapons.

In 1905, however, those discoveries were in the future. In fact, for Einstein, almost everything was in the future. Having had a rather undistinguished academic career, he was, at the age of 26, working as a patent clerk in the Swiss capital of Bern. He had got the job in 1902 on the recommendation of a friend's father, and it had just been upgraded from a temporary to a permanent position. What was more unusual about this young Technical Expert (Third Class) was that in his spare time, he tinkered around with theoretical physics. And he was simply brilliant at it.

Today, we tend to refer to 1905 as Einstein's *annus mirabilis* – his miraculous year – and not without good reason. Special relativity was just one aspect of what amounted to a single-handed revolution in physics. Here's the time line:

- 17 March: Einstein submits a paper on the photoelectric effect and the quantum nature of light, suggesting that light comes in the bullets of energy we now call photons (he won the 1921 Nobel Prize for this work);
- 30 April: he completes a paper on the size of molecules (for which he receives his Ph.D from the University of Zurich);
- 11 May: he submits a paper on the motion of small particles suspended in a liquid, leading eventually to the proof that atoms exist;
- 30 June: he submits a paper on his new theory of motion, the Special Theory of Relativity;
- 27 September: he submits a short supplementary note on some consequences of special relativity, including *that* equation.

Given such a breathtaking performance, there is little wonder that the world celebrated the centenary of Einstein's *annus mirabilis* with an International Year of Physics. A worldwide programme of events in both science and the arts included conferences, lectures, displays, exhibitions, concerts and plays. As a result, 2005 was an outstandingly successful Einstein Year. You may have noticed, however, that 2005 was some time ago. So why make a fuss about it now – especially when most people involved with the celebration felt truly Einsteined-out by the end of it?

GRAVITY OR ITS EQUIVALENT

The answer lies in what came next – because that was even better. By 1907, Einstein had a couple more publications under his belt and was beginning to get some recognition in scientific circles, although his application for a post at the University of Bern that year had been turned down. He was still at the Patent Office. But it was while sitting there at his desk, no doubt musing about Life, the Universe and Everything, that Einstein had what he later described as 'der glücklichste Gedanke meines Lebens' – 'the happiest thought of my life'. Wow – Einstein's happiest thought. What on Earth could that be about?

In fact, the idea was off the Earth rather than on it. Einstein was thinking about how special relativity might modify Newton's famous theory of gravitation. Arguably the greatest intellectual feat of all time, Newton's theory had proved dazzlingly successful in explaining the motions of objects in the Solar System right down to the finest detail. Just one minuscule aspect of Mercury's orbit didn't seem to fit, but everything else did. So, mused Einstein, how would relativity alter it, given that Newtonian gravity took no account whatever of time, and he now knew that time and space were intimately linked?

For some bizarre reason, Einstein then imagined himself falling from the roof of a house, and realized that in this rather inconvenient circumstance he would feel no gravitational force. He would certainly feel something when he hit the ground, but that doesn't matter in a thought experiment such as this. Einstein reasoned that he would be in a state of free fall, and if his pipe fell out of his mouth or coins fell out of his pocket, they would appear to float around him as if there were no gravity. We fortunate occupants of the twenty-first century are, of course, used to seeing TV images of orbiting astronauts surrounded by the weightless detritus of their trade – floating pens, cameras, food capsules, scientific instruments and so on. But in Einstein's day it was an entirely novel idea, and it quickly led him to the next step, the realization that the effects of a gravitational field and an applied acceleration are identical. If you were sitting in a windowless compartment on a rocket in space, for example, and someone lit the fuse, you would be unable to deduce whether the force you felt was due to the acceleration of the rocket, or to gravity. Therefore – locally at least – they must be the same thing.

This gleeful thought was a major breakthrough, now called the Principle of Equivalence – and 2007 is its centenary. In fact, it wasn't until 1912 that Einstein set out a formal statement of the principle, putting it in terms of the equivalence of the gravitational mass of an object (the way it responds to the pull of gravity) and its inertial mass (the way it responds to a force like the thrust of a rocket). Einstein then soared in his thinking, bringing together the mathematical tools needed to develop a new theory of gravity based upon the idea of accelerated reference frames. (Imagine yourself back in the Airbus. When it makes its take-off run with those four giant turbofans at full power, you and everyone else on board are in an accelerated reference frame. It feels great.)

Einstein quickly realized that much of this boiled down to a problem of geometry – because the laws of relativity that apply in ordinary, or Euclidean space (as exemplified by Minkowski space–time) don't work any more. But if you invoke a geometrical system called a four-dimensional Riemannian manifold, then the accelerated reference frames become as docile as kittens. Well, nearly – the mathematical formulation is still exceedingly difficult. You might be forgiven for thinking, as I did, that a Riemannian manifold is something you'd find under the bonnet of your car, but it's merely a particularly complex model of space developed in the 1850s by a gifted German mathematician called Bernhard Riemann (1826–66).

What followed, of course, was the General Theory of Relativity, a startling new theory of gravity that made the wildly improbable assertion that space–time itself can bend, warped by the presence of matter – which, in turn, responds to the distorted geometry of space–time by moving within it. The final step in the argument was beautifully summarized by the late Sir Fred Hoyle in a popular article some years ago:

> Einstein's remarkable idea was to regard the difference between Riemannian space–time and Minkowski space–time as the true meaning of the phenomenon of gravitation. To this end he modified Newton's equations of motion so as to form a comprehensive scheme for calculating not just the motions of particles in a prescribed space–time like that of Minkowski, but a determination of what the more complex Riemannian space–time had to be.

The new theory was stunning in its implications. Shortly before submitting his description of it for publication, in November 1915, Einstein realized that it exactly accounted for the observed anomaly in Mercury's orbit. 'For a few days, I was beside myself with joyous excitement,' he wrote later. And, of course, the dramatic verification of the theory's prediction that the Sun's gravity bends light, using observations of the total solar eclipse of 25 May 1919, is now the stuff of legend. As *The Times* of 7 November 1919 blared: 'Revolution in science – New Theory of the Universe – Newtonian ideas overthrown'. None of which was any exaggeration.

More than ninety years after its formulation, general relativity is still the best theory of gravity we have. It has survived all the tests that have been thrown at it, and has successfully predicted the existence of black holes, the expanding Universe, gravitational lenses, gravitational waves, and so on. It underpins cosmology – the science of the history and evolution of the Universe as a whole. Everyone is familiar with the idea that space–time is curved, and Einstein is regarded as the greatest genius of the twentieth century, not to mention a few other centuries besides. The one thing that general relativity can't cope with is gravity on the very smallest scale, since the theory is based on space–time as a continuous medium rather than a succession of distinct steps or quanta – and we know that this is how the submicroscopic world works. The search for a theory of quantum gravity is well under way . . . but that is a story for another time.

FROM HAPPIEST THOUGHT TO BIGGEST BLUNDER . . .

Meanwhile, general relativity is at the heart of one of the most exciting questions facing cosmologists today. As recently as the mid-1990s, we believed that the expansion of the Universe – a consequence of the Big Bang some 13.7 billion years ago – was gradually slowing down as a result of the mutual gravitational attraction of everything within it. An entirely reasonable assumption, you'd think, but a few heretical souls in the astronomical community had some doubts about this model. They wondered whether a kind of dark energy, or 'springiness' of space, might be starting to counter the deceleration, pushing the Universe into an era of accelerated expansion. It was a rather esoteric point until, quite suddenly in 1998, two separate groups of scientists (one of which, I'm delighted to say, was based in Australia) produced hard evidence that the Universe is, indeed, expanding more rapidly today than it was seven or eight billion years ago.

The evidence came in the form of observations of a particular kind of supernova – the so-called Type Ia – at very great distances. Supernovae of this type are caused by old stars exploding violently as a result of matter being deposited on them from a nearby companion star, and provide extremely bright standard candles, easily outshining their host galaxies. What caused all the excitement was that these remote supernovae were dimmer than they ought to be, given their estimated distances – and hence look-back times – from our Galaxy. This suggested that, yes, the expansion of the Universe is accelerating, a result that has now been confirmed by a number of different methods. Moreover, we now know that the dark energy driving the acceleration is the largest single component of the Universe, amounting to some 75 per cent of its total mass/energy density. So what is it? When consideration was given to this question, an intriguing possibility emerged.

Some fourteen months after completing his General Theory of Relativity, Einstein had realized that his equations represent a Universe that must either expand or contract – it can't remain static. That was long before Hubble's 1929 discovery of the real Universe's overall expansion, so Einstein thought he had a serious problem on his hands. In order to fix it, he introduced a new element into his equations, calling it the 'cosmological constant' (conventionally symbolized by the Greek letter lambda, Λ).

This new quantity would represent a property of space itself, allowing an attractive or repulsive force to be introduced at a constant rate throughout the whole Universe, compensating its natural tendency to expand or contract. The value of Λ would have to be determined by observations, of course. The problem duly sorted (mathematically, at least), Einstein sat back feeling rather pleased with himself. However, as soon as the expansion of the real Universe was discovered, he quickly withdrew the idea. Years later, the great Ukrainian–American physicist George Gamow (1904–68) disclosed that 'when I was discussing cosmological problems with Einstein, he remarked that the introduction of the cosmological term was the biggest blunder he ever made in his life'.

Once the expansion of the Universe had been firmly established by Hubble and others, most cosmologists simply assumed that the value of Λ was zero, and forgot about it. Then, in the late 1990s, when astronomy was overwhelmed by the euphoria of the newly found accelerating Universe, the obvious question was asked. Could the dark energy be something to do with that long-neglected orphan of general relativity, the cosmological constant? If it had the form of a negative pressure, and Λ had a value small enough that it only began to overcome gravity when the characteristic distances separating galaxies had become very great, then it might just fit the bill.

There were other theoretical possibilities, too, but they required the introduction of 'new physics' – phenomena that are not predicted by relativity, such as quantum gravity and string theory. Among them was the whimsically named 'quintessence', echoing the fifth element of ancient Greek philosophy. Again, this would have to be a dark energy with negative pressure, but a key difference between it and the cosmological constant is that quintessence evolves with time, leaving its imprint on the Universe only in the relatively recent past.

No one really knows what causes dark energy. The best guesses involve a seething foam of virtual particles at the quantum level, popping in and out of existence and imbuing the fabric of space with negative pressure. Theories on this bizarre area of quantum physics are many and various – and far from complete. But a good start on understanding the problem might be to identify which model of dark energy best fits the astronomical observations. Cosmological constant or quintessence – or something else? The problem is, though, that most of the required observations don't yet exist.

A number of groups throughout the world are now actively engaged on the process of obtaining them, typically by extending the supernova observations to greater distances and greater numbers of objects. But the best chance of really tying down the intimate details of dark energy comes from more subtle (and more difficult) observations. The fact is that the nature of dark energy has a significant influence on the geometry of the Universe. Therefore, if that can be probed at different stages in the Universe's history, there is a real chance that the correct model can be identified and its characteristics precisely determined.

We already have an accurate knowledge of this large-scale geometry at two key times in cosmic history. One is in the very early Universe. Detailed observations of the cosmic microwave background radiation (the flash of the Big Bang, seen at a look-back time of almost 13.7 billion years) made recently with the WMAP spacecraft have revealed what the Universe was like in its infancy. And large-scale surveys of the three-dimensional distribution of galaxies in today's Universe have been made with the 3.9-metre Anglo-Australian Telescope (the 2dF Galaxy Redshift Survey) and the 2.5-metre Sloan Telescope. Comparison of the Universe's characteristics at these two periods has already allowed a wealth of information on its evolution to be deduced. The missing ingredient is a similar 3-D survey of galaxies at great enough distances that they correspond to a look-back time of about half the age of the Universe – a time seven billion years or so ago, when dark energy first began to make its presence felt. But to do the job properly requires a survey of around a million faint galaxies, a hugely ambitious programme.

The hardware requirements for this are simple: an 8-metre-class telescope equipped with a device to allow the distances of galaxies to be measured thousands at a time – and lots of observing time available to do it. Prime candidates for the host facility are the northern Gemini telescope in Hawaii (a multinational venture that involves both Britain and Australia) or its near neighbour on the summit of Mauna Kea, the Japanese Subaru telescope. That part, at least, is straightforward. The tricky bit is the auxiliary equipment, which needs thousands of miniature robots to accurately position optical fibres in the focus of the telescope. There, the light from these faint galaxies can be intercepted and fed to sensitive spectroscopic instruments.

I don't want to sound like a car salesman at this point, but I think most astronomers would agree that the leading institution in the world for building such devices is the one I work for – the Anglo-Australian Observatory. The organization has a proven track record in building and deploying robotic fibre-optics equipment on both its own and other telescopes. Thus, the AAO can expect to be deeply involved with this project, from both an instrumental and a scientific perspective. Finally, there is the question of the availability of observing time – but that is a decision for the telescope's user community as a whole. Since enthusiasm for this project is today almost palpable throughout the world of astronomy, the chances of getting enough telescope time appear to be very good. The new survey and its exciting outcomes are something we can all look forward to as the first decade of the twenty-first century draws to a close.

Meanwhile, what's happening with the supernovae? At the time of writing (January 2006), the most prolific observing team is an international group called the Supernova Legacy Survey, and their preliminary results are showing a decided preference for – wait for it – yes, the cosmological constant. The group reports that the negative pressure of dark energy seems to have changed by less than 20 per cent since the Universe was about half its current size, a finding consistent with dark energy being due to the most conservative of the current models, good old Λ. If that is confirmed, it will be a truly remarkable finding. It means that even when Einstein thought he was blundering, he was actually right. What a guy.

. . . AND BACK AGAIN

Although the Universe at large provides an excellent laboratory for testing the predictions of general relativity, there are many other possible approaches to validating the theory. The deflection of light around massive bodies, for example, can now be checked to a high degree of accuracy using radio telescopes. The technique of very long baseline interferometry, which uses arrays of radio telescopes to measure the positions of celestial targets with almost unbelievable precision, has confirmed Einstein's gravitational deflection to about 2 parts in 10,000. A related phenomenon, the so-called Shapiro delay experienced by radiation passing a massive body, has been most recently checked using telemetry signals from the Cassini spacecraft en route to Saturn, yielding results that agree with general relativity to within 1 part in 100,000. And at an even more esoteric level, the Gravity Probe B spacecraft, currently in Earth orbit, is checking two predictions of general relativity that relate to the distortion of space–time caused by the Earth itself – frame-dragging and geodetic precession. You were probably just thinking of trying the same thing from your backyard.

But why are we so obsessed with continuing to check general relativity, when its predictions have been so triumphantly confirmed already? And not just once, but many times over? There is a very good answer to that question, and it is perhaps best illustrated by returning to the main theme of this article. Indeed, no celebration of the centenary of the equivalence principle would be complete without some mention of its experimental verification, and just what that means.

You'll recall that the heart of the equivalence principle – and the heart of general relativity itself – is that the gravitational mass and the inertial mass of an object are the same thing. (In fact, this is sometimes called the weak equivalence principle, its strong counterpart including gravitational energy as well as ordinary matter.) One of the consequences of the equivalence principle is that objects will fall under gravity with the same acceleration, irrespective of their internal structure and composition. This harks back to Galileo's famous experiment at the Leaning Tower of Pisa in the 1590s, and most of us have been familiar with the acceleration due to gravity at the Earth's surface

(9.8 metres per second per second) since our schooldays, often from first-hand experience. But the bottom line in all this is that some of the more exotic theories of gravitation – such as those attempting to unify the fundamental forces of nature (like string theory) – would, if correct, lead to a violation of the equivalence principle. Hunting for subtle violations is therefore a great way to discover whether 'new physics' is, in fact, at work.

How can one do this? The laboratory method involves comparing the responses of two differing test bodies to the same gravitational pull – lumps of copper and aluminium sitting in the Earth's gravitational field, for example. The technique owes its origin to a gifted Hungarian nobleman, Baron Loránd Eötvös (1848–1919), who performed such experiments with a sophisticated torsion balance in the 1890s and early 1900s. His work demonstrated no difference in the acceleration experienced by differing test masses to within one part in a hundred million, and it was this result that led to Einstein's adoption of the equivalence principle. The rather striking Hungarian name Eötvös, by the way, is pronounced a bit like Oat-fosh, which explains the whimsical name of the research collaboration doing the very best work of this kind today: they are at the University of Washington in Seattle, and are called the Eöt-Wash group.

Using extraordinarily sensitive balances, Eöt-Wash scientists have confirmed the equivalence principle to better than one part in 10^{12} using the gravitational attraction not just of the Earth, but also of the Sun and our own Galaxy. In the late 1980s, they famously put paid to a flurry of excitement over the existence of a so-called fifth fundamental force. Their experiments (and eventually those of other groups, too) showed no evidence of violation – and hence no fifth force. But even the spectacular accuracy achieved by Eöt-Wash will soon be surpassed by refined lunar laser-ranging experiments, in which light is bounced off reflectors left on the Moon by Apollo astronauts. These experiments will check the strong equivalence principle using the Earth and Moon as test bodies; violations of a few parts in 10^{14} are expected to be detectable. And finally, in this head-spinning search for tiny deviations, space missions over the next few years will use enclosed test bodies in orbit to achieve even more stunning gains in accuracy. The most ambitious, the proposed STEP mission (Satellite Test of the Equivalence Principle), is expected to provide results at a level of one part in 10^{18} – one in a billion billion.

Such fastidious explorations of the reliability of general relativity are very cheap compared with the gigantic particle physics experiments that are now under development. They, too, are looking for anomalies in our current model of the Universe. Some $2.3 billion is being invested in the Large Hadron Collider, for example, an ambitious European particle accelerator due to be fired up for the first time in mid-2007. But wouldn't it be astonishing if a whole era of 'new physics' came from nothing more than the detection of a minuscule deviation from the equivalence principle? A deviation so impossibly small that finding it would be like discovering a solitary huntsman spider in a farmer's field. The size of Asia.

FURTHER READING

Hoyle, F., 1987, 'Relativity', in *The Astronomy Encyclopaedia*, first edition (ed. Patrick Moore), pp. 359–61, Mitchell Beazley, London.

Institute of Physics Publishing Ltd., 2005, *Physics World* 'Einstein 2005' edition, vol.18, no.1.

New Scientist, 2004, 'State of the Universe', (A *New Scientist* Supplement, 9 October 2004), Reed Business Information Ltd, London.

Nicolson, Iain, 2001, 'A Universe of darkness', in *2002 Yearbook of Astronomy* (ed. Sir Patrick Moore), pp. 243–64, Macmillan, London.

O'Connor, John J. and Robertson, Edmund F., January 2006, The MacTutor History of Mathematics Archive, http://www-history.mcs.st-andrews.ac.uk/history/index.html, entries on Einstein and related topics.

Probing the Atmosphere of Venus

DAVID M. HARLAND

Forty years ago, on 18 October 1967, the Soviet Union's Venera 4 became the first space probe to make *in situ* measurements of the atmosphere of Venus.

VENUS IN THE SKY

In the autumn of 1609, armed with the newly invented telescope, Galileo Galilei observed that Venus shows lunar-like illumination phases. This contradicted the Ptolemaic concept of a 'celestial sphere' revolving around the Earth, and proved the proposition of Nicolaus Copernicus that – with the exception of the Moon – the 'wandering bodies' move around the Sun instead of the Earth. When Venus is closest to Earth, it is at inferior conjunction. However, at this time it presents its darkened hemisphere to us, and it is lost in the solar glare. When its disc is fully illuminated the planet is at superior conjunction, and is again unobservable. It is therefore best placed for observation when at elongation.

ROTATIONAL PERIOD

On noting bright, dusky markings in 1667, G.D. Cassini estimated that Venus rotated in 23 hours 21 minutes. However, despite many years of studying the planet, his son, J.J. Cassini, was unable to confirm this. In 1725 Francesco Bianchini perceived surface detail that suggested the period of rotation was some twenty-four days. When M.V. Lomonosov observed Venus transiting the Sun in 1761 he realized from the fuzzy edge of the planet's disc that it possessed a dense atmosphere. During the transit of 1769, D. Rittenhouse saw light refracting around the part of the planet that had yet to move on to the solar disc. The extension of these 'cusps' when the planet was a thin crescent in the sky suggested to J.H. Mädler in 1849 that sunlight was being refracted over the poles. In 1898 H.N. Russell noted that when Venus was within a degree of the Sun the cusps extended almost fully around the disc. Having seen nothing more than a few dusky markings over many years of observing the planet, William Herschel concluded the surface was masked by impenetrable cloud. After observing the planet between 1877 and 1890, G.V. Schiaparelli decided that its axial rotation was synchronized with its orbital period of 225 days, which meant that it maintained one hemisphere in sunlight and the other in darkness.

In 1921 W.H. Pickering departed from the two 'camps' that favoured its rotation as being either essentially 24 hours or 225 days, by offering a figure of 68 hours, and also posed the radical suggestion that the spin axis was tipped at 85°. Thermocouple measurements in the late 1920s by S.B. Nicholson and E. Pettit, using the 100-inch reflector on Mount Wilson (then the largest such telescope in the world), revealed the atmosphere on the darkened hemisphere to be not as cold as would be the case if the rotation was synchronous, which suggested the period was several months. Spectroscopic observations by Gunter Roth in 1953 measured the Doppler shift across the planet's disc, and indicated a period of fifteen days. It was evident from the lack of agreement between observers over the years that Venus was a very tricky object to study. F.E. Ross experimented with photographing the planet through a variety of filters, and in 1927 discovered that ultra-violet showed detail that was not visible to the naked eye. As ultraviolet cannot penetrate deep into the atmosphere, this structure was evidently at high altitude. Follow-up observations in the 1950s prompted G.P. Kuiper to suggest a rotational period of several weeks, with the axis tilted at about 30°. A study by C. Boyer identified a Y-shaped pattern with a four-day retrograde rotation inclined at 180°. Although the possibility of the planet being inverted was ridiculed, when large radio telescopes were used as radars in the early 1960s they were able to use the Doppler effect to verify this; the surprise was the period, since at 243 days the planet takes longer to turn on its axis than it does to travel around the Sun.

CONDITIONS ON THE SURFACE

Water vapour is difficult to identify unambiguously in a planet's atmosphere by telescopic spectroscopy because the signal is swamped by the water vapour in our own atmosphere, but in 1897 Johnstone Stoney reported Venus's atmosphere to be laden with water vapour. A polarization study by B. Lyot in 1929 indicated that the clouds appeared so bright because tiny droplets of liquid suspended in the upper atmosphere were reflecting sunlight to space. In 1915 C.E. Housden, who believed the rotation to be synchronous, proposed that heated air would rise at the subsolar point and flow at high altitude around to the dark hemisphere, where it would chill, descend, and be drawn back on to the daylit hemisphere at low level. And because he also believed the atmosphere to be wet, he predicted there must be an ice cap on the frozen hemisphere. In 1918 Svante Arrhenius, noting that Venus must be hotter than Earth by virtue of its being closer to the Sun, and believing the enshrouding cloud to be composed of water droplets, argued that there must be vast swamps of luxuriant vegetation, as on Earth several hundred million years ago.

In 1932 W.S. Adams and T. Dunham detected three absorption bands in the infrared which were later identified as being due to carbon dioxide. The presence of such a 'heavy' gas in the upper atmosphere meant that the lower atmosphere would be rich in carbon dioxide and, since this is a 'greenhouse' gas, it followed that the surface must be even warmer than the planet's proximity to the Sun would imply. In 1937 Arthur Adel said the surface temperature probably exceeded 50°C. In 1939 Rupert Wildt ventured that it very likely exceeded the boiling point of water, and suggested the clouds comprised droplets of formaldehyde, a compound of carbon, hydrogen and oxygen whose formation might be induced by ultraviolet irradiation, and which is white in the presence of water vapour. However, a spectroscopic search for appropriate absorption bands was inconclusive. H. Suess, believing Venus to be hot and arid, argued that the clouds contained chloride salts which precipitated when the oceans evaporated, but again there was no spectroscopic evidence. Nevertheless, in 1955 F.L. Whipple and D.H. Menzel, accepting Lyot's polarimetry indicating the clouds were composed of droplets, and believing this to be water, posited such a vigorous hydrological cycle in the predominantly carbon dioxide atmosphere that erosion by carbonic acid that formed as the water absorbed carbon dioxide would have left no exposed land, turning the surface into a global ocean. Also in 1955, Fred Hoyle argued that the clouds were a dense smog of dust motes and droplets of hydrocarbons. He said that if oil that had accumulated at shallow depth in the crust were to broach the surface, it would evaporate and upon being oxidized would draw oxygen from the atmosphere. This would continue either until all the oil had been oxidized or until all the surface water had evaporated and terminated the liberation of oxygen by the dissociation of water vapour in the upper atmosphere. The presence of the smoggy clouds, Hoyle said, meant the oxygen had run out first, the surface was arid, and was awash with oil.

The introduction of a sensitive radiometer in 1956 enabled the temperature of the surface to be measured directly by its microwave emissions, but the value in excess of 300°C was puzzling, since even though the insolation impinging on the atmosphere was twice that at Earth's distance from the Sun, some 85 per cent of it was being reflected by the clouds. Thus, as the 'space age' dawned, it was not known whether Venus was wet and rich in vegetation, oily, or an arid desert.

OUR FIRST CLOSE LOOK

Venera 1, the first spacecraft aimed towards the planet, was launched by the Soviet Union on 12 February 1961. Although contact was lost several weeks later, when the probe was some 7.5 million kilometres from Earth, the mission represented a partial success in that the 'escape stage' had established a trajectory that produced a 100,000-kilometre fly-by in May, which demonstrated that interplanetary flights were feasible. The motions of Earth and Venus around the Sun yield opportunities to send probes on 'fast' trajectories to Venus at nineteen-month intervals, so NASA had to wait. Its first mission on 22 July 1962 was frustrated when the Atlas launcher malfunctioned and ditched Mariner 1, built by the Jet Propulsion Laboratory of the California Institute of Technology in Pasadena, into the Atlantic Ocean. Luckily, the 'launch window' remained open for several weeks, and once the fault had been rectified Mariner 2 was successfully dispatched on 27 August. A 16,000-kilometre fly-by was intended, but the trajectory was slightly off, and the closest approach on 14 December was at twice this distance. The spacecraft aimed a battery of 'remote sensing' instruments at the planet to find out whether the high surface temperature derived from microwave radiometry was correct. In fact, the results indicated it to be even hotter, at 480°C. The surface pressure was not known, but liquid water would not be stable at this temperature. The fact that the spacecraft did not detect a planetary magnetic field was consistent with the extremely slow rotation, because the Earth's field is believed to be induced by electric currents circulating in its rapidly rotating iron core. As the first successful interplanetary mission, this demonstrated that a fly-by probe with appropriate instruments could provide evidence to sort the 'wheat' from the 'chaff' in the basket of competing theories.

PROBING FOR THE SURFACE

The Soviets exploited the launch windows of 1962 and 1963, but their spacecraft were either lost in launch accidents or stranded in 'parking orbit' by their escape stages. On 27 March 1964 the first of a heavier type of probe was stranded, but a second was successfully dispatched on 2 April 1964, at which time it was named Zond 1. Unfortunately, after making several manoeuvres to refine its trajectory it fell silent. On 12 November 1965 an even heavier probe named Venera 2 was safely dispatched, but it fell silent shortly before making a 24,000-kilometre fly-by in February 1966. The instrument unit of its partner, Venera 3, had been replaced by a 1-metre-diameter spherical capsule constructed to survive 250-g deceleration during atmospheric braking. It was launched on 16 November 1965, and refined its trajectory to reach the planet in March 1966, but at that time, having succumbed to some sort of failure, it was inert.

Venera 4, which was similar, was launched on 12 June 1967, and on approaching Venus on 18 October 1967 it successfully released its probe an hour before the main component, dubbed the 'bus', was destroyed as it entered the atmosphere. The trajectory, and therefore the probe's entry point, were constrained by the requirement that it intersect the atmosphere at the correct angle – too shallow and it would bounce off, too steep and it would burn up – and that it have a line of sight to Earth to transmit its results. It penetrated the equatorial zone some 1,500 kilometres beyond the dark side of the terminator. Once the probe had slowed to 300 metres per second, it opened its parachute and began to transmit. As a radio altimeter measured the altitude, sensors measured the ambient temperature, pressure and air composition. By the time the transmission ended, the pressure had risen to 22 bars. Although the Soviets said the probe was disabled on striking the surface, this was inconsistent with the final temperature of 280°C. When NASA's Mariner 5 flew by the next day, its trajectory took it behind the planet as seen from Earth, and measurements of the manner in which its radio signal was attenuated by the planet's atmosphere provided a profile from which extrapolation indicated the surface pressure to be between 75 and 100 bars. Evidently, Venera 4 had succumbed to the hostile conditions at an altitude of 27 kilometres, but by providing the first *in situ* measurements of the composition of the atmosphere it marked a significant advance. A nitrogen atmosphere with up to 10 per cent carbon dioxide was expected, but the carbon dioxide fraction turned out to be at least 90 per cent. By suggesting a process known as a 'runaway greenhouse', this discovery offered insight into the extreme conditions.

Although the surface would remain beyond reach until a stronger probe could be developed, it was decided to use the next launch window to send another pair of such probes, but with smaller parachutes so as to descend more rapidly and penetrate more deeply before they succumbed. On 16 May 1969 Venera 5's final measurements were 320°C and 27 bars at an altitude of 25 kilometres, from which the surface pressure was extrapolated to be 140 bars. The readings from Venera 6 the next day were similar, but its final radio altimeter reading indicated an altitude of 12 kilometres, which implied a relatively mild 60 bars and 400°C at the surface. Clearly something was amiss: either the altimeter had malfunctioned, or the probe had been above an extremely mountainous area, and on balance, it seemed that the altimeter was at fault. The chemical analyses confirmed the high carbon dioxide concentration: fully 95 per cent. Most of the rest was an inert gas (later established to be nitrogen). Oxygen was less than 0.4 per cent. Although the upper atmosphere contained water vapour it was by no means saturated, and the clouds were not water droplets. The hot lower atmosphere was arid.

Having found Venus's atmosphere to be denser than expected, the Soviets redesigned their probe to withstand an incredible 180 bars. Following a parachute descent of 26 minutes on 15 December 1970,

Venera 7 appeared to fall silent, but later analysis found the signal had continued at barely 1 per cent of its previous strength for another 23 minutes, from which it was concluded that the probe had rolled over on touching down and aimed its antenna away from Earth. Although the telemetry system had malfunctioned by fixating on the temperature sensor, by correlating the temperature profile with the Doppler on the radio signal (showing how the probe had been slowed by the thickening air), it was possible to calculate the pressure at the surface to be about 100 bars. With conditions on the surface established, it was possible to design a probe to carry out a detailed programme of surface studies. As developing this would take time, another interim mission was ordered for the next window. The mass saved by trimming the pressure vessel for 'only' 100 bars was used to improve the thermal shielding, and a second antenna was added to enable the probe to maintain contact no matter how it came to rest. Venera 8's arrival on 22 July 1972 was just after local dawn, as far on to the day-side hemisphere as it was possible to land and have a line of sight to Earth. All of the instruments functioned perfectly for 50 minutes on the surface, until the probe was disabled by the thermal stress. Conditions at the surface were 470(±8)°C and 90(±2) bars. The chemical analysis refined the atmospheric composition as 96 per cent carbon dioxide, 3 per cent nitrogen, and at most 0.1 per cent oxygen. The wind speeds during the descent decreased from 100 metres per second at an altitude of 48 kilometres (which marked the base of the cloud deck) to less than 1 metre per second at 10 kilometres. Confident that their probe would survive to operate on the surface, the Soviets had added a gamma-ray spectrometer, the results of which suggested a potassium-rich granitic rock. This success brought the first phase of Soviet exploration to a conclusion.

On 3 November 1973, NASA launched Mariner 10, which used a gravitational 'slingshot' at a range of 5,750 kilometres from Venus on 5 February 1974 in order to head for Mercury. The science operations were conducted during an eight-day fly-by sequence. Although no detail was apparent in the visible spectrum, the camera had an ultraviolet filter and this confirmed that the Y-shaped pattern circles the planet in just four days (see also Figure 1). This rapid circulation prevents the atmosphere on the night side from cooling down; indeed, the infrared radiometer found the temperature of the cloud tops to be a uniform −23°C across both hemispheres.

Figure 1. The faint Y-shaped marking in the upper atmosphere of Venus is visible in this ultraviolet image obtained by the Pioneer Venus 1 orbiter spacecraft on 26 February 1979. (Image courtesy NASA/JPL.)

Having demonstrated that their probes could survive the descent, the Soviets were eager to see what the surface looked like. The requirement for a line of sight to enable a probe to transmit its data to Earth had effectively restricted them to the night side. To land in full daylight, to have sufficient illumination for photography, it would be necessary to relay the transmission. After releasing its probe about two days out on a trajectory which would intercept the planet's trailing hemisphere, the new spacecraft was to execute a deflection manoeuvre to enable it to pass 1,600 kilometres ahead of the planet, where it would fire its engine to enter an eccentric orbit in which, as it climbed to apoapsis, it would be in position to relay its probe's signal. After initial deceleration, the new robust probes were to use parachutes in the altitude range between 65 and 50 kilometres in order to provide time to sample the cloud layer, and then release their chutes to pass through the hot atmosphere as rapidly as possible and thus maximize their surface time. The free-fall descent was feasible because the air was so thick that even without 'chutes they would strike the surface at only five metres per second. The spherical instrument unit was set on a ring-shaped shock absorber sufficiently wide to ensure the probe would remain upright, even on a slope.

The first image of the planet's surface was provided by Venera 9 on 22 October 1975 (see Figure 2a). This took the form of a 180° monochrome panorama built up over twenty minutes by a line-scan-facsimile camera. It showed angular rocks ranging up to several tens of centimetres across, sitting among small, dark particles. Venera 10, which landed three days later and 2,500 kilometres away to the south, found a landscape of fewer, rather slabbier rocks that either formed a level outcrop or the fragmented crust of a thin sheet of lava (see Figure 2b). The cracks between the light-toned slabs contained a dark, loosely consolidated material. The gamma-ray spectrometer results indicated both sites to be basaltic in nature. Despite the overcast, 2.5 per cent of the incident insolation penetrated to the surface, but this was so diffused as to give no hint of the Sun's position in the sky.

Figure 2a. (top) The first ever view of the surface of Venus from Venera 9.
Figure 2b. (bottom) The surface of Venus from Venera 10.

THE WEATHER SYSTEM

In 1978, NASA dispatched two spacecraft, one of which (Pioneer 12) was to enter orbit around Venus to conduct long-term remote sensing of its atmosphere and map the surface by radar, and the other (Pioneer 13) was to drop probes into the atmosphere at a variety of sites. Pioneer 12 arrived first, and entered orbit on 4 December. Five days later the bus of Pioneer 13 released its main probe at a range of eleven million kilometres from the planet on a trajectory to enter the atmosphere near the Equator on the dawn side of the terminator. The three small probes were ejected one million kilometres nearer, on slightly divergent trajectories: one heading for the atmosphere far to the north, on the night side; a second just south of the Equator on the day side; and the third closer to the Equator near local midnight. The large probe deployed a parachute at an altitude of 68 kilometres to slow its descent while sampling the clouds, but this was released at 47 kilometres in order to enable the probe to descend more rapidly in the inhospitable lower atmosphere. The smaller probes did not have parachutes. As the probes could not sample their environment during the initial deceleration, a mass spectrometer on the bus reported the condition of the upper atmosphere prior to the vehicle burning up. Although not expected to survive the impact, the 'day' probe transmitted from the surface for over an hour, falling silent when its battery was exhausted. The overall results showed there to be a layer of haze (a fine smog) in the altitude range 70–90 kilometres, the main cloud base was at 48 kilometres, the air was clear down to a thin layer of haze at 31 kilometres, below which it was clear (see also Figure 3). The maximum opacity was at 50 kilometres.

Because the lower atmosphere was stagnant, the base of the troposphere (the convective part of the atmosphere, which on Earth is the lowest layer) was at an altitude of 48 kilometres, at the base of the cloud deck. When Pioneer 12 fell into the atmosphere in 1992, its data had established that the circulation system is a single Hadley 'cell' on either side of the Equator. The air rises in the equatorial zone, flows at high altitude into the polar zone, then descends. The returning airflow occurs in the middle atmosphere. The lower atmosphere is divorced from the 'weather system'. This circulation derives from the planet's slow rotation. On the rapidly rotating Earth, the Coriolis effect

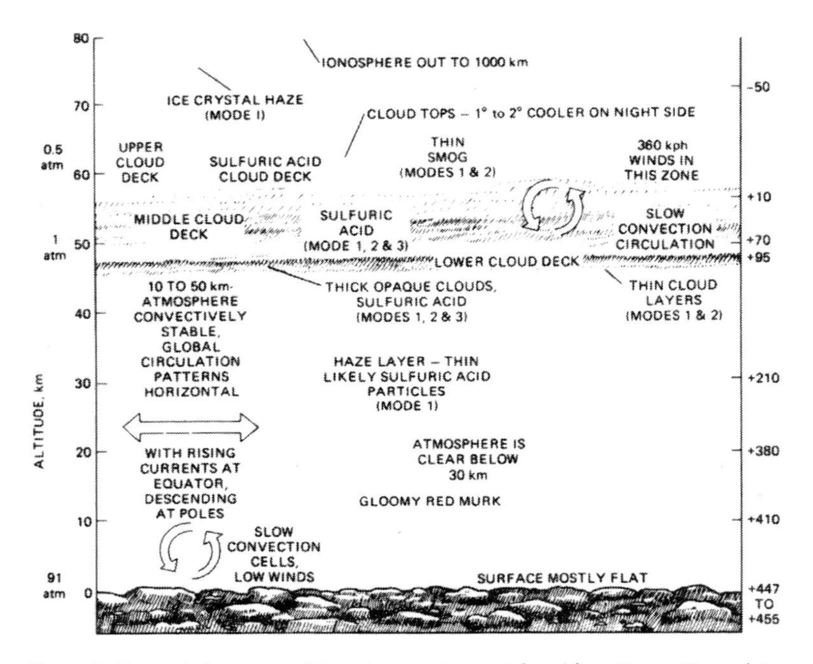

Figure 3. The vertical structure of Venus' atmosphere as inferred from Pioneer Venus data. (Image courtesy NASA/JPL.)

disrupts this simple circulation system by inducing swirling airflows and tropical, temperate and polar components. In Venus's upper atmosphere, the winds of 100 metres per second race from east to west with the planet's retrograde rotation, and the Y-pattern is caused by the fact that poleward flow is at barely 10 per cent of this rate. The pattern is apparent in ultraviolet light because some chemical whose concentration varies across the upper atmosphere shows bright where ultraviolet is reflected and dark where it is absorbed. In fact, the weather system is more complex than this, as there is turbulence where sunlight penetrates deeper at the subsolar point and gives rise to vigorous isolated convection cells which cause hot gas to 'bubble out' from the top of the cloud deck, and these create turbulent eddies in the zonal flow as this races around the planet.

In 1969, based on measurements of the index of refractivity, it was proposed that the condensates in the atmosphere were acid-laden water droplets. The mass spectrometer on the large Pioneer probe confirmed some 75–85 per cent of the cloud to be composed of aerosols of sulphuric acid. This is thought to have formed by photochemical oxidation at altitudes exceeding sixty kilometres. The dissociation of carbon dioxide or sulphur dioxide in the upper atmosphere produces atomic oxygen that oxidizes SO_2 to SO_3, which is hydrated into sulphuric acid (H_2SO_4) droplets. As the droplets 'rain out' and fall, they are thermally disrupted on reaching the 100°C temperature at an altitude of about forty-nine kilometres. They yield SO_3 which, upon encountering carbon monoxide, regenerates sulphur dioxide and carbon dioxide, which completes the cycle. This cycle of precipitation operates in the upper atmosphere, where the temperature is moderate. In the lower atmosphere, there is a steep thermal profile in which the temperature decreases by about 8°C per kilometre of altitude. Hence, although for a specific elevation the surface temperature is uniform both from pole to pole and from daylight into darkness, the surface temperature varies across the thirteen-kilometre height range from the summit of the tallest mountain to the floor of the deepest depression.

At no point on the surface is water stable. The planet's remaining water is in the cooler upper atmosphere, but it must be progressively diminishing because the hydrogen atoms released by photodissociation will tend to leak to space. Liberated hydroxyl radicals will combine with rising sulphur dioxide and enhance the manufacture of sulphuric acid. Any free oxygen that reaches the surface will oxidize the hot rock, removing it from the atmosphere. Sulphurous gases are present in our atmosphere only in trace amounts. They are released by volcanic activity, but unless this is on an enormous scale the sulphur is either dissolved in the water droplets in clouds or, in arid regions, is bound up with oxygen-rich radicals or other trace gases to form particulates that fall to the ground. When an explosive volcano sends a sulphurous plume into the stratosphere, the droplets of sulphuric acid that form are distributed around the globe, where they reflect sunlight and cool the lower atmosphere.

Even though most of the sunlight reaching Venus is reflected, the high concentration of carbon dioxide maintains the lower atmosphere at a high temperature. One theory is that, in the case of Venus, catastrophic volcanism triggered a 'runaway' process. The Pioneer orbiter produced a low-resolution radar map of the surface. In 1983 the Soviets placed two Veneras into orbit to improve on this, and in 1990

NASA sent its Magellan orbiter to map at high resolution. The results suggested the planet was substantially resurfaced by volcanism, perhaps a mere 500 million years ago. This raised the possibility that the atmosphere was 'pumped up' with sulphurous chemicals at that time. Because the hot lower atmosphere is arid, sulphur dioxide from volcanic eruptions cannot be washed out: once released it will remain in the atmosphere and provide a reservoir for the chemical processes high above which produce the sulphuric acid clouds. Might Venus owe its hostile condition to recent geological activity? Was it ever more Earth-like?

EARTH'S NON-IDENTICAL TWIN

Venus is slightly smaller than Earth: its diameter is 95 per cent, its volume is 86 per cent, and its mass is 82 per cent. The total amount of carbon dioxide in Venus's atmosphere may be comparable to that which Earth would have if all the carbon dioxide in its carbonate rock could be liberated – or, to put it another way, as Earth may have been before the carbonate formed. If all the carbon dioxide in Venus's atmosphere could be drawn down into the rock, it would produce a residual nitrogen-based atmosphere with a comparatively mild surface pressure of 3 bars. As Venus accreted from the solar nebula, it should have acquired as much water as did Earth. Although Venus is closer to the Sun, the early Sun was less radiant than today. If Venus's surface temperature was near water's triple point, it may have had oceans and a vigorous hydrological cycle in which water vapour combined with carbon dioxide to form carbonic acid that weathered rock to produce carbonates, which were washed into the oceans to settle out as sediment – as occurs on Earth. However, when the Sun heated up, the oceans (it is speculated) were evaporated to make a supersaturated atmosphere, and the exacerbated greenhouse effect further raised the temperature of the lower atmosphere. As ultraviolet dissociated water in the upper atmosphere, the deuterium isotope of hydrogen would have been preferentially retained as the lighter isotope leaked away to space. The 100:1 ratio of deuterium to hydrogen measured by the mass spectrometer on the large Pioneer probe implies that Venus has lost a great deal of water. With the onset of arid conditions, there would have been no way to remove carbon dioxide from the atmosphere, and volcanism would not only have increased this concentration but also issued the sulphur compounds which had the unfortunate effect of completely changing the nature of the weather system.

RECENT OBSERVATIONS

In 1988 it was realized that the upper atmosphere was transparent to narrow spectral bands in the near-infrared, providing 'windows' to observe the middle atmosphere. In principle, the absorption features at wavelengths in these bands would allow the minority constituents of the atmosphere to be determined all the way down to the surface. On its indirect route to Jupiter, NASA's Galileo spacecraft flew by Venus on 10 February 1990. Its infrared spectrometer was able to make such 'soundings': at a wavelength of 2.3 microns it was able to observe the turbulence at the base of the main cloud deck. The heat from the surface was attenuated as it passed through the clouds, but the different terrains were apparent because the lower-lying regions were hotter. The view could be enhanced by the process of 'de-clouding', in which the 2.3-micron signal representing the upper atmosphere was subtracted from that at 1.18 microns representing the lower atmosphere and surface. Galileo's plasma wave spectrometer detected broadband electromagnetic pulses from lightning in the lower atmosphere. On Earth, lightning occurs when updrafts cause moist air to condense out droplets of rain, with a build-up of static electricity which discharges between clouds and to the ground. However, Venus's lower atmosphere is utterly arid. Terrestrial lightning can also occur in the plume of gas and dust emitted by an explosive volcano. The pressure at the Venusian surface would inhibit plumes, but remote sensing by the Pioneer orbiter established that between 1978 and 1986 the amount of sulphur dioxide at an altitude of eighty kilometres diminished by a factor of ten, prompting the proposal that a major eruption had occurred shortly prior to the spacecraft's arrival. However, when the Cassini spacecraft made a very close fly-by on 26 April 1998 its radio and plasma wave spectrometer detected no evidence of lightning, suggesting that if the production of lightning was related to volcanism, this activity was not continuous.

VENUS EXPRESS

On 9 November 2005 the European Space Agency dispatched Venus Express on a 'fast' trajectory leading to arrival on 11 April 2006. In July, having manoeuvred into its operating orbit, it will use new sensors operating across an unprecedented range of wavelengths to investigate the composition and circulation of the atmosphere and its interaction with the 'solar wind', and seek evidence that volcanic activity is ongoing.

THE BIG ISSUE

At the dawn of the 'space age', we knew little for certain about Venus as a world. We now know that its atmosphere and surface are both remarkably different from Earth's, and are left wondering why the two planets, outwardly near-twins, are, in fact, so different, and whether what turned Venus into a veritable hell planet might one day befall Earth as well.

FURTHER READING

David Grinspoon, 1999, *Venus Revealed: A New Look Below the Clouds of Our Mysterious Twin Planet*, Perseus Books, London.

Patrick Moore, 2006, *Patrick Moore on Venus*, Cassell, London.

Two Great Hawaii Telescopes: UKIRT and JCMT

DEREK WARD-THOMPSON

Mauna Kea in Hawaii is one of the world's best locations for astronomical observing. It is an extinct volcano, whose summit is more than 14,000 feet above sea level. At this altitude it is literally above the clouds on most normal days, and this is why some of the world's largest optical telescopes are located there. However, it is more than just an optical observatory. It is also home to some of the world's largest infrared telescopes, as well as telescopes that work at even more exotic wavelengths.

ATOP MAUNA KEA

There are two telescopes on Mauna Kea in particular that are unique in their own special ways, and they were both built in the UK. These are the United Kingdom Infrared Telescope (UKIRT) and the James Clerk Maxwell Telescope (JCMT), which is named after a famous nineteenth-century Scottish physicist. UKIRT works at wavelengths in the near infrared, just beyond the wavelength of visible light. The JCMT works at much longer wavelengths, between the infrared and the radio, in a régime known as the submillimetre waveband. This can be thought of as either very far infrared wavelengths, or ultrahigh-frequency radio wavelengths. The JCMT itself is in part a hybrid of these two wavelength regions. It looks rather like a radio telescope, but it has cameras rather like an infrared telescope.

The reason that Mauna Kea is such an excellent location for these telescopes is that it is not only above the clouds, but it is also above almost all of the water vapour, or moisture, in the earth's atmosphere. It is water vapour that blocks out almost all of the far infrared and submillimetre waves from reaching the Earth's surface at sea level. But on Mauna Kea, above most of the moisture in the earth's atmosphere, these telescopes can detect very faint radiation at these wavelengths from space. UKIRT has been among the world's leading telescopes in infrared astronomy for more than three decades, since it was built in 1979, and the JCMT has been the world's largest dedicated sub-millimetre telescope ever since it was opened in 1987. Both remain at the forefront of their respective fields.

Both telescopes employed radical new design techniques when they were built. UKIRT looks like an optical telescope, with a giant glass mirror (Figure 1). However, its mirror was made using a revolutionary 'float glass' design, which made it thinner and therefore lighter than any previous mirror of similar size. The lighter mirror meant that the whole structure of the telescope could be lighter, and hence less bulky. This is important for the operation of the telescope.

Figure 1. UKIRT looks like an optical telescope, but its revolutionary design makes it ideal for work in the infrared. Image courtesy Joint Astronomy Center, Hawaii.

OBSERVING AT INFRARED AND SUBMILLIMETRE WAVELENGTHS

It is difficult to observe in the infrared because everything around us on Earth glows at infrared wavelengths, because it is warm and infrared radiation is just heat. In particular, people emit infrared radiation due to normal body heat, which is why rescue services use infrared cameras to find people who are lost on mountains at night, for example. Therefore, the astronomers must stay in a shielded control room when operating UKIRT. Furthermore, even the metal frame of the telescope itself emits infrared radiation, simply because it is at the temperature of the surrounding air. Consequently, building an infrared telescope is rather like building an optical telescope out of fluorescent light tubes. UKIRT's lightweight design minimizes the emission of infrared radiation from the telescope itself, making it far more sensitive to the very faint radiation it is trying to detect from space.

The design of the JCMT was also revolutionary when it was built. It has a dish like a radio telescope to catch the submillimetre radiation from space (Figure 2). The dish is 15 metres in diameter. However, it is not made from one solid sheet of metal, but rather it is made from hundreds of individual panels. These panels can each be moved separately by means of electronic sensors on the back of the dish. In this way the shape of the dish can be made as near to perfect as possible. Typically the surface is kept to an accuracy of around 25 microns (1 micron is one thousandth of a millimetre). The very high surface accuracy of the dish makes the telescope very much more sensitive to faint levels of radiation.

One reason why astronomers study these wavelengths is that it is possible to see parts of the Universe in the far infrared and submillimetre that are hidden to astronomers who work only in visible light. This is because the space between the stars is not entirely empty, but contains minute fractions of gas and dust. The amounts are so small that it is still closer to a vacuum than anything that can be achieved in a laboratory on Earth. Nonetheless, the space between the stars is so vast that the amount of gas and dust becomes significant, and the dust begins to block out the visible light.

The dust itself is made of silicates, rather like the sand on a beach, though the size of the individual dust grains is much smaller than the

Figure 2. JCMT looks like a radio telescope with 15-metre-diameter dish, but its surface accuracy means it can operate at submillimetre wavelengths. Image courtesy Joint Astronomy Center, Hawaii.

grains of sand on a beach. In fact, the dust particles are typically the same size as particles of cigarette smoke. Then, just as it is sometimes difficult to see across a smoke-filled room, it is also sometimes difficult to see parts of space that are dusty. That is where the infrared and submillimetre come in. At these wavelengths it is possible to see through the dust and to understand what is going on behind.

This is important because if we want to see great distances within our own Galaxy, the Milky Way, then the amount of dust becomes so great that almost no visible light can get through. So, for example, if we want to see to the very centre of our Galaxy (Figure 3) we must go to longer wavelengths. In the infrared we can see through the dust to the individual stars and star clusters that make up the centre of our Galaxy. In the submillimetre we can see the clouds of material in the centre of our Galaxy that are in the process of forming new stars (Figure 4).

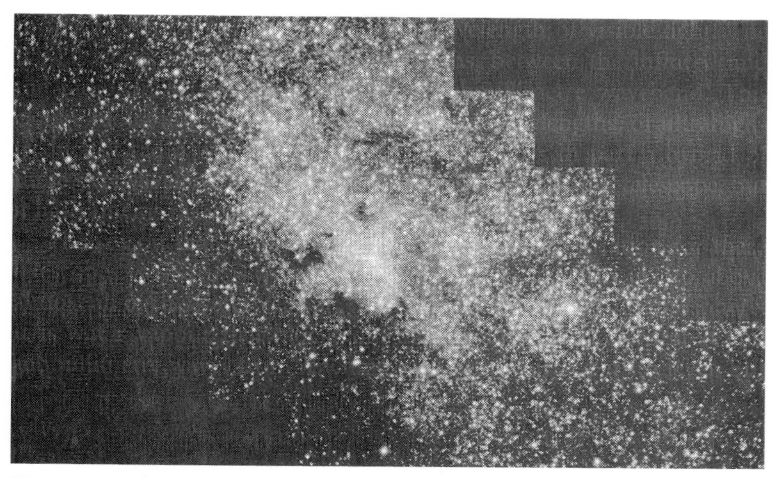

Figure 3. An infrared picture of the centre of our Galaxy. It is not possible to see these stars in the visible because of all the dust in the Galaxy. Image courtesy Antonio Chrysostomou (Univ. of Hertfordshire, UK) and Joint Astronomy Center, Hawaii.

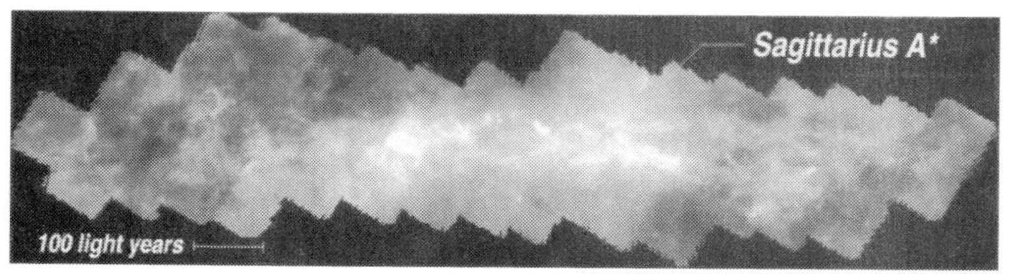

Figure 4. A false-colour submillimetre image of the centre of our Galaxy. Each of the bright areas is a place where new stars are being born. Image courtesy Joint Astronomy Center, Hawaii and Univ. of Cambridge, UK.

STELLAR NURSERIES AND YOUNG STARS

In fact, the study of the formation of new stars and planets is one of the key areas that infrared and submillimetre astronomy have opened up in recent years. This is because the regions of space in which new stars and planets form usually have more than average amounts of dust within them. Many of these areas are familiar to optical astronomers as some of the more famous nebulae. For example, the Horsehead Nebula in Orion appears as a dark silhouette in visible light because it is a giant cloud of dust that just happens to appear to have this peculiar shape and is blocking out the background starlight.

Visible light can tell us nothing of what is happening inside the Horsehead Nebula because it appears completely dark (Figure 5a). But when we go to the longer infrared and submillimetre wavelengths we can see right into the heart of the nebula. Recent submillimetre images have shown that in the 'throat' of the horse there appears to be a very

(a)

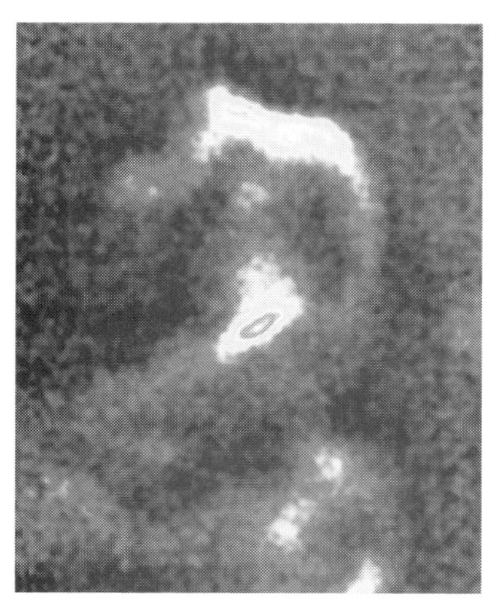

(b)

Figure 5. The Horsehead Nebula seen at optical (a) and submillimetre (b) wavelengths. The optical image shows only the dark outline of the nebula. The submillimetre picture shows what is happening in the centre of the nebula. A lump in the horse's 'throat' is actually forming new stars. Images courtesy European Southern Observatory, ESO (Figure 5a) and of the author (Figure 5b).

Figure 6. An infrared image of the ring around Vega seen face on. This is like the rings around Saturn but very much bigger. The ring is larger than our entire Solar System. Image courtesy K.Y.L. Su (Univ. of Arizona Steward Observatory) and NASA Jet Propulsion Laboratory-Caltech.

dense clump of gas and dust (Figure 5b). This clump is many times more massive than our own Sun and is in the process of collapsing under gravity, under its own weight, to form new stars deep inside the nebula. In a few million years these new stars will evaporate the surrounding nebula and will become visible. Without infrared and submillimetre telescopes we would not have been able to see what was happening inside the Horsehead Nebula.

The formation of planets is another topic to which infrared and submillimetre astronomy has contributed significantly. We have long known about the planets that orbit our Sun, such as Venus, Mars and Jupiter, but we know much less about planets around other stars. In addition, we do not know exactly how the planets that we do see, including our own planet Earth, were originally formed. They are really nothing more than the leftover bits and pieces after the Sun was born. However, the details of how they form remain something of a mystery. Therefore, to study how the planets formed we need to be able to see in great detail other planetary systems that are still in the process of forming today.

The star Vega in the constellation Lyra is now known to have a ring around it, rather like a giant version of the rings of Saturn (Figure 6).

However, the ring around Vega is larger than our entire Solar System. It is believed to be a much younger version of our Solar System in which planets have not yet finished forming. The ring around Vega was not seen in visible light because of the dust it contains, but when it was observed in the infrared it was seen very clearly.

Another nearby star, Epsilon Eridani, has also been seen to have a giant ring around it. This time the ring was observed in the submillimetre by the JCMT (Figure 7). The fact that it was observed only at much longer wavelengths shows that this is an even younger system. Furthermore, in the detailed images that the JCMT's cameras produced, this ring can be seen to contain denser clumps. These are believed to be

Figure 7. A submillimetre false-colour image of the ring around Epsilon Eridani. The lumps in the ring are going to collapse under their own weight to form new planets. Image courtesy J. Greaves et al., Joint Astronomy Center, Hawaii, Univ. of California, Los Angeles and Royal Observatory, Edinburgh.

planets actually in the process of being born. The clumps will collapse under their own weight and will eventually be seen as a brand-new planetary system. By observing these clumps over a number of years astronomers have been able to watch them orbiting their star, Epsilon Eridani, just like the planets in our own Solar System orbit the Sun. Such detailed studies of newly forming planets would not have been possible without telescopes like the JCMT.

BACK IN TIME

Another reason for studying longer-wavelength astronomy like the infrared and submillimetre is that sometimes visible light is redshifted to these longer wavelengths. The redshift is caused by the well-known Doppler Effect, by which an object moving away at speed has its emission shifted to longer wavelengths. This same effect produces an apparent shift in the note of an ambulance siren as it speeds away from us. Distant galaxies are moving away from us at very high speeds and so their emission is also shifted to longer wavelengths. Furthermore, the astronomer Edwin Hubble discovered that the further away a galaxy is the faster it is moving, and hence the more it is redshifted.

The most distant galaxies therefore have the highest redshifts. Some galaxies are so far away that their optical light is redshifted all the way into the submillimetre, so to study these galaxies in detail astronomers must look in the submillimetre. In addition, the further away a galaxy is the longer it has taken for the light from that galaxy to reach us here on Earth. Some galaxies observed in the submillimetre are so far away that we are seeing them now as they were only a relatively short time after the Big Bang (Figure 8), so we are seeing very young galaxies at a time when even the Universe itself was still young. By studying these very young galaxies astronomers can learn about how our Galaxy must have been when it was very young, and even about how our Galaxy itself may have first been formed.

Astronomers working in the infrared and submillimetre at UKIRT and JCMT are learning about some of the fundamental questions in the Universe. Pictures that can see deep into the heart of dark nebulae see the places where new stars are about to be born. Studying the infrared and submillimetre dust rings around nearby stars shows planetary systems like our own Solar System at an earlier evolutionary

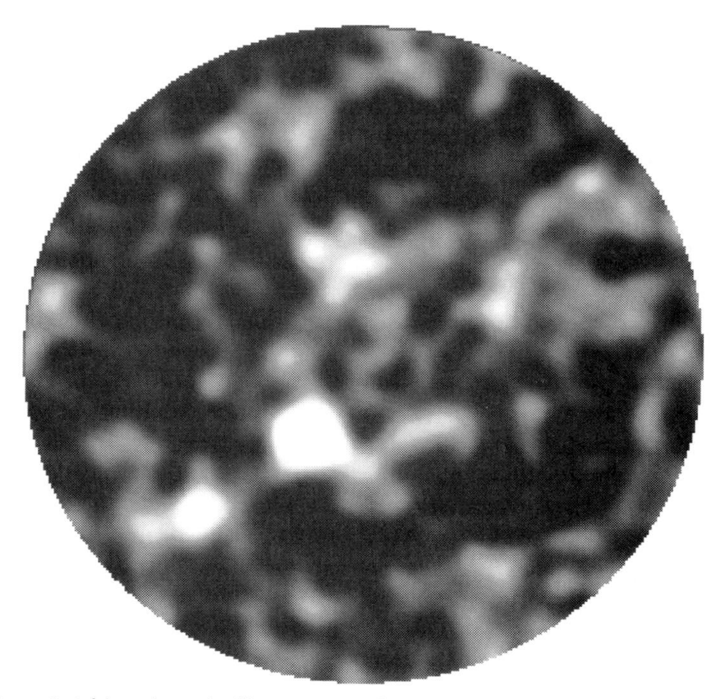

Figure 8. A false-colour submillimetre picture of some very distant and very young galaxies. When the light left these galaxies the Universe was less than one-fifth of its present age. The light from the galaxies has been redshifted into the submillimetre. Image courtesy D. Hughes et al., Royal Observatory, Edinburgh and Joint Astronomy Center, Hawaii.

stage. Images of the centre of our Galaxy together with pictures of some of the most distant galaxies in the Universe show us how galaxies themselves are formed and evolve over the history of the Universe. Revolutionary telescopes like UKIRT and the JCMT have made all of this work possible and have added significantly to our understanding of the Universe in which we live and our place in it.

UKIRT and JCMT are operated by the Joint Astronomy Center, Hawaii, on behalf of the UK Particle Physics and Astronomy Research Council, the Canadian National Reseach Council and the Netherlands Organisation for Scientific Research.

Ireland's Astronomical Muse: Sir Robert Stawell Ball and the Victorian World of Astronomy

ALLAN CHAPMAN

Most people who are interested in the history of astronomy and who have a taste for rooting around in second-hand bookshops will have encountered *The Story of the Heavens*, *Great Astronomers*, and *Starland*, not to mention around ten further titles which bear the name Sir Robert Stawell Ball. Yet who was this prolific writer, lecturer, and communicator, who also held the academic titles of Andrews Professor at Trinity College Dublin, Lowndean Professor at Cambridge, and who by the age of 34 had become Astronomer Royal for Ireland and a Fellow of the Royal Society?

Sir Robert Ball was a product of that brilliant, colourful, and sometimes eccentric world of intellectual Victorian Ireland. A world, indeed, that is often passed over by historians, who tend to concentrate their attention upon Ireland's tragedies, such as the Potato Famine, or troubled politics, while ignoring the enormously rich intellectual culture that flourished, especially around Dublin and down the east coast of the still constitutionally unified Emerald Isle of Queen Victoria's day. Whereas poets and writers, such as Oscar Wilde and James Joyce, might spring to mind, we so often forget Victorian Ireland's dazzling scientific community. Mention Ireland, and how many people think of the brilliant astronomer, mathematician and linguist Sir William Rowan Hamilton, the historian of astronomy Agnes Clerke, the Revd Dr Thomas Romney Robinson (Director of the Armagh Observatory), the physicist Father Nicholas Callan, Sir William Wilde (Oscar Wilde's father and eminent Dublin surgeon and Royal Ophthalmologist), or Sir Robert Stawell Ball? Most of them, it is true, belonged to what was called the 'Englishry', or 'Protestant Ascendancy', although some, such as the distinguished scientific and literary sisters Agnes and Mary Ellen Clerke and Father Callan, were Roman Catholic. All of them, however, saw themselves as Irish.

THE FORMATIVE YEARS

Robert Ball was born in Dublin on 1 July 1840, the son of Dr Robert Ball (who was descended from a seventeenth-century Devonshire family) and his wife Amelia, a Somerset girl. Dr Robert Ball was a Dublin civil servant, antiquary and scholar, with a passion for science, who had met his wife at the British Association for the Advancement of Science meeting held in Bristol in 1836, which led the humorous Robert (the astronomer) to say that he was – metaphorically speaking – a child of the British Association! Robert Ball Senior was involved with several Irish learned societies, and among other things was one of the founders of the Dublin Zoo. A large, happy family grew up at their home at 3 Granby Row, Rutland Square, Dublin, for Dr Robert and Amelia Ball had six children in addition to Robert the astronomer. It was also a distinguished family. One of Robert's brothers, Charles, became a famous Dublin surgeon, and won a knighthood and became an FRCS, while brother Dr Valentine became Director of the Dublin Science and Art Museum, and received the honour of a Companion of the Bath and an FRS. Indeed, all three brothers held professorships at Trinity College Dublin, while Robert's sisters all married successful professional men.

Young Robert was sent away to be educated in England, but after his father's sudden death in 1857 he was brought home to Ireland to enter Trinity College Dublin, which institution had given Robert Senior his honorary doctorate in recognition of his services to science and learning. Here he found his feet, and quickly rose from being considered a rather average school pupil (because he was not a natural classical scholar) to establishing himself as a brilliant mathematical and scientific student. He won prizes, made numerous friends, and read a book which led him to a deeper fascination with astronomy. This was *The Orbs of Heaven* (1860), by the American Ormsby McKnight Mitchell.

Then in 1865 he was introduced by his Trinity College friend Dr Johnstone Stoney to William Parsons, third Earl of Rosse, as a prospective tutor for his and the Countess's three youngest sons, and the two years he spent at Birr Castle were absolutely formative to his future professional life. With his naturally genial disposition, Ball made friends wherever he went, and the years at Birr saw him form lifelong friendships with his pupils and with the Rosse family. Before his sudden death in 1867, Lord Rosse, a former president of the Royal Society, had taken it upon himself to introduce young Ball to pretty well everyone who was anyone in British science in Birr, Dublin, and in London at the Royal Society and other learned societies. That pioneer of stellar spectroscopy, the English 'grand amateur' Sir William Huggins, was made known to Ball by Lord Rosse, who took Ball to see Huggins's great private observatory at Tulse Hill, south London, along with the Irish variable-star observer John Birmingham. And let us not forget that one of Ball's pupils at Birr Castle was Sir Charles Parsons, who would go on to become one of the outstanding mechanical engineers of the late Victorian age, and whose steamship *SS Turbinia* would steal the show at the Spithead Review of 1897, when its revolutionary steam turbine engines outran every other ship in the Royal Navy.

It was also at Birr that Robert Ball's taste for serious astronomical research developed. For while the great 72-inch-aperture reflector of 52 feet focal length, which in its refurbished state still dominates Birr Castle Park, had really served its purpose of resolving the nebulae by 1865, it was still the largest telescope in the world, and Ball was given pretty much a free hand to observe with it as he chose. Just imagine what an inspiration it must have been for a 25-year-old to be given free rein with such a vast telescope! Though he tells us that Birr was not, for meteorological reasons, a good place for astronomical observation, Ball used the 'Leviathan of Parsonstown' (as Birr was called 140 years ago) to see the sky as no one else could see it. And on the night of 13 November 1866, he watched out for, and observed by naked eye, the great Leonid Meteor Storm. Indeed, Ball later told us that Lord Rosse and he had wondered, following a suggestion from James Glaisher of Greenwich, whether the constellation of Leo would once more blaze with meteors in 1866, as it had in 1833 and 1800. Although Robert Ball was by no means the only astronomer to witness the spectacular Leonids of 1866, he played a significant part in establishing the idea that certain meteor groups at least were genuinely periodic.

A GREAT TALENT EMERGES

Following Lord Rosse's death, Ball's increasingly illustrious reputation enabled him at the age of twenty-seven to move into a distinguished post as Professor of Applied Mathematics and Mechanism at Dublin's Royal College of Science. Here he began to show evidence of that gift which, by 1900, would make his name synonymous throughout the English-speaking world with popular astronomy: his talent for popular lecturing. Students flocked to him, for he had that rare ability to render complex ideas lucid, and to carry his audience with him no matter how intellectually challenging the going became. In his lectures, Robert Ball used lantern slides, both painted on glass and as photographic slides (though in the 1880s 'magic lanterns' could be dangerous machines, especially if, in this pre-electric age, the illuminant came from 'lime light', for such a light – immortalized in popular parlance from its use in early theatre spotlights – was generated by using pre-prepared bags of hydrogen and oxygen to feed an intensely hot flame that caused a silicate compound to incandesce to a brilliant pale lime-green). Ball tells us that he had once, as an undergraduate in the early 1860s, attended an illustrated lecture by Dr Robinson of Armagh in the Metropolitan Hall, Dublin, where the operator, using the projector's oxygen bag, into which some pressurized hydrogen had been accidentally intruded, to demonstrate the rapid burning of phosphorus, set off a terrific oxy-hydrogen explosion, which blew up the apparatus. Mercifully, no one seems to have been seriously hurt; but within a few years such hazardous visual aids necessitating oxygen and hydrogen flames had been replaced, first by electric carbon arcs and then, by the mid-1880s, with electric light bulbs!

In 1874 the Andrews Professorship of Astronomy at Trinity College Dublin fell vacant following the resignation of Professor Franz Friedrich Ernst Brünnow, and Robert Ball was appointed to succeed him. This was the senior astronomical chair in Ireland, and carried with it not only the title of Astronomer Royal for Ireland but also the directorship of Ireland's oldest research observatory at Dunsink, some four miles north-west of Dublin. Honours were now coming thick and fast, as Ball was elected Fellow of the Royal Society in 1873, Fellow of the Royal Astronomical Society in 1875, received various medals, and was knighted in 1886.

In addition to 'grand amateur' establishments such as Birr, and Markree Castle, Sligo, Ireland had several public or academic observatories in Ball's time. These were the Archbishop's Observatory at Armagh (1791), and the Queen's College Observatory at Cork (1878), though Dunsink (1785) was the oldest. Dunsink was the official Observatory of Trinity College Dublin, and after becoming Andrews Professor, Ball and his wife Frances Elizabeth (whom he had married in 1868) moved into the grand and spacious Astronomer's Residence, as working time became divided between astronomical observation at Dunsink and teaching in the university. Robert Ball enjoyed practical observation, and he set out a programme of research.

THE WORK AT DUNSINK

Though possessing a variety of instruments, Dunsink in the 1870s had two principal ones. Firstly, there was the large transit circle, that was set to describe a vertical circle in the plane of the meridian. Using a micrometer eyepiece in conjunction with an exact regulator clock, the observer employed the transit to take right ascension and declination observations of the Sun, Moon, planets and stars, as they came to the meridian, which data could be used in the construction of exact astronomical catalogues. The transit was further used for time signals and clock corrections. But more significant was the 11¾-inch-aperture equatorial telescope, with optics by the Frenchman Robert Aglaé Cauchoix and engineering by Thomas Grubb. Though the object glass itself was over forty years old, and had been involved in a blistering lawsuit within the early Royal Astronomical Society, its superlative optics and modern 1863 Grubb engineering gave Ball access to an excellent research telescope.

The large refractor was an ideal instrument for the investigation to which Ball chose to address himself, namely, the micrometric positions of particular classes of stars. The large light-grasp of the 11¾-inch object glass and the exquisitely engineered equatorial mount with its clock drive gave very stable star images over many hours of the night, exactly what was needed for micrometric work. They were also perfect for an academic observatory, as such observations presupposed a high level of geometry and spherical trigonometry, with each set of observations having to be followed by a rigorous mathematical analysis in the computing room.

The re-measurement of a number of stellar parallaxes which aimed to confirm and to refine earlier mid-century measurements by Friedrich Wilhelm Bessel and others – especially of the parallax of 61 Cygni – constituted one of Robert Ball's research projects. But the main project to which he addressed himself while at Dunsink was the micrometric position of 368 small red stars. Following from a suggestion by Johnstone Stoney and Giovanni V. Schiaparelli, it was then thought that certain red stars were relatively close (in cosmological terms) to our Solar System, and might even be moving through space as parts of a cluster to which our own Sun belonged, and that, being close, should exhibit large stellar parallaxes and proper motions. Only an exhaustive measurement of each selected red star, with relation to visually adjacent red and other stars, could settle the issue one way or the other. The man hours involved must have been enormous, spread as they mainly were between 1876 and 1881, as each star's position had to be measured several times and the separation angles – reckoned as only a few arcseconds and decimal fractions of a second – checked and re-checked against adjacent stars in the field.

At the end of it all the result turned out to be negative, with not a single red star parallax of significance. Stoney and Schiaparelli had been wrong! Yet one might say that Ball *had* made a discovery in so far as he had shown that small red stars were *not* especially local to the Sun. In many respects, however, Ball instinctively belonged to what was rapidly becoming a rather old-fashioned tradition in academic astronomical research. By the late 1870s, when he was new in office at Dunsink, painstaking visual micrometric work through the telescope was being superseded by photography, while the intellectual cutting edge of all astronomical research by 1885 had ceased to be celestial geometry, which had now been replaced by spectroscopy and astrophysics. Although Ball was interested in these new fields, he never really did serious research in astrophysics. Instead, as celestial geometry slipped from the forefront of astronomical research, his attention focused upon two areas: pure mathematical geometry and astronomical popularizing. Another factor, moreover, played a significant rôle in ending his career as a visual observer: eye trouble. His right eye in particular became increasingly diseased, so that by 1897 it had to be surgically removed, obliging Sir Robert thereafter to wear a glass eye.

AN UNUSUAL THEORY

Robert Ball made no great discoveries in observational astronomy at Dunsink, or at Cambridge after 1892, and it was in the realm of pure geometry that he felt his most significant academic contribution to lie. At Birr Castle he had produced trigonometrical correction formulae for Lord Rosse, whereby the nebulae observations made from an altazimuth-mounted 72-inch telescope could be related more exactly to the spherical sky, and as the years went by he came to devote more attention to perfecting what he called his 'Theory of Screws'. This line of research had first caught his imagination in the spring of 1869, following Dr Johnstone Stoney's lecture to the Royal Dublin Society, and it most definitely did *not* involve woodwork, screws, or bolts!

Instead, the 'Screws' idea stemmed initially from the mathematical and dynamic behaviour of rotating pendulums. The orbital courses of pendulums as long, rigid structures in motion had fascinated scientists for centuries, and Christiaan Huygens and Robert Hooke in the seventeenth century had conducted experimental and mathematical investigations into the arcs described by suspended pendula. But imagine what orbital path a conical-bob pendulum would describe around its suspension point! This, however, was only the starting point of Ball's interest in the subject. Over the next thirty years he developed his 'Theory of Screws' into an abstruse branch of pure mathematics and geometry, as he began to analyse the 'twists', 'wrenches' and other curvilinear forces acting within moving solid bodies. This analysis of the kinematics, harmonics and vibrational cycles, and of the resulting helical (or screw) patterns acting within rotating solids was for the pure mathematicians only, and Ball even told his own son that if he explained it to him for six months without a break, it would still remain incomprehensible to a layman. So I shall leave well alone!

A KEEN SENSE OF FUN

It is clear from many sources, not to mention the famous cartoon entitled 'Popular Astronomy' by the artist 'Spy' which appeared in the magazine *Vanity Fair* in 1904, that Sir Robert Ball had, in addition to his astronomical and mathematical interests, a strong sense of humour, and he was clearly a brilliant raconteur. He tells us of an incident that happened at Dunsink which also has an element of the ghost story. Working on his own one night in May 1880 in the 11¾-inch telescope dome, Ball was suddenly surprised by the outbreak of 'a terrific uproar' coming from under his feet, 'as if a number of furies were hurling bricks at each other across the entire space under the floor'. Then came a great crashing sound, and Ball admitted that for a while he was 'terribly frightened'. When day broke, the wooden floorboards under the dome were taken up, where it transpired that the vibrations caused by a group of visitors the day before had dislodged a draught-trap or under-ceiling attached beneath the joists, the collapse of which had produced the noise, rather than a marauding banshee! He also left a highly entertaining account of the whirlwind visit to Dublin of Dom Pedro, Emperor of Brazil, in 1876. Dom Pedro was an intellectual monarch fascinated by science and technology, added to which he was famous for his eccentricities and slovenly dress. His Majesty wanted to visit Sir Howard Grubb's great telescope factory, which he did early on a Sunday morning, the Lord Mayor of Dublin (who knew nothing of astronomy) having previously called in Ball, as Astronomer Royal of Ireland, to act as go-between. All went well, as His Majesty inspected the 24-inch-diameter lens which Grubb was figuring for the great Vienna refractor, but on leaving, Dom Pedro absentmindedly placed Sir Howard's brand-new silk top hat upon his head, and left behind 'what we call in Ireland "an old Cawbeen"', or his own battered hat. Rather amused, no one said anything, though some time later the apologetic Imperial Secretary came back to return Sir Howard Grubb's hat and collect the shapeless Imperial 'Cawbeen'. It seems that the Emperor not infrequently picked up other people's hats and left his own behind!

THE GREAT POPULARIZER

To most people, the name of Sir Robert Ball conjures up the image of one of astronomy's most successful popularizers, and this must have derived at least in part from his raconteur's ability to tell stories and hold an audience's attention through the 'hard' bits of a lecture. Rotund, with ample 'corporation' duplicating the shape of the large celestial globe in the 'Spy' cartoon of 1904, frock-coated and with a broad, beaming red face, this was the figure who was to address around one million men and women across Great Britain, America, Canada and elsewhere from the late 1870s down to 1910. Lecturing in town halls, great public buildings, theatres, chapels, not to mention his favourite venue, the Birmingham and Midlands Institute, Sir Robert Ball took 'popular astronomy' to the great wide English-speaking world. Of course, Victorian and Edwardian Britain and America had a well-established and thriving lecture circuit, as famous lecturers in all fields – explorers, soldiers, missionaries, writers, preachers, scientists and so on – used the railway system and fast ocean-going liners to take their respective messages to vast audiences nationwide and beyond.

By 1885, moreover, every town of any importance would have had at least one large public hall, where amid hissing gas lights and comfortable red plush seats hundreds if not thousands of people could assemble to listen with bated breath to the person at the front who brought in ideas and lantern-slide images which thrilled and delighted. It is perhaps sad that in our own day lectures have so often become synonymous with a monotone voice supplying a half-audible commentary to a rapid succession of PowerPoint graphics. But 120 years ago, a lecture could be a riveting, life-changing experience for members of the audience. To the Victorians, lecturing was a performance art, and a top-flight lecturer like Sir Robert Ball was in crowd-drawing competition with theatrical personalities such as the Shakespearean actor Sir Henry Irving, or the music hall doyenne Marie Lloyd. After all, home was often a quiet and unexciting place, and the Victorians loved nothing more than crowding into great shows and public spectacles for their entertainment and edification; for three decades Sir Robert Ball formed part of that world.

Ball was meticulous in the preparation of his lectures. As time went on, he seems to have worked from a largely memorized written script, into which even appropriate gestures were cued – as for an actor – and, in an age without amplification, he must have mastered the orator's art of making every syllable crystal clear to 2,000 people without shouting.

AN INSPIRING PERSONALITY

In addition, in the words of his RAS obituarist Edward Ball Knobel, to being able to excite 'interest and enthusiasm for his subject by his inspiring personality', Sir Robert Ball became a best-selling author. The titles of three of his popular books were mentioned at the beginning of this article, but in all he wrote thirteen, as well as university texts. All are written in a lucid and completely accessible English style which anyone could understand. And if he could write English prose of this quality, one perhaps gets a sense of what his lectures sounded like.

Nor must we forget the rôle which Ball seems to have played in that energizing of popular astronomy, and the founding of astronomical societies, which took place in the last twenty years of the nineteenth century. The dormant Leeds Astronomical Society was brought back into thriving and enduring existence as a result of Sir Robert's inspiration in 1892, while in 1901 he gave a high-profile lecture in Cardiff which inspired the Astronomical Society of Wales. It does seem, however, that he approached lecturing as a money-earning activity, be the lectures organized by a commercial agency, by the charitable Gilchrist Trust for working men, or by a local society, for in 1908 the minute book of the Manchester Astronomical Society lamented 'Sir R. Ball's fee being too high for the Socy. to meet'. This is surprising in many ways, as the Manchester Astronomical Society was blessed with a large and quite wealthy membership. It would be interesting to know what fee he was asking on this occasion, though as Roger Jones has shown in his listed article below, Ball could sometimes demand as much as £40. And to put things into perspective, such a sum – for an evening's work – would have been only slightly less than what a labouring man could expect to earn from a whole year of back-breaking toil in the 1890s.

In addition to his professional work at Dublin, Dunsink and Cambridge (where he succeeded John Couch Adams in 1892), Sir Robert enjoyed golf, photography and an active social life. His obituarists and all people who left recollections of him emphasized his 'charming personality. His kindly and sympathetic nature, his full appreciation of the labours of others, and his keen sense of humour made him greatly beloved and respected by all his friends' (Knobel).

Sir Robert Ball's career went through several changes. From a brilliant start as an undergraduate and a professorship by the age of twenty-seven, his work as an academic research astronomer had, in many ways, reached its peak by the mid-1880s, as visual celestial geometry declined in importance. Whereas his academic career was enhanced by his published work in the pure mathematics of 'Screw Theory', it was as an astronomical popularizer that he found his fame, and he took 'popular astronomy' to more people than did anyone before the television age. He died in Cambridge, on 25 November 1913, from what may have been diabetic complications, and was buried in St Giles Churchyard, Cambridge. He left £12,045.

BIBLIOGRAPHY

W. Valentine Ball (ed.), 1915, *The Reminiscences and Letters of Sir Robert Ball*, Cassell, London.

F.W.D. and G.T.B., 1915, 'Sir Robert Stawell Ball, 1840–1913', obituary, *Proceedings of the Royal Society*, Series A, vol. XCI, September, pp. xvii–xxi.

E.[dward] B.[all] K.[nobel], 1915, 'Robert Stawell Ball', obituary, *Monthly Notices of the Royal Astronomical Society*, 75, pp. 230–6.

Patrick Wayman, 2004, 'Sir Robert Stawell Ball', *New Dictionary of National Biography*, Oxford University Press.

Pedro Ruiz Castell, 2004, 'Astronomy and its audiences: Robert Ball and popular astronomy in Victorian Britain', *The Antiquarian Astronomer*, No. 1, pp. 34–9.

A. Chapman, 1998, *The Victorian Amateur Astronomer: Independent Astronomical Research in Britain 1820–1920*, Praxis-Wiley, Chichester.

I. S. Glass, 1997, *Victorian Telescope Makers: The Lives and Letters of Thomas and Howard Grubb*, Institute of Physics, Bristol.

Roger Jones, 2005, 'Sir Robert Ball: Victorian Astronomer and Lecturer *par excellence*', *The Antiquarian Astronomer*, No. 2, pp. 27–36.

Susan McKenna-Lawlor, 1985, 'Robert Stawell Ball: mathematician and astronomer', in C. Mollan et al. (eds), *Some People and Places in Irish Science and Technology*, Royal Irish Academy, Dublin, pp. 56–7.

Charles Mollan, William Davis, and Brendan Finucane, 1990, *More People and Places in Irish Science and Technology*, Royal Irish

Academy. (Does not discuss Ball, but like *Some People and Places* (above) supplies a great deal of historical information about Irish science.)

James Moseley, 1979, 'Sir Robert Stawell Ball FRS', *Journal of the British Interplanetary Society*, 32, p. 157.

Frank M. Turner, 1980, 'Public science in Britain, 1880–1919', *Isis*, 71, pp. 589–608.

Part III

Miscellaneous

Some Interesting Variable Stars

JOHN ISLES

All variable stars are of potential interest, and hundreds of them can be observed with the slightest optical aid, even with a pair of binoculars. The stars in the list that follows include many that are popular with amateur observers, as well as some less well-known objects that are nevertheless suitable for study visually. The periods and ranges of many variables are not constant from one cycle to another, and some are completely irregular.

Finder charts are given after the list for those stars marked with an asterisk. These charts are adapted with permission from those issued by the Variable Star Section of the British Astronomical Association. Apart from the eclipsing variables and others in which the light changes are purely a geometrical effect, variable stars can be divided broadly into two classes: the pulsating stars, and the eruptive or cataclysmic variables.

Mira (Omicron Ceti) is the best-known member of the long-period subclass of pulsating red-giant stars. The chart is suitable for use in estimating the magnitude of Mira when it reaches naked-eye brightness – typically from about a month before the predicted date of maximum until two or three months after maximum. Predictions for Mira and other stars of its class follow the section of finder charts.

The semi-regular variables are less predictable, and generally have smaller ranges. V Canum Venaticorum is one of the more reliable ones, with steady oscillations in a six-month cycle. Z Ursae Majoris, easily found with binoculars near Delta, has a large range, and often shows double maxima owing to the presence of multiple periodicities in its light changes. The chart for Z is also suitable for observing another semi-regular star, RY Ursae Majoris. These semi-regular stars are mostly red giants or supergiants.

The RV Tauri stars are of earlier spectral class than the semi-regulars, and in a full cycle of variation they often show deep minima and double maxima that are separated by a secondary minimum. U Monocerotis is one of the brightest RV Tauri stars.

Among eruptive variable stars is the carbon-rich supergiant R Coronae Borealis. Its unpredictable eruptions cause it not to brighten, but to fade. This happens when one of the sooty clouds that the star throws out from time to time happens to come in our direction and blots out most of the star's light from our view. Much of the time R Coronae is bright enough to be seen with binoculars, and the chart can be used to estimate its magnitude. During the deepest minima, however, the star needs a telescope of 25-centimetre or larger aperture to be detected.

CH Cygni is a symbiotic star – that is, a close binary comprising a red giant and a hot dwarf star that interact physically, giving rise to outbursts. The system also shows semi-regular oscillations, and sudden fades and rises that may be connected with eclipses.

Observers can follow the changes of these variable stars by using the comparison stars whose magnitudes are given below each chart. Observations of variable stars by amateurs are of scientific value, provided they are collected and made available for analysis. This is done by several organizations, including the British Astronomical Association (see the list of astronomical societies in this volume), the American Association of Variable Star Observers (25 Birch Street, Cambridge, Mass. 02138), and the Royal Astronomical Society of New Zealand (PO Box 3181, Wellington).

Star	RA		Declination		Range	Type	Period	Spectrum
	h	m	°	′			(days)	
R Andromedae	00	24.0	+38	35	5.8–14.9	Mira	409	S
W Andromedae	02	17.6	+44	18	6.7–14.6	Mira	396	S
U Antliae	10	35.2	−39	34	5–6	Irregular	—	C
Theta Apodis	14	05.3	−76	48	5–7	Semi-regular	119	M
R Aquarii	23	43.8	−15	17	5.8–12.4	Symbiotic	387	M+Pec
T Aquarii	20	49.9	−05	09	7.2–14.2	Mira	202	M
R Aquilae	19	06.4	+08	14	5.5–12.0	Mira	284	M
V Aquilae	19	04.4	−05	41	6.6–8.4	Semi-regular	353	C
Eta Aquilae	19	52.5	+01	00	3.5–4.4	Cepheid	7.2	F–G
U Arae	17	53.6	−51	41	7.7–14.1	Mira	225	M
R Arietis	02	16.1	+25	03	7.4–13.7	Mira	187	M
U Arietis	03	11.0	+14	48	7.2–15.2	Mira	371	M
R Aurigae	05	17.3	+53	35	6.7–13.9	Mira	458	M
Epsilon Aurigae	05	02.0	+43	49	2.9–3.8	Algol	9892	F+B
R Boötis	14	37.2	+26	44	6.2–13.1	Mira	223	M

Star	RA		Declination		Range	Type	Period	Spectrum
	h	m	°	′			(days)	
X Camelopardalis	04	45.7	+75	06	7.4–14.2	Mira	144	K–M
R Cancri	08	16.6	+11	44	6.1–11.8	Mira	362	M
X Cancri	08	55.4	+17	14	5.6–7.5	Semi-regular	195?	C
R Canis Majoris	07	19.5	−16	24	5.7–6.3	Algol	1.1	F
VY Canis Majoris	07	23.0	−25	46	6.5–9.6	Unique	—	M
S Canis Minoris	07	32.7	+08	19	6.6–13.2	Mira	333	M
R Canum Ven.	13	49.0	+39	33	6.5–12.9	Mira	329	M
*V Canum Ven.	13	19.5	+45	32	6.5–8.6	Semi-regular	192	M
R Carinae	09	32.2	−62	47	3.9–10.5	Mira	309	M
S Carinae	10	09.4	−61	33	4.5–9.9	Mira	149	K–M
l Carinae	09	45.2	−62	30	3.3–4.2	Cepheid	35.5	F–K
Eta Carinae	10	45.1	−59	41	−0.8–7.9	Irregular	—	Pec
R Cassiopeiae	23	58.4	+51	24	4.7–13.5	Mira	430	M
S Cassiopeiae	01	19.7	+72	37	7.9–16.1	Mira	612	S
W Cassiopeiae	00	54.9	+58	34	7.8–12.5	Mira	406	C
Gamma Cas.	00	56.7	+60	43	1.6–3.0	Gamma Cas.	—	B
Rho Cassiopeiae	23	54.4	+57	30	4.1–6.2	Semi-regular	—	F–K
R Centauri	14	16.6	−59	55	5.3–11.8	Mira	546	M
S Centauri	12	24.6	−49	26	7–8	Semi-regular	65	C
T Centauri	13	41.8	−33	36	5.5–9.0	Semi-regular	90	K–M
S Cephei	21	35.2	+78	37	7.4–12.9	Mira	487	C
T Cephei	21	09.5	+68	29	5.2–11.3	Mira	388	M
Delta Cephei	22	29.2	+58	25	3.5–4.4	Cepheid	5.4	F–G
Mu Cephei	21	43.5	+58	47	3.4–5.1	Semi-regular	730	M
U Ceti	02	33.7	−13	09	6.8–13.4	Mira	235	M
W Ceti	00	02.1	−14	41	7.1–14.8	Mira	351	S
*Omicron Ceti	02	19.3	−02	59	2.0–10.1	Mira	332	M
R Chamaeleontis	08	21.8	−76	21	7.5–14.2	Mira	335	M
T Columbae	05	19.3	−33	42	6.6–12.7	Mira	226	M
R Comae Ber.	12	04.3	+18	47	7.1–14.6	Mira	363	M
*R Coronae Bor.	15	48.6	+28	09	5.7–14.8	R Coronae Bor.	—	C
S Coronae Bor.	15	21.4	+31	22	5.8–14.1	Mira	360	M
T Coronae Bor.	15	59.6	+25	55	2.0–10.8	Recurrent nova	—	M+Pec
V Coronae Bor.	15	49.5	+39	34	6.9–12.6	Mira	358	C
W Coronae Bor.	16	15.4	+37	48	7.8–14.3	Mira	238	M
R Corvi	12	19.6	−19	15	6.7–14.4	Mira	317	M
R Crucis	12	23.6	−61	38	6.4–7.2	Cepheid	5.8	F–G
R Cygni	19	36.8	+50	12	6.1–14.4	Mira	426	S
U Cygni	20	19.6	+47	54	5.9–12.1	Mira	463	C
W Cygni	21	36.0	+45	22	5.0–7.6	Semi-regular	131	M

Star	RA		Declination		Range	Type	Period	Spectrum
	h	m	°	′			(days)	
RT Cygni	19	43.6	+48	47	6.0–13.1	Mira	190	M
SS Cygni	21	42.7	+43	35	7.7–12.4	Dwarf nova	50±	K+Pec
*CH Cygni	19	24.5	+50	14	5.6–9.0	Symbiotic	—	M+B
Chi Cygni	19	50.6	+32	55	3.3–14.2	Mira	408	S
R Delphini	20	14.9	+09	05	7.6–13.8	Mira	285	M
U Delphini	20	45.5	+18	05	5.6–7.5	Semi-regular	110?	M
EU Delphini	20	37.9	+18	16	5.8–6.9	Semi-regular	60	M
Beta Doradûs	05	33.6	–62	29	3.5–4.1	Cepheid	9.8	F–G
R Draconis	16	32.7	+66	45	6.7–13.2	Mira	246	M
T Eridani	03	55.2	–24	02	7.2–13.2	Mira	252	M
R Fornacis	02	29.3	–26	06	7.5–13.0	Mira	389	C
R Geminorum	07	07.4	+22	42	6.0–14.0	Mira	370	S
U Geminorum	07	55.1	+22	00	8.2–14.9	Dwarf nova	105±	Pec+M
Zeta Geminorum	07	04.1	+20	34	3.6–4.2	Cepheid	10.2	F–G
Eta Geminorum	06	14.9	+22	30	3.2–3.9	Semi-regular	233	M
S Gruis	22	26.1	–48	26	6.0–15.0	Mira	402	M
S Herculis	16	51.9	+14	56	6.4–13.8	Mira	307	M
U Herculis	16	25.8	+18	54	6.4–13.4	Mira	406	M
Alpha Herculis	17	14.6	+14	23	2.7–4.0	Semi-regular	—	M
68, u Herculis	17	17.3	+33	06	4.7–5.4	Algol	2.1	B+B
R Horologii	02	53.9	–49	53	4.7–14.3	Mira	408	M
U Horologii	03	52.8	–45	50	6–14	Mira	348	M
R Hydrae	13	29.7	–23	17	3.5–10.9	Mira	389	M
U Hydrae	10	37.6	–13	23	4.3–6.5	Semi-regular	450?	C
VW Hydri	04	09.1	–71	18	8.4–14.4	Dwarf nova	27±	Pec
R Leonis	09	47.6	+11	26	4.4–11.3	Mira	310	M
R Leonis Minoris	09	45.6	+34	31	6.3–13.2	Mira	372	M
R Leporis	04	59.6	–14	48	5.5–11.7	Mira	427	C
Y Librae	15	11.7	–06	01	7.6–14.7	Mira	276	M
RS Librae	15	24.3	–22	55	7.0–13.0	Mira	218	M
Delta Librae	15	01.0	–08	31	4.9–5.9	Algol	2.3	A
R Lyncis	07	01.3	+55	20	7.2–14.3	Mira	379	S
R Lyrae	18	55.3	+43	57	3.9–5.0	Semi-regular	46?	M
RR Lyrae	19	25.5	+42	47	7.1–8.1	RR Lyrae	0.6	A–F
Beta Lyrae	18	50.1	+33	22	3.3–4.4	Eclipsing	12.9	B
U Microscopii	20	29.2	–40	25	7.0–14.4	Mira	334	M
*U Monocerotis	07	30.8	–09	47	5.9–7.8	RV Tauri	91	F–K
V Monocerotis	06	22.7	–02	12	6.0–13.9	Mira	340	M
R Normae	15	36.0	–49	30	6.5–13.9	Mira	508	M
T Normae	15	44.1	–54	59	6.2–13.6	Mira	241	M

Star	RA h	RA m	Declination °	Declination ′	Range	Type	Period (days)	Spectrum
R Octantis	05	26.1	–86	23	6.3–13.2	Mira	405	M
S Octantis	18	08.7	–86	48	7.2–14.0	Mira	259	M
V Ophiuchi	16	26.7	–12	26	7.3–11.6	Mira	297	C
X Ophiuchi	18	38.3	+08	50	5.9–9.2	Mira	329	M
RS Ophiuchi	17	50.2	–06	43	4.3–12.5	Recurrent nova	—	OB+M
U Orionis	05	55.8	+20	10	4.8–13.0	Mira	368	M
W Orionis	05	05.4	+01	11	5.9–7.7	Semi-regular	212	C
Alpha Orionis	05	55.2	+07	24	0.0–1.3	Semi-regular	2335	M
S Pavonis	19	55.2	–59	12	6.6–10.4	Semi-regular	381	M
Kappa Pavonis	18	56.9	–67	14	3.9–4.8	W Virginis	9.1	G
R Pegasi	23	06.8	+10	33	6.9–13.8	Mira	378	M
X Persei	03	55.4	+31	03	6.0–7.0	Gamma Cas.	—	O9.5
Beta Persei	03	08.2	+40	57	2.1–3.4	Algol	2.9	B
Zeta Phoenicis	01	08.4	–55	15	3.9–4.4	Algol	1.7	B+B
R Pictoris	04	46.2	–49	15	6.4–10.1	Semi-regular	171	M
RS Puppis	08	13.1	–34	35	6.5–7.7	Cepheid	41.4	F–G
L^2 Puppis	07	13.5	–44	39	2.6–6.2	Semi-regular	141	M
T Pyxidis	09	04.7	–32	23	6.5–15.3	Recurrent nova	7000±	Pec
U Sagittae	19	18.8	+19	37	6.5–9.3	Algol	3.4	B+G
WZ Sagittae	20	07.6	+17	42	7.0–15.5	Dwarf nova	1900±	A
R Sagittarii	19	16.7	–19	18	6.7–12.8	Mira	270	M
RR Sagittarii	19	55.9	–29	11	5.4–14.0	Mira	336	M
RT Sagittarii	20	17.7	–39	07	6.0–14.1	Mira	306	M
RU Sagittarii	19	58.7	–41	51	6.0–13.8	Mira	240	M
RY Sagittarii	19	16.5	–33	31	5.8–14.0	R Coronae Bor.	—	G
RR Scorpii	16	56.6	–30	35	5.0–12.4	Mira	281	M
RS Scorpii	16	55.6	–45	06	6.2–13.0	Mira	320	M
RT Scorpii	17	03.5	–36	55	7.0–15.2	Mira	449	S
Delta Scorpii	16	00.3	–22	37	1.6–2.3	Irregular	—	B
S Sculptoris	00	15.4	–32	03	5.5–13.6	Mira	363	M
R Scuti	18	47.5	–05	42	4.2–8.6	RV Tauri	146	G–K
R Serpentis	15	50.7	+15	08	5.2–14.4	Mira	356	M
S Serpentis	15	21.7	+14	19	7.0–14.1	Mira	372	M
T Tauri	04	22.0	+19	32	9.3–13.5	T Tauri	—	F–K
SU Tauri	05	49.1	+19	04	9.1–16.9	R Coronae Bor.	—	G
Lambda Tauri	04	00.7	+12	29	3.4–3.9	Algol	4.0	B+A
R Trianguli	02	37.0	+34	16	5.4–12.6	Mira	267	M
R Ursae Majoris	10	44.6	+68	47	6.5–13.7	Mira	302	M
T Ursae Majoris	12	36.4	+59	29	6.6–13.5	Mira	257	M
*Z Ursae Majoris	11	56.5	+57	52	6.2–9.4	Semi-regular	196	M

Star	RA		Declination		Range	Type	Period	Spectrum
	h	m	°	′			(days)	
*RY Ursae Majoris	12	20.5	+61	19	6.7–8.3	Semi-regular	310?	M
U Ursae Minoris	14	17.3	+66	48	7.1–13.0	Mira	331	M
R Virginis	12	38.5	+06	59	6.1–12.1	Mira	146	M
S Virginis	13	33.0	–07	12	6.3–13.2	Mira	375	M
SS Virginis	12	25.3	+00	48	6.0–9.6	Semi-regular	364	C
R Vulpeculae	21	04.4	+23	49	7.0–14.3	Mira	137	M
Z Vulpeculae	19	21.7	+25	34	7.3–8.9	Algol	2.5	B+A

V CANUM VENATICORUM 13h 19.5m +45° 32′ (2000)

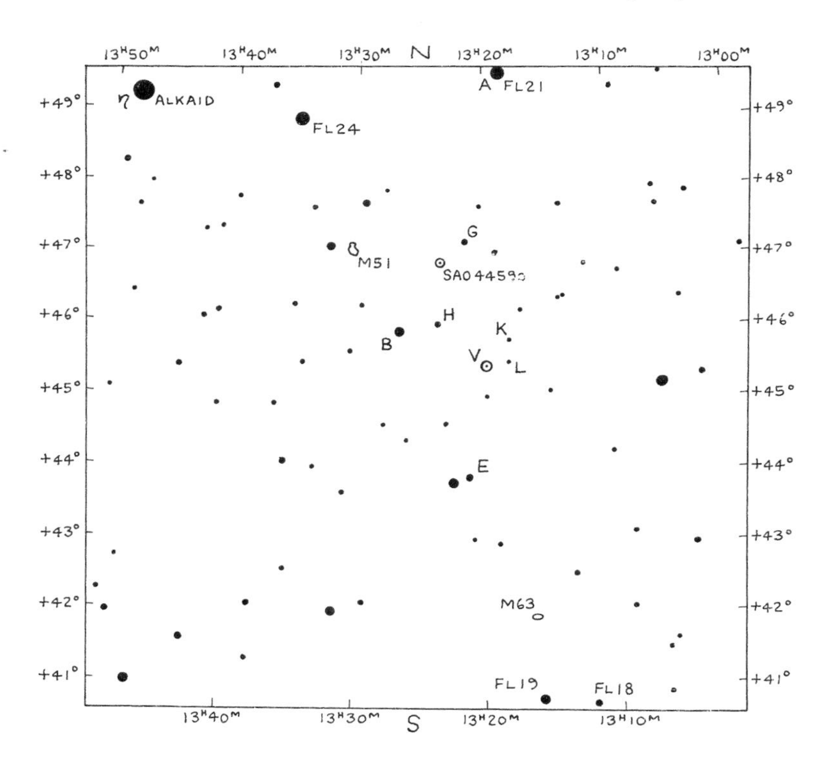

A	5.1	H	7.8
B	5.9	K	8.4
E	6.5	L	8.6
G	7.1		

o (MIRA) CETI 02h 19.3m −02° 59′ (2000)

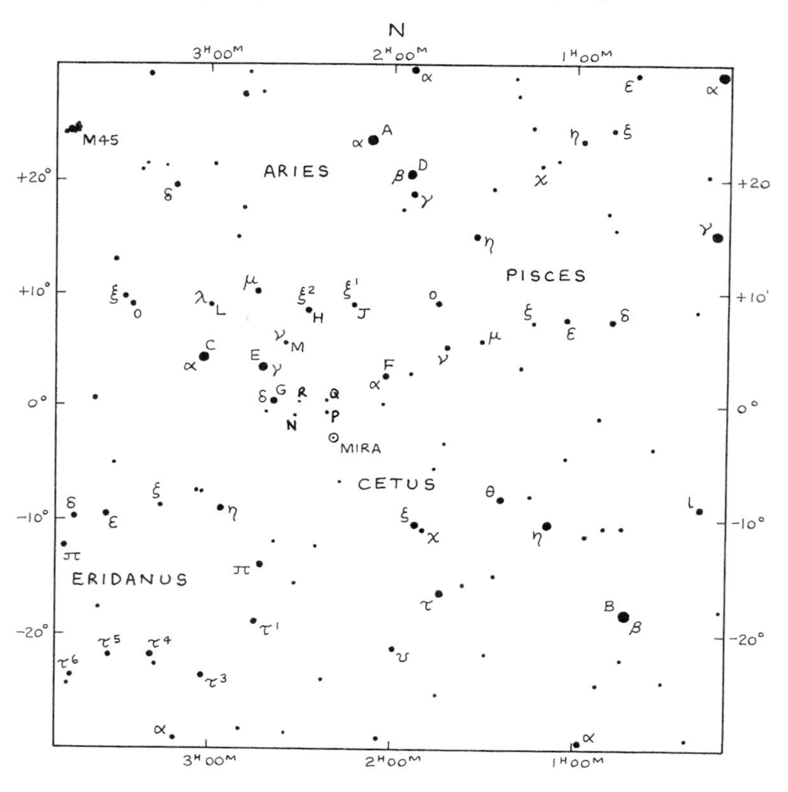

A 2.2	J 4.4
B 2.4	L 4.9
C 2.7	M 5.1
D 3.0	N 5.4
E 3.6	P 5.5
F 3.8	Q 5.7
G 4.1	R 6.1
H 4.3	

R CORONAE BOREALIS 15h 48.6m +28° 09′ (2000)

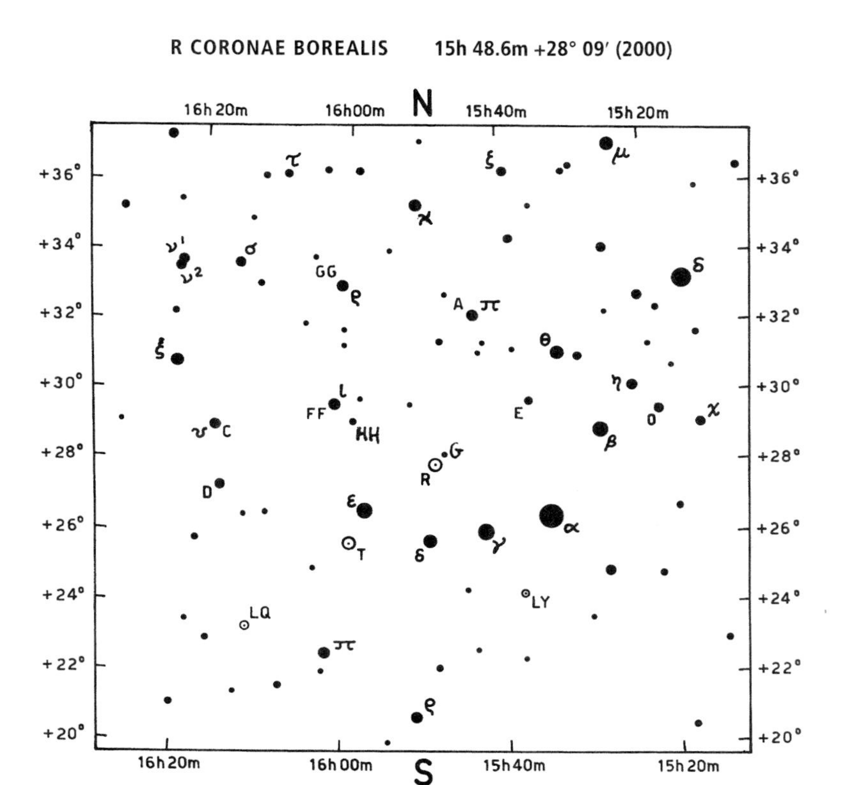

FF	5.0	C	5.8
GG	5.4	D	6.2
A	5.6	E	6.5
		HH	7.1
		G	7.4

CH CYGNI 19h 24.5m +50° 14′ (2000)

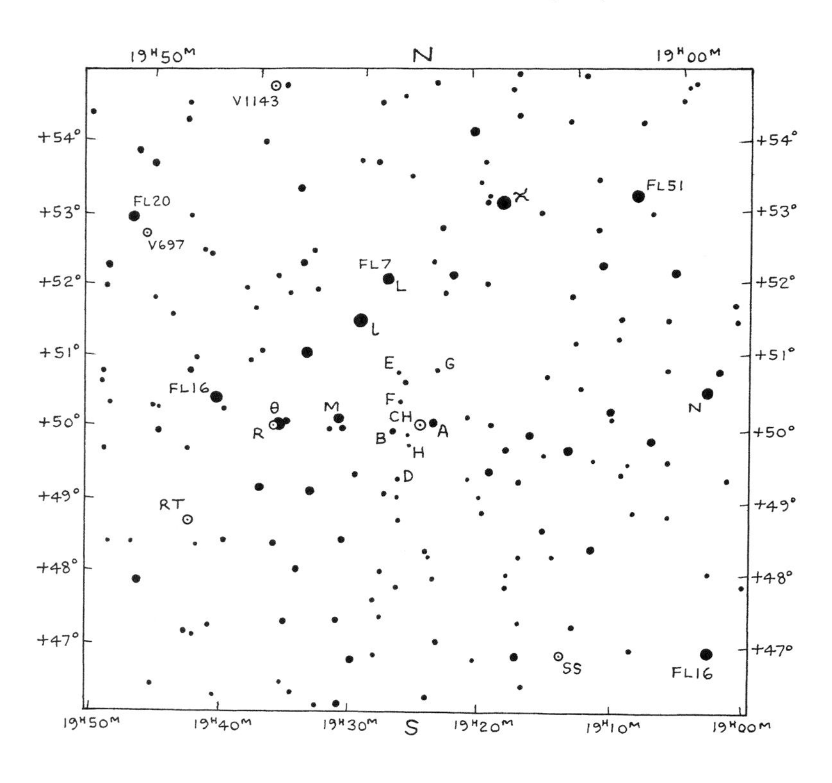

N 5.4	D 8.0
M 5.5	E 8.1
L 5.8	F 8.5
A 6.5	G 8.5
B 7.4	H 9.2

U MONOCEROTIS 07h 30.8m −09° 47′ (2000)

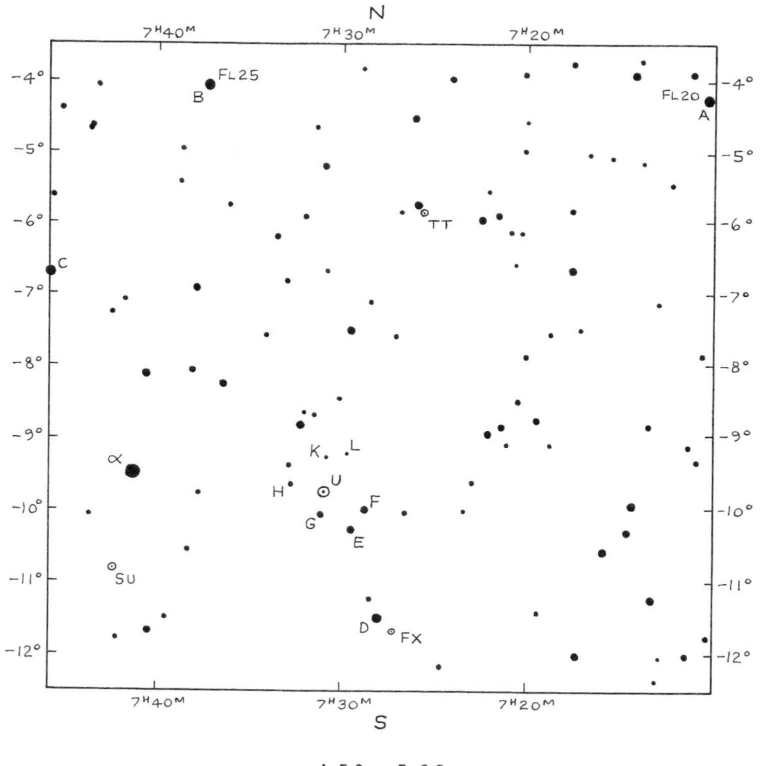

A 5.0	F 6.6
B 5.2	G 7.0
C 5.7	H 7.5
D 5.9	K 7.8
E 6.0	L 8.0

RY URSAE MAJORIS 12h 20.5m +61° 19′ (2000)
Z URSAE MAJORIS 11h 56.5m +57° 52′ (2000)

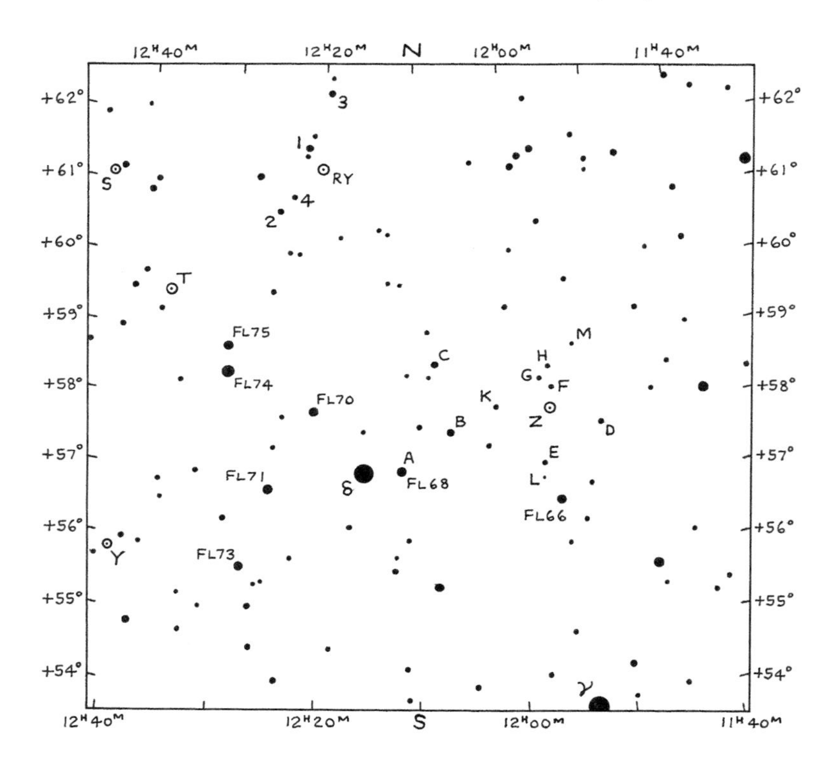

A	6.5	F	8.6	M	9.1
B	7.2	G	8.7	1	6.9
C	7.6	H	8.8	2	7.4
D	8.0	K	8.9	3	7.7
E	8.3	L	9.0	4	7.8

Mira Stars: Maxima, 2007

JOHN ISLES

Below are the predicted dates of maxima for Mira stars that reach magnitude 7.5 or brighter at an average maximum. Individual maxima can in some cases be brighter or fainter than average by a magnitude or more, and all dates are only approximate. The positions, extreme ranges and mean periods of these stars can be found in the preceding list of interesting variable stars.

Star	Mean Magnitude at Maximum	Dates of Maxima
R Andromedae	6.9	15 May
W Andromedae	7.4	23 Apr
R Aquarii	6.5	21 Nov
R Aquilae	6.1	1 Jul
R Bootis	7.2	5 Feb, 16 Sep
R Cancri	6.8	15 Sep
S Canis Minoris	7.5	1 Apr
R Carinae	4.6	16 Jul
S Carinae	5.7	13 May, 9 Oct
R Cassiopeiae	7.0	29 Oct
R Centauri	5.8	25 Sep
T Cephei	6.0	13 Dec
U Ceti	7.5	15 Jan, 6 Sep
Omicron Ceti	3.4	14 Mar
T Columbae	7.5	19 Apr, 1 Dec
S Coronae Borealis	7.3	23 Sep
V Coronae Borealis	7.5	9 Mar
R Corvi	7.5	1 May
R Cygni	7.5	30 Oct
U Cygni	7.2	30 Jul
RT Cygni	7.3	26 Jun

Star	Mean Magnitude at Maximum	Dates of Maxima
Chi Cygni	5.2	25 Sep
R Geminorum	7.1	21 Dec
U Herculis	7.5	25 Aug
R Horologii	6.0	24 Nov
R Hydrae	4.5	4 Nov
R Leonis	5.8	28 Feb
R Leonis Minoris	7.1	16 Dec
R Leporis	6.8	24 Jul
RS Librae	7.5	23 Feb, 28 Sep
V Monocerotis	7.0	6 Aug
R Normae	7.2	18 Jul
T Normae	7.4	11 Aug
V Ophiuchi	7.5	16 Aug
X Ophiuchi	6.8	17 Feb
U Orionis	6.3	21 Jan
R Sagittarii	7.3	26 Sep
RR Sagittarii	6.8	4 Mar
RT Sagittarii	7.0	12 Oct
RU Sagittarii	7.2	26 Feb, 24 Oct
RR Scorpii	5.9	31 Aug
RS Scorpii	7.0	28 Jun
S Sculptoris	6.7	22 Dec
R Serpentis	6.9	18 Oct
R Trianguli	6.2	15 Jun
R Ursae Majoris	7.5	19 Aug
R Virginis	6.9	22 Mar, 15 Aug
S Virginis	7.0	19 Jan

Some Interesting Double Stars

BOB ARGYLE

The positions, angles and separations given below correspond to epoch 2006.0.

No.	RA		Declin-ation		Star	Magni-tudes	Separa-tion	PA	Cata-logue	Comments
	h	m	°	′			arcsec	°		
1	00	31.5	−62	58	β Tuc	4.4, 4.8	27.1	169	LCL 119	Both again difficult doubles.
2	00	49.1	+57	49	η Cas	3.4, 7.5	13.1	320	Σ60	Easy. Creamy, bluish.
3	00	55.0	+23	38	36 And	6.0, 6.4	1.0	320	Σ73	P = 168 years. Both yellow. Slowly opening.
4	01	13.7	+07	35	ζ Psc	5.6, 6.5	23.1	63	Σ100	Yellow, reddish-white.
5	01	39.8	−56	12	p Eri	5.8, 5.8	11.6	189	Δ5	Period = 483 years.
6	01	53.5	+19	18	γ Ari	4.8, 4.8	7.5	1	Σ180	Very easy. Both white.
7	02	02.0	+02	46	α Psc	4.2, 5.1	1.8	267	Σ202	Binary, period = 933 years.
8	02	03.9	+42	20	γ And	2.3, 5.0	9.6	63	Σ205	Yellow, blue. Relatively fixed.
					γ2 And	5.1, 6.3	0.3	102	OΣ38	BC. Needs 30 cm. Closing.
9	02	29.1	+67	24	ι Cas AB	4.9, 6.9	2.6	230	Σ262	AB is long-period binary. P = 620 years.
					ι Cas AC	4.9, 8.4	7.2	118		
10	02	33.8	−28	14	ω For	5.0, 7.7	10.8	245	HJ 3506	Common proper motion.
11	02	43.3	+03	14	γ Cet	3.5, 7.3	2.6	298	Σ299	Not too easy.

No.	RA		Declin-ation		Star	Magni-tudes	Separa-tion	PA	Cata-logue	Comments
	h	m	°	′			arcsec	°		
12	02	58.3	−40	18	θ Eri	3.4, 4.5	8.3	90	PZ 2	Both white.
13	02	59.2	+21	20	ε Ari	5.2, 5.5	1.5	208	Σ333	Binary. Little motion. Both white.
14	03	00.9	+52	21	Σ331 Per	5.3, 6.7	12.0	85	–	Fixed.
15	03	12.1	−28	59	α For	4.0, 7.0	5.1	300	HJ 3555	P = 269 years. B variable?
16	03	48.6	−37	37	f Eri	4.8, 5.3	8.2	215	Δ16	Pale yellow. Fixed.
17	03	54.3	−02	57	32 Eri	4.8, 6.1	6.9	348	Σ470	Fixed.
18	04	32.0	+53	55	1 Cam	5.7, 6.8	10.3	308	Σ550	Fixed.
19	04	50.9	−53	28	ι Pic	5.6, 6.4	12.4	58	Δ18	Good object for small apertures. Fixed.
20	05	13.2	−12	56	κ Lep	4.5, 7.4	2.2	357	Σ661	Visible in 7.5 cm.
21	05	14.5	−08	12	β Ori	0.1, 6.8	9.5	204	Σ668	Companion once thought to be close double.
22	05	21.8	−24	46	41 Lep	5.4, 6.6	3.4	93	HJ 3752	Deep yellow pair in a rich field.
23	05	24.5	−02	24	η Ori	3.8, 4.8	1.7	78	DA 5	Slow-moving binary.
24	05	35.1	+09	56	λ Ori	3.6, 5.5	4.3	44	Σ738	Fixed.
25	05	35.3	−05	23	θ Ori AB	6.7, 7.9	8.6	32	Σ748	Trapezium in M42.
					θ Ori CD	5.1, 6.7	13.4	61		
26	05	38.7	−02	36	σ Ori AC	4.0, 10.3	11.4	238	Σ762	Quintuple. A is a close double.
					σ Ori ED	6.5, 7.5	30.1	231		
27	05	40.7	−01	57	ζ Ori	1.9, 4.0	2.2	166	Σ774	Can be split in 7.5 cm. Long-period binary.
28	06	14.9	+22	30	η Gem	var, 6.5	1.6	255	β1008	Well seen with 20 cm. Primary orange.
29	06	46.2	+59	27	12 Lyn AB	5.4, 6.0	1.7	67	Σ948	AB is binary, P = 706 years.
					12 Lyn AC	5.4, 7.3	8.7	309		

No.	RA		Declin-ation		Star	Magni-tudes	Separa-tion	PA	Cata-logue	Comments
	h	m	°	′			arcsec	°		
30	07	08.7	−70	30	γ Vol	3.9, 5.8	14.1	298	Δ42	Very slow binary.
31	07	16.6	−23	19	h3945 CMa	4.8, 6.8	26.8	51	–	Contrasting colours.
32	07	20.1	+21	59	δ Gem	3.5, 8.2	5.6	227	Σ1066	Not too easy. Yellow, pale blue.
33	07	34.6	+31	53	α Gem	1.9, 2.9	4.4	59	Σ1110	Widening. Easy with 7.5 cm.
34	07	38.8	−26	48	κ Pup	4.5, 4.7	9.8	318	H III 27	Both white.
35	08	12.2	+17	39	ζ Cnc AB	5.6, 6.0	1.0	48	Σ1196	Period (AB) = 60 years. Near maximum separation.
					ζ Cnc AB-C	5.0, 6.2	5.9	70	Σ1196	Period (AB-C) = 1,150 years.
36	08	44.7	−54	43	δ Vel	2.1, 5.1	0.7	324	I 10	Difficult close pair. Period = 142 years.
37	08	46.8	+06	25	ε Hyd	3.3, 6.8	2.9	303	Σ1273	PA slowly increasing. A is a very close pair.
38	09	18.8	+36	48	38 Lyn	3.9, 6.6	2.8	230	Σ1338	Almost fixed.
39	09	47.1	−65	04	μ Car	3.1, 6.1	5.0	128	RMK 11	Fixed. Fine in small telescopes.
40	10	20.0	+19	50	γ Leo	2.2, 3.5	4.4	126	Σ1424	Binary, period = 619 years. Both orange.
41	10	32.0	−45	04	s Vel	6.2, 6.5	13.5	218	PZ 3	Fixed.
42	10	46.8	−49	26	μ Vel	2.7, 6.4	2.5	55	R 155	P = 138 years. Near widest separation.
43	10	55.6	+24	45	54 Leo	4.5, 6.3	6.6	111	Σ1487	Slowly widening. Pale yellow and white.

No.	RA		Declin-ation		Star	Magni-tudes	Separa-tion	PA	Cata-logue	Comments
	h	m	°	′			arcsec	°		
44	11	18.2	+31	32	ξ UMa	4.3, 4.8	1.7	233	Σ1523	Binary, 60 years. Needs 7.5 cm.
45	11	21.0	–54	29	π Cen	4.3, 5.0	0.2	165	I 879	Binary, 38.7 years. Very close. Needs 40 cm.
46	11	23.9	+10	32	ι Leo	4.0, 6.7	1.9	103	Σ1536	Binary, period = 186 years.
47	11	32.3	–29	16	N Hya	5.8, 5.9	9.5	210	H III 96	Fixed.
48	12	14.0	–45	43	D Cen	5.6, 6.8	2.8	243	RMK 14	Orange and white. Closing.
49	12	26.6	–63	06	α Cru	1.4, 1.9	4.0	112	Δ252	Third star in a low-power field.
50	12	41.5	–48	58	γ Cen	2.9, 2.9	0.6	337	HJ 4539	Period = 84 years. Closing. Both yellow.
51	12	41.7	–01	27	γ Vir	3.5, 3.5	0.7	59	Σ1670	Periastron in 2005. Now widening quickly.
52	12	46.3	–68	06	β Mus	3.7, 4.0	1.3	47	R 207	Both white. Closing slowly. P = 383 years.
53	12	54.6	–57	11	μ Cru	4.3, 5.3	34.9	17	Δ126	Fixed. Both white.
54	12	56.0	+38	19	α CVn	2.9, 5.5	19.3	229	Σ1692	Easy. Yellow, bluish.
55	13	22.6	–60	59	J Cen	4.6, 6.5	60.0	343	Δ133	Fixed. A is a close pair.
56	13	24.0	+54	56	ζ UMa	2.3, 4.0	14.4	152	Σ1744	Very easy. Naked-eye pair with Alcor.
57	13	51.8	–33	00	3 Cen	4.5, 6.0	7.9	106	H III 101	Both white. Closing slowly.
58	14	39.6	–60	50	α Cen	0.0, 1.2	9.0	234	RHD 1	Finest pair in the sky. P = 80 years. Closing.
59	14	41.1	+13	44	ζ Boo	4.5, 4.6	0.6	296	Σ1865	Both white. Closing – highly inclined orbit.

No.	RA		Declin-ation		Star	Magni-tudes	Separa-tion	PA	Cata-logue	Comments
	h	m	°	′			arcsec	°		
60	14	45.0	+27	04	ε Boo	2.5, 4.9	2.9	345	Σ1877	Yellow, blue. Fine pair.
61	14	46.0	−25	27	54 Hya	5.1, 7.1	8.3	122	H III 97	Closing slowly.
62	14	49.3	−14	09	μ Lib	5.8, 6.7	1.9	2	β106	Becoming wider. Fine in 7.5 cm.
63	14	51.4	+19	06	ξ Boo	4.7, 7.0	6.2	311	Σ1888	Fine contrast. Easy.
64	15	03.8	+47	39	44 Boo	5.3, 6.2	1.9	57	Σ1909	Period = 206 years. Beginning to close.
65	15	05.1	−47	03	π Lup	4.6, 4.7	1.7	64	HJ 4728	Widening.
66	15	18.5	−47	53	μ Lup AB	5.1, 5.2	0.8	120	HJ 4753	AB closing. Underobserved.
					μ Lup AC	4.4, 7.2	24.0	129	Δ180	AC almost fixed.
67	15	23.4	−59	19	γ Cir	5.1, 5.5	0.8	350	HJ 4757	Closing. Needs 20 cm. Long-period binary.
68	15	32.0	+32	17	η CrB	5.6, 5.9	0.5	138	Σ1937	Both yellow. P = 41 yrs. Will now start to widen.
69	15	34.8	+10	33	δ Ser	4.2, 5.2	4.3	173	Σ1954	Long-period binary.
70	15	35.1	−41	10	γ Lup	3.5, 3.6	0.8	277	HJ 4786	Binary. Period = 190 years. Needs 20 cm.
71	15	56.9	−33	58	ξ Lup	5.3, 5.8	10.2	49	PZ 4	Fixed.
72	16	14.7	+33	52	σ CrB	5.6, 6.6	7.1	237	Σ2032	Long-period binary. Both white.
73	16	29.4	−26	26	α Sco	1.2, 5.4	2.7	277	GNT 1	Red, green. Difficult from mid-northern latitudes.
74	16	30.9	+01	59	λ Oph	4.2, 5.2	1.6	35	Σ2055	P = 129 years. Fairly difficult in small apertures.

No.	RA		Declin-ation		Star	Magni-tudes	Separa-tion	PA	Cata-logue	Comments
	h	m	°	′			arcsec	°		
75	16	41.3	+31	36	ζ Her	2.9, 5.5	1.1	205	Σ2084	Period = 34 years. Now widening. Needs 20 cm.
76	17	05.3	+54	28	μ Dra	5.7, 5.7	2.3	9	Σ2130	Period = 672 years.
77	17	14.6	+14	24	α Her	var, 5.4	4.6	104	Σ2140	Red, green. Long-period binary.
78	17	15.3	–26	35	36 Oph	5.1, 5.1	4.9	143	SHJ 243	Period = 471 years.
79	17	23.7	+37	08	ρ Her	4.6, 5.6	4.1	318	Σ2161	Slowly widening.
80	18	01.5	+21	36	95 Her	5.0, 5.1	6.4	257	Σ2264	Colours thought variable in C19.
81	18	05.5	+02	30	70 Oph	4.2, 6.0	5.2	135	Σ2272	Opening. Easy in 7.5 cm.
82	18	06.8	–43	25	h5014 CrA	5.7, 5.7	1.7	4	–	Period = 450 years. Needs 10 cm.
83	18	35.9	+16	58	OΣ358 Her	6.8, 7.0	1.6	151	–	Period = 380 years.
84	18	44.3	+39	40	ε^1 Lyr	5.0, 6.1	2.4	348	Σ2382	Quadruple system with ε^2. Both pairs
85	18	44.3	+39	40	ε^2 Lyr	5.2, 5.5	2.4	79	Σ2383	visible in 7.5 cm.
86	18	56.2	+04	12	θ Ser	4.5, 5.4	22.4	104	Σ2417	Fixed. Very easy.
87	19	06.4	–37	04	γ CrA	4.8, 5.1	1.3	27	HJ 5084	Beautiful pair. Period = 122 years.
88	19	30.7	+27	58	β Cyg AB	3.1, 5.1	34.3	54	Σ I 43	Glorious. Yellow, blue-greenish.
					β Cyg Aa	3.1, 5.2	0.2	100	MCA 55	Aa. Period = 97 years. Closing.
89	19	45.0	+45	08	δ Cyg	2.9, 6.3	2.7	221	Σ2579	Slowly widening. Period = 780 years.

No.	RA		Declin-ation		Star	Magni-tudes	Separa-tion	PA	Cata-logue	Comments
	h	m	°	′			arcsec	°		
90	19	48.2	+70	16	ε Dra	3.8, 7.4	3.2	17	Σ2603	Slow binary.
91	20	46.7	+16	07	γ Del	4.5, 5.5	9.1	265	Σ2727	Easy. Yellowish. Long-period binary.
92	20	47.4	+36	29	λ Cyg	4.8, 6.1	0.9	10	OΣ413	Difficult binary in small apertures.
93	20	59.1	+04	18	ε Equ AB	6.0, 6.3	0.6	284	Σ2737	Fine triple. AB is closing.
					ε Equ AC	6.0, 7.1	10.3	66		
94	21	06.9	+38	45	61 Cyg	5.2, 6.0	31.1	151	Σ2758	Nearby binary. Both orange. Period = 659 years.
95	21	19.9	−53	27	θ Ind	4.5, 7.0	6.8	271	HJ 5258	Pale yellow and reddish. Long-period binary.
96	21	44.1	+28	45	μ Cyg	4.8, 6.1	1.7	314	Σ2822	Period = 789 years.
97	22	03.8	+64	37	ξ Cep	4.4, 6.5	8.3	274	Σ2863	White and blue. Long-period binary.
98	22	26.6	−16	45	53 Aqr	6.4, 6.6	1.4	27	SHJ 345	Long-period binary; periastron in 2023.
99	22	28.8	−00	01	ζ Aqr	4.3, 4.5	2.1	177	Σ2909	Period = 587 years. Slowly widening.
100	23	59.4	+33	43	Σ3050 And	6.6, 6.6	2.1	334	–	Period = 350 years.

Some Interesting Nebulae, Clusters and Galaxies

Object	RA		Declination		Remarks
	h	m	°	′	
M31 Andromedae	00	40.7	+41	05	Andromeda Galaxy, visible to naked eye.
H VIII 78 Cassiopeiae	00	41.3	+61	36	Fine cluster, between Gamma and Kappa Cassiopeiae.
M33 Trianguli	01	31.8	+30	28	Spiral. Difficult with small apertures.
H VI 33–4 Persei, C14	02	18.3	+56	59	Double cluster; Sword-handle.
Δ142 Doradus	05	39.1	–69	09	Looped nebula round 30 Doradus. Naked eye. In Large Magellanic Cloud.
M1 Tauri	05	32.3	+22	00	Crab Nebula, near Zeta Tauri.
M42 Orionis	05	33.4	–05	24	Orion Nebula. Contains the famous Trapezium, Theta Orionis.
M35 Geminorum	06	06.5	+24	21	Open cluster near Eta Geminorum.
H VII 2 Monocerotis, C50	06	30.7	+04	53	Open cluster, just visible to naked eye.
M41 Canis Majoris	06	45.5	–20	42	Open cluster, just visible to naked eye.
M47 Puppis	07	34.3	–14	22	Mag. 5.2. Loose cluster.
H IV 64 Puppis	07	39.6	–18	05	Bright planetary in rich neighbourhood.
M46 Puppis	07	39.5	–14	42	Open cluster.
M44 Cancri	08	38	+20	07	Praesepe. Open cluster near Delta Cancri. Visible to naked eye.
M97 Ursae Majoris	11	12.6	+55	13	Owl Nebula, diameter 3′. Planetary.
Kappa Crucis, C94	12	50.7	–60	05	'Jewel Box'; open cluster, with stars of contrasting colours.
M3 Can. Ven.	13	40.6	+28	34	Bright globular.
Omega Centauri, C80	13	23.7	–47	03	Finest of all globulars. Easy with naked eye.
M80 Scorpii	16	14.9	–22	53	Globular, between Antares and Beta Scorpii.
M4 Scorpii	16	21.5	–26	26	Open cluster close to Antares.

Object	RA		Declination		Remarks
	h	m	°	′	
M13 Herculis	16	40	+36	31	Globular. Just visible to naked eye.
M92 Herculis	16	16.1	+43	11	Globular. Between Iota and Eta Herculis.
M6 Scorpii	17	36.8	−32	11	Open cluster; naked eye.
M7 Scorpii	17	50.6	−34	48	Very bright open cluster; naked eye.
M23 Sagittarii	17	54.8	−19	01	Open cluster nearly 50′ in diameter.
H IV 37 Draconis, C6	17	58.6	+66	38	Bright planetary.
M8 Sagittarii	18	01.4	−24	23	Lagoon Nebula. Gaseous. Just visible with naked eye.
NGC 6572 Ophiuchi	18	10.9	+06	50	Bright planetary, between Beta Ophiuchi and Zeta Aquilae.
M17 Sagittarii	18	18.8	−16	12	Omega Nebula. Gaseous. Large and bright.
M11 Scuti	18	49.0	−06	19	Wild Duck. Bright open cluster.
M57 Lyrae	18	52.6	+32	59	Ring Nebula. Brightest of planetaries.
M27 Vulpeculae	19	58.1	+22	37	Dumb-bell Nebula, near Gamma Sagittae.
H IV 1 Aquarii, C55	21	02.1	−11	31	Bright planetary, near Nu Aquarii.
M15 Pegasi	21	28.3	+12	01	Bright globular, near Epsilon Pegasi.
M39 Cygni	21	31.0	+48	17	Open cluster between Deneb and Alpha Lacertae. Well seen with low powers.

(M = Messier number; NGC = New General Catalogue number; C = Caldwell number.)

Our Contributors

Dr Richard McKim has analysed all the BAA Mars observations since the 1980 opposition; his monograph entitled *Telescopic Martian Dust Storms* was the first such publication. He has many other publications concerning the atmospheres of Venus, Jupiter and Saturn, and a number of astronomical biographies. He is a chemist by training, a teacher by profession and a past president of the British Astronomical Association. In 2003, minor planet 1996 AC was renamed (7845) McKim in recognition of his astronomical work.

Professor Richard Ellis is the Steele Professor of Astronomy at the California Institute of Technology in Pasadena, California, and a Welshman by birth. He moved to the USA in 1999 after a 5-year term as Director of the Institute of Astronomy, Cambridge, and was previously Professor of Astronomy at the University of Durham. A regular observer of distant galaxies at the Keck telescopes, Professor Ellis leads Caltech's efforts to construct the Thirty Meter Telescope, an ambitious venture undertaken in collaboration with the University of California, Canada and the US National Observatory.

Dr Duncan Steel lives in Canberra, where he works for the Australian subsidiary of Ball Aerospace, a major US space contractor. In the past he has worked for both NASA and ESA, and at universities in England, the US, New Zealand and Sweden. Duncan is the author of four popular-level books on astronomical subjects, over 130 scientific research papers, and more than a thousand articles for newspapers and magazines. He has also appeared in numerous radio and TV documentaries. An expert on near-Earth asteroids and comets, this year's article is Duncan's third contribution to the *Yearbook of Astronomy*.

Professor Chris Kitchin was formerly director of the University of Hertfordshire Observatory. He is an astrophysicist with a great eagerness in encouraging a popular interest in astronomy. He is the author of several books, and appears regularly on television.

Nick James B.Sc., C.Eng. is the papers secretary of the British Astronomical Association and Assistant Director of its Comet Section. Professionally he is an engineer working in the space industry responsible for a team developing space communication and tracking systems. He has had a long-term interest in astronomical imaging, starting with film and progressing more recently to CCDs and digital cameras. He is joint author, with Gerald North, of *Observing Comets*, published by Springer in 2003.

Professor Fred Watson is Astronomer-in-Charge of the Anglo-Australian Observatory at Coonabarabran in north-western New South Wales. He is an Adjunct Professor in the School of Physical and Chemical Sciences at the Queensland University of Technology, and an honorary Associate Professor of Astronomy in the University of Southern Queensland. A regular contributor to the *Yearbook of Astronomy*, his new book *Stargazer: The Life and Times of the Telescope* is published in Australia by Allen & Unwin.

Dr David M. Harland gained his B.Sc. in astronomy in 1977 and then a doctorate in computational science. Subsequently, he has taught computer science, worked in industry and managed academic research. In 1995 he 'retired' and has since published many books on space themes.

Dr Derek Ward-Thompson is a Reader in the University of Wales (Cardiff) Department of Physics and Astronomy. He has worked extensively with UKIRT and JCMT over the last twenty years, and is a former member of the board of directors of the JCMT. He has just completed a sabbatical year at the Observatoire de Bordeaux, where he was working on preparation for the European Space Agency's Herschel Space Telescope, due to be launched in 2008. He is currently working on a project on NASA's Spitzer Space Telescope.

Dr Allan Chapman, of Wadham College, Oxford, is probably Britain's leading authority on the history of astronomy. He has published many research papers and several books, as well as numerous popular accounts. He is a frequent and welcome contributor to the *Yearbook*.

Astronomical Societies in the British Isles

British Astronomical Association
Assistant Secretary: Burlington House, Piccadilly, London W1V 9AG.
Meetings: Lecture Hall of Scientific Societies, Civil Service Commission Building, 23 Savile Row, London W1. Last Wednesday each month (Oct.–June), 5 p.m. and some Saturday afternoons.

Association for Astronomy Education
Secretary: Teresa Grafton, The Association for Astronomy Education, c/o The Royal Astronomical Society, Burlington House, Piccadilly, London W1V 0NL.

Astronomical Society of Edinburgh
Secretary: Graham Rule, 105/19 Causewayside, Edinburgh EH9 1QG.
Website: www.roe.ac.uk/asewww/; *Email:* asewww@roe.ac.uk
Meetings: City Observatory, Calton Hill, Edinburgh. 1st Friday each month, 8 p.m.

Astronomical Society of Glasgow
Secretary: Mr David Degan, 5 Hillside Avenue, Alexandria, Dunbartonshire G83 0BB.
Website: www.astronomicalsocietyofglasgow.org.uk
Meetings: Royal College, University of Strathclyde, Montrose Street, Glasgow. 3rd Thursday each month, Sept.–Apr., 7.30 p.m.

Astronomical Society of Haringey
Secretary: Jerry Workman, 91 Greenslade Road, Barking, Essex IG11 9XF.
Meetings: Palm Court, Alexandra Palace, 3rd Wednesday each month, 8 p.m.

Astronomy Ireland
Secretary: Tony Ryan, PO Box 2888, Dublin 1, Eire.
Website: www.astronomy.ie; *Email:* info@astronomy.ie
Meetings: 2nd Monday of each month. Telescope meetings every clear Saturday.

Federation of Astronomical Societies
Secretary: Clive Down, 10 Glan-y-Llyn, North Cornelly, Bridgend, County Borough CF33 4EF.
Email: clivedown@btinternet.com

Junior Astronomical Society of Ireland
Secretary: K. Nolan, 5 St Patrick's Crescent, Rathcoole, Co. Dublin.
Meetings: The Royal Dublin Society, Ballsbridge, Dublin 4. Monthly.

Society for Popular Astronomy
Secretary: Guy Fennimore, 36 Fairway, Keyworth, Nottingham NG12 5DU.
Website: www.popastro.com; *Email:* SPAstronomy@aol.com
Meetings: Last Saturday in Jan., Apr., July, Oct., 2.30 p.m. in London.

Webb Society
Secretary: M.B. Swan, Carrowreagh, Kilshanny, Kilfenora, Co. Clare, Eire.

Aberdeen and District Astronomical Society
Secretary: Ian C. Giddings, 95 Brentfield Circle, Ellon, Aberdeenshire AB41 9DB.
Meetings: Robert Gordon's Institute of Technology, St Andrew's Street, Aberdeen. Fridays, 7.30 p.m.

Abingdon Astronomical Society (was **Fitzharry's Astronomical Society**)
Secretary: Chris Holt, 9 Rutherford Close, Abingdon, Oxon OX14 2AT.
Website: www.abingdonastro.org.uk; *Email:* info@abingdonastro.co.uk
Meetings: All Saints' Methodist Church Hall, Dorchester Crescent, Abingdon, Oxon. 2nd Monday Sept.–June, 8 p.m. and additional beginners' meetings and observing evenings as advertised.

Altrincham and District Astronomical Society
Secretary: Derek McComiskey, 33 Tottenham Drive, Manchester M23 9WH.
Meetings: Timperley Village Club. 1st Friday Sept.–June, 8 p.m.

Andover Astronomical Society
Secretary: Mrs S. Fisher, Staddlestones, Aughton, Kingston, Marlborough, Wiltshire SN8 3SA.
Meetings: Grately Village Hall. 3rd Thursday each month, 7.30 p.m.

Astra Astronomy Section
Secretary: c/o Duncan Lunan, Flat 65, Dalraida House, 56 Blythswood Court, Anderston, Glasgow G2 7PE.
Meetings: Airdrie Arts Centre, Anderson Street, Airdrie. Weekly.

Astrodome Mobile School Planetarium
Contact: Peter J. Golding, 53 City Way, Rochester, Kent ME1 2AX.
Website: www.astrodome.clara.co.uk; *Email:* astrodome@clara.co.uk

Aylesbury Astronomical Society
Secretary: Alan Smith, 182 Marley Fields, Leighton Buzzard, Bedfordshire LU7 8WN.
Meetings: 1st Monday in month at 8 p.m., venue in Aylesbury area. Details from Secretary.

Bassetlaw Astronomical Society
Secretary: Andrew Patton, 58 Holding, Worksop, Notts S81 0TD.
Meetings: Rhodesia Village Hall, Rhodesia, Worksop, Notts. 2nd and 4th Tuesdays of month at 7.45 p.m.

Batley & Spenborough Astronomical Society
Secretary: Robert Morton, 22 Links Avenue, Cleckheaton, West Yorks BD19 4EG.
Meetings: Milner K. Ford Observatory, Wilton Park, Batley. Every Thursday, 8 p.m.

Bedford Astronomical Society
Secretary: Mrs L. Harrington, 24 Swallowfield, Wyboston, Bedfordshire MK44 3AE.
Website: www.observer1.freeserve.co.uk/bashome.html
Meetings: Bedford School, Burnaby Rd, Bedford. Last Wednesday each month.

Bingham & Brooks Space Organization
Secretary: N. Bingham, 15 Hickmore's Lane, Lindfield, West Sussex.

Birmingham Astronomical Society
Contact: P. Bolas, 4 Moat Bank, Bretby, Burton-on-Trent DE15 0QJ.
Website: www.birmingham-astronomical.co.uk; *Email:* pbolas@aol.com
Meetings: Room 146, Aston University. Last Tuesday of month. Sept.–June (except Dec., moved to 1st week in Jan.).

Blackburn Leisure Astronomy Section
Secretary: Mr H. Murphy, 20 Princess Way, Beverley, East Yorkshire HU17 8PD.
Meetings: Blackburn Leisure Welfare. Mondays, 8 p.m.

Blackpool & District Astronomical Society
Secretary: Terry Devon, 30 Victory Road, Blackpool, Lancashire FY1 3JT.
Website: www.blackpoolastronomy.org.uk; *Email:* info@blackpoolastronomy.org.uk
Meetings: St Kentigern's Social Centre, Blackpool. 1st Wednesday of the month, 7.45 p.m.

Bolton Astronomical Society
Secretary: Peter Miskiw, 9 Hedley Street, Bolton, Lancashire BL1 3LE.
Meetings: Ladybridge Community Centre, Bolton. 1st and 3rd Tuesdays Sept.–May, 7.30 p.m.

Border Astronomy Society
Secretary: David Pettitt, 14 Sharp Grove, Carlisle, Cumbria CA2 5QR.
Website: www.members.aol.com/P3pub/page8.html
Email: davidpettitt@supanet.com
Meetings: The Observatory, Trinity School, Carlisle. Alternate Thursdays, 7.30 p.m., Sept.–May.

Boston Astronomers
Secretary: Mrs Lorraine Money, 18 College Park, Horncastle, Lincolnshire LN9 6RE.
Meetings: Blackfriars Arts Centre, Boston. 2nd Monday each month, 7.30 p.m.

Bradford Astronomical Society
Contact: Mrs J. Hilary Knaggs, 6 Meadow View, Wyke, Bradford BD12 9LA.
Website: www.bradford-astro.freeserve.co.uk/index.htm
Meetings: Eccleshill Library, Bradford. Alternate Mondays, 7.30 p.m.

Braintree, Halstead & District Astronomical Society
Secretary: Mr J. R. Green, 70 Dorothy Sayers Drive, Witham, Essex CM8 2LU.
Meetings: BT Social Club Hall, Witham Telephone Exchange. 3rd Thursday each month, 8 p.m.

Breckland Astronomical Society (was **Great Ellingham and District Astronomy Club**)
Contact: Martin Wolton, Willowbeck House, Pulham St Mary, Norfolk IP21 4QS.
Meetings: Great Ellingham Recreation Centre, Watton Road (B1077), Great Ellingham, 2nd Friday each month, 7.15 p.m.

Bridgend Astronomical Society
Secretary: Clive Down, 10 Glan-y-Llyn, Broadlands, North Cornelly, Bridgend County CF33 4EF.
Email: clivedown@btinternet.com
Meetings: Bridgend Bowls Centre, Bridgend. 2nd Friday, monthly, 7.30 p.m.

Bridgwater Astronomical Society
Secretary: Mr G. MacKenzie, Watergore Cottage, Watergore, South Petherton, Somerset TA13 5JQ.
Website: www.ourworld.compuserve.com/hompages/dbown/Bwastro.htm
Meetings: Room D10, Bridgwater College, Bath Road Centre, Bridgwater. 2nd Wednesday each month, Sept.–June.

Bridport Astronomical Society
Secretary: Mr G.J. Lodder, 3 The Green, Walditch, Bridport, Dorset DT6 4LB.
Meetings: Walditch Village Hall, Bridport. 1st Sunday each month, 7.30 p.m.

Brighton Astronomical and Scientific Society
Secretary: Ms T. Fearn, 38 Woodlands Close, Peacehaven, East Sussex BN10 7SF.
Meetings: St John's Church Hall, Hove. 1st Tuesday each month, 7.30 p.m.

Bristol Astronomical Society
Secretary: Dr John Pickard, 'Fielding', Easter Compton, Bristol BS35 5SJ.
Meetings: Frank Lecture Theatre, University of Bristol Physics Dept., alternate Fridays in term time, and Westbury Park Methodist Church Rooms, North View, other Fridays.

Callington Community Astronomy Group
Secretary: Beccy Watson. *Tel:* 07732 945671
Email: Beccyboo@kimwatson99.fsnet.co.uk
Website: www.callington-astro.org.uk
Meetings: Callington Space Centre, Callington Community College, Launceston Road, Callington, Cornwall PL17 7DR. 1st and 3rd Saturday of each month, 7.30 p.m., Sept.–July.

Cambridge Astronomical Society
Secretary: Brian Lister, 80 Ramsden Square, Cambridge CB4 2BL.
Meetings: Institute of Astronomy, Madingley Road. 3rd Friday each month.

Cardiff Astronomical Society
Secretary: D.W.S. Powell, 1 Tal-y-Bont Road, Ely, Cardiff CF5 5EU.
Meetings: Dept. of Physics and Astronomy, University of Wales, Newport Road, Cardiff. Alternate Thursdays, 8 p.m.

Castle Point Astronomy Club
Secretary: Andrew Turner, 3 Canewdon Hall Close, Canewdon, Rochford, Essex SS4 3PY.
Meetings: St Michael's Church Hall, Daws Heath. Wednesdays, 8 p.m.

Chelmsford Astronomers
Secretary: Brendan Clark, 5 Borda Close, Chelmsford, Essex.
Meetings: Once a month.

Chester Astronomical Society
Secretary: Mrs S. Brooks, 39 Halton Road, Great Sutton, South Wirral LL66 2UF.
Meetings: All Saints' Parish Church, Chester. Last Wednesday each month except Aug. and Dec., 7.30 p.m.

Chester Society of Natural Science, Literature and Art
Secretary: Paul Braid, 'White Wing', 38 Bryn Avenue, Old Colwyn, Colwyn Bay LL29 8AH.
Email: p.braid@virgin.net
Meetings: Once a month.

Chesterfield Astronomical Society
President: Mr D. Blackburn, 71 Middlecroft Road, Stavely, Chesterfield, Derbyshire S41 3XG. Tel: 07909 570754.
Website: www.chesterfield-as.org.uk
Meetings: Barnet Observatory, Newbold, each Friday.

Clacton & District Astronomical Society
Secretary: C. L. Haskell, 105 London Road, Clacton-on-Sea, Essex.

Cleethorpes & District Astronomical Society
Secretary: C. Illingworth, 38 Shaw Drive, Grimsby, South Humberside.
Meetings: Beacon Hill Observatory, Cleethorpes. 1st Wednesday each month.

Cleveland & Darlington Astronomical Society
Contact: Dr John McCue, 40 Bradbury Rd., Stockton-on-Tees, Cleveland TS20 1LE.
Meetings: Grindon Parish Hall, Thorpe Thewles, near Stockton-on-Tees. 2nd Friday, monthly.

Cork Astronomy Club
Secretary: Charles Coughlan, 12 Forest Ridge Crescent, Wilton, Cork, Eire.
Meetings: 1st Monday, Sept.–May (except bank holidays).

Cornwall Astronomical Society
Secretary: J.M. Harvey, 1 Tregunna Close, Porthleven, Cornwall TR13 9LW.
Meetings: Godolphin Club, Wendron Street, Helston, Cornwall. 2nd and 4th Thursday of each month, 7.30 for 8 p.m.

Cotswold Astronomical Society
Secretary: Rod Salisbury, Grove House, Christchurch Road, Cheltenham, Gloucestershire GL50 2PN.
Website: www.members.nbci.com/CotswoldAS
Meetings: Shurdington Church Hall, School Lane, Shurdington, Cheltenham. 2nd Saturday each month, 8 p.m.

Coventry & Warwickshire Astronomical Society
Secretary: Steve Payne, 68 Stonebury Avenue, Eastern Green, Coventry CV5 7FW.
Website: www.cawas.freeserve.co.uk; *Email:* sjp2000@thefarside57.freeserve.co.uk
Meetings: The Earlsdon Church Hall, Albany Road, Earlsdon, Coventry. 2nd Friday, monthly, Sept.–June.

Crawley Astronomical Society
Secretary: Ron Gamer, 1 Pevensey Close, Pound Hill, Crawley, West Sussex RH10 7BL.
Meetings: Ifield Community Centre, Ifield Road, Crawley. 3rd Friday each month, 7.30 p.m.

Crayford Manor House Astronomical Society
Secretary: Roger Pickard, 28 Appletons, Hadlow, Kent TM1 0DT.
Meetings: Manor House Centre, Crayford. Monthly during term time.

Crewkerne and District Astronomical Society (CADAS)
Chairman: Kevin Dodgson, 46 Hermitage Street, Crewkerne, Somerset TA18 8ET.
Email: crewastra@aol.com

Croydon Astronomical Society
Secretary: John Murrell, 17 Dalmeny Road, Carshalton, Surrey.
Meetings: Lecture Theatre, Royal Russell School, Combe Lane, South Croydon. Alternate Fridays, 7.45 p.m.

Derby & District Astronomical Society
Secretary: Ian Bennett, Freers Cottage, Sutton Lane, Etwall.
Web site: www.derby-astro-soc.fsnet/index.html;
Email: bennett.lovatt@btinternet.com
Meetings: Friends Meeting House, Derby. 1st Friday each month, 7.30 p.m.

Doncaster Astronomical Society
Secretary: A. Anson, 15 Cusworth House, St James Street, Doncaster DN1 3AY
Web site: www.donastro.freeserve.co.uk; *Email:* space@donastro.freeserve.co.uk
Meetings: St George's Church House, St George's Church, Church Way, Doncaster. 2nd and 4th Thursday of each month, commencing at 7.30 p.m.

Dumfries Astronomical Society
Secretary: Mr J. Sweeney, 3 Lakeview, Powfoot, Annan DG13 5PG.
Meetings: Gracefield Arts Centre, Edinburgh Road, Dumfries. 3rd Tuesday Aug.–May, 7.30 p.m.

Dundee Astronomical Society
Secretary: G. Young, 37 Polepark Road, Dundee, Tayside DD1 5QT.
Meetings: Mills Observatory, Balgay Park, Dundee. 1st Friday each month, 7.30 p.m. Sept.–Apr.

Easington and District Astronomical Society
Secretary: T. Bradley, 52 Jameson Road, Hartlepool, Co. Durham.
Meetings: Easington Comprehensive School, Easington Colliery. Every 3rd Thursday throughout the year, 7.30 p.m.

Eastbourne Astronomical Society
Secretary: Peter Gill, 18 Selwyn House, Selwyn Road, Eastbourne, East Sussex BN21 2LF.
Meetings: Willingdon Memorial Hall, Church Street, Willingdon. One Saturday per month, Sept.–July, 7.30 p.m.

East Riding Astronomers
Secretary: Tony Scaife, 15 Beech Road, Elloughton, Brough, North Humberside HU15 1JX.
Meetings: As arranged.

East Sussex Astronomical Society
Secretary: Marcus Croft, 12 St Mary's Cottages, Ninfield Road, Bexhill-on-Sea, East Sussex.
Website: www.esas.org.uk
Meetings: St Marys School, Wrestwood Road, Bexhill. 1st Thursday of each month, 8 p.m.

Edinburgh University Astronomical Society
Secretary: c/o Dept. of Astronomy, Royal Observatory, Blackford Hill, Edinburgh.

Ewell Astronomical Society
Secretary: Richard Gledhill, 80 Abinger Avenue, Cheam SM2 7LW.
Website: www.ewell-as.co.uk
Meetings: St Mary's Church Hall, London Road, Ewell. 2nd Friday of each month except August, 7.45 p.m.

Exeter Astronomical Society
Secretary: Tim Sedgwick, Old Dower House, Half Moon, Newton St Cyres, Exeter, Devon EX5 5AE.
Meetings: The Meeting Room, Wynards, Magdalen Street, Exeter. 1st Thursday of month.

Farnham Astronomical Society
Secretary: Laurence Anslow, 'Asterion', 18 Wellington Lane, Farnham, Surrey GU9 9BA.
Meetings: Central Club, South Street, Farnham. 2nd Thursday each month, 8 p.m.

Foredown Tower Astronomy Group
Secretary: M. Feist, Foredown Tower Camera Obscura, Foredown Road, Portslade, East Sussex BN41 2EW.
Meetings: At the above address, 3rd Tuesday each month. 7 p.m. (winter), 8 p.m. (summer).

Greenock Astronomical Society
Secretary: Carl Hempsey, 49 Brisbane Street, Greenock.
Meetings: Greenock Arts Guild, 3 Campbell Street, Greenock.

Grimsby Astronomical Society
Secretary: R. Williams, 14 Richmond Close, Grimsby, South Humberside.
Meetings: Secretary's home. 2nd Thursday each month, 7.30 p.m.

Guernsey: La Société Guernesiasie Astronomy Section
Secretary: Debby Quertier, Lamorna, Route Charles, St Peter Port, Guernsey GY1 1QS. and Jessica Harris, Keanda, Les Sauvagees, St Sampson's, Guernsey GY2 4XT.
Meetings: Observatory, Rue du Lorier, St Peter's. Tuesdays, 8 p.m.

Guildford Astronomical Society
Secretary: A. Langmaid, 22 West Mount, The Mount, Guildford, Surrey GU2 5HL.
Meetings: Guildford Institute, Ward Street, Guildford. 1st Thursday each month except Aug., 7.30 p.m.

Gwynedd Astronomical Society
Secretary: Mr Ernie Greenwood, 18 Twrcelyn Street, Llanerchymedd, Anglesey LL74 8TL.
Meetings: Dept. of Electronic Engineering, Bangor University. 1st Thursday each month except Aug., 7.30 p.m.

The Hampshire Astronomical Group
Secretary: Geoff Mann, 10 Marie Court, 348 London Road, Waterlooville, Hampshire PO7 7SR.
Website: www.hantsastro.demon.co.uk; *Email:* Geoff.Mann@hazleton97.fsnet.co.uk
Meetings: 2nd Friday, Clanfield Memorial Hall, all other Fridays Clanfield Observatory.

Hanney & District Astronomical Society
Secretary: Bob Church, 47 Upthorpe Drive, Wantage, Oxfordshire OX12 7DG.
Meetings: Last Thursday each month, 8 p.m.

Harrogate Astronomical Society
Secretary: Brian Bonser, 114 Main Street, Little Ouseburn TO5 9TG.
Meetings: National Power HQ, Beckwith Knowle, Harrogate. Last Friday each month.

Hastings and Battle Astronomical Society
Secretary: K.A. Woodcock, 24 Emmanuel Road, Hastings, East Sussex TN34 3LB.
Email: keith@habas.freeserve.co.uk
Meetings: Herstmonceux Science Centre. 2nd Saturday of each month, 7.30 p.m.

Havering Astronomical Society
Secretary: Frances Ridgley, 133 Severn Drive, Upminster, Essex RM14 1PP.
Meetings: Cranham Community Centre, Marlborough Gardens, Upminster, Essex. 3rd Wednesday each month except July and Aug., 7.30 p.m.

Heart of England Astronomical Society
Secretary: John Williams, 100 Stanway Road, Shirley, Solihull B90 3JG.
Website: www.members.aol.com/hoeas/home.html; *Email:* hoeas@aol.com
Meetings: Furnace End Village, over Whitacre, Warwickshire. Last Thursday each month, except June, July & Aug., 8 p.m.

Hebden Bridge Literary & Scientific Society, Astronomical Section
Secretary: Peter Jackson, 44 Gilstead Lane, Bingley, West Yorkshire BD16 3NP.
Meetings: Hebden Bridge Information Centre. Last Wednesday, Sept.–May.

Herschel Astronomy Society
Secretary: Kevin Bishop, 106 Holmsdale, Crown Wood, Bracknell, Berkshire RG12 3TB.
Meetings: Eton College. 2nd Friday each month, 7.30 p.m.

Highlands Astronomical Society
Secretary: Richard Green, 11 Drumossie Avenue, Culcabock, Inverness IV2 3SJ.
Meetings: The Spectrum Centre, Inverness. 1st Tuesday each month, 7.30 p.m.

Hinckley & District Astronomical Society
Secretary: Mr S. Albrighton, 4 Walnut Close, The Bridleways, Hartshill, Nuneaton, Warwickshire CV10 0XH.
Meetings: Burbage Common Visitors Centre, Hinckley. 1st Tuesday Sept.–May, 7.30 p.m.

Horsham Astronomy Group (was **Forest Astronomical Society**)
Secretary: Dan White, 32 Burns Close, Horsham, West Sussex RH12 5PF.
Email: secretary@horshamastronomy.com
Meetings: 1st Wednesday each month.

Howards Astronomy Club
Secretary: H. Ilett, 22 St George's Avenue, Warblington, Havant, Hampshire.
Meetings: To be notified.

Huddersfield Astronomical and Philosophical Society
Secretary: Lisa B. Jeffries, 58 Beaumont Street, Netherton, Huddersfield, West Yorkshire HD4 7HE.
Email: l.b.jeffries@hud.ac.uk
Meetings: 4a Railway Street, Huddersfield. Every Wednesday and Friday, 7.30 p.m.

Hull and East Riding Astronomical Society
President: Sharon E. Long
Email: charon@charon.karoo.co.uk
Website: http://www.heras.org.uk
Meetings: The Wilberforce Building, Room S25, University of Hull, Cottingham Road, Hull. 2nd Monday each month, Sept.–May, 7.30–9.30 p.m.

Ilkeston & District Astronomical Society
Secretary: Mark Thomas, 2 Elm Avenue, Sandiacre, Nottingham NG10 5EJ.
Meetings: The Function Room, Erewash Museum, Anchor Row, Ilkeston. 2nd Tuesday monthly, 7.30 p.m.

Ipswich, Orwell Astronomical Society
Secretary: R. Gooding, 168 Ashcroft Road, Ipswich.
Meetings: Orwell Park Observatory, Nacton, Ipswich. Wednesdays, 8 p.m.

Irish Astronomical Association
President: Terry Moseley, 31 Sunderland Road, Belfast BT6 9LY, Northern Ireland.
Email: terrymosel@aol.com
Meetings: Ashby Building, Stranmillis Road, Belfast. Alternate Wednesdays, 7.30 p.m.

Irish Astronomical Society
Secretary: James O'Connor, PO Box 2547, Dublin 15, Eire.
Meetings: Ely House, 8 Ely Place, Dublin 2. 1st and 3rd Monday each month.

Isle of Man Astronomical Society
Secretary: James Martin, Ballaterson Farm, Peel, Isle of Man IM5 3AB.
Email: ballaterson@manx.net
Meetings: Isle of Man Observatory, Foxdale. 1st Thursday of each month, 8 p.m.

Isle of Wight Astronomical Society
Secretary: J. W. Feakins, 1 Hilltop Cottages, High Street, Freshwater, Isle of Wight.
Meetings: Unitarian Church Hall, Newport, Isle of Wight. Monthly.

Keele Astronomical Society
Secretary: Natalie Webb, Department of Physics, University of Keele, Keele, Staffordshire ST5 5BG.
Meetings: As arranged during term time.

Kettering and District Astronomical Society
Asst. Secretary: Steve Williams, 120 Brickhill Road, Wellingborough, Northamptonshire.
Meetings: Quaker Meeting Hall, Northall Street, Kettering, Northamptonshire. 1st Tuesday each month, 7.45 p.m.

King's Lynn Amateur Astronomical Association
Secretary: P. Twynman, 17 Poplar Avenue, RAF Marham, King's Lynn.
Meetings: As arranged.

Lancaster and Morecambe Astronomical Society
Secretary: Mrs E. Robinson, 4 Bedford Place, Lancaster LA1 4EB.
Email: ehelenerob@btinternet.com
Meetings: Church of the Ascension, Torrisholme. 1st Wednesday each month except July and Aug.

Lancaster University Astronomical Society
Secretary: c/o Students' Union, Alexandra Square, University of Lancaster.
Meetings: As arranged.

Laymans Astronomical Society
Secretary: John Evans, 10 Arkwright Walk, The Meadows, Nottingham.
Meetings: The Popular, Bath Street, Ilkeston, Derbyshire. Monthly.

Leeds Astronomical Society
Secretary: Mark A. Simpson, 37 Roper Avenue, Gledhow, Leeds LS8 1LG.
Meetings: Centenary House, North Street. 2nd Wednesday each month, 7.30 p.m.

Leicester Astronomical Society
Secretary: Dr P.J. Scott, 21 Rembridge Close, Leicester LE3 9AP.
Meetings: Judgemeadow Community College, Marydene Drive, Evington, Leicester. 2nd and 4th Tuesdays each month, 7.30 p.m.

Letchworth and District Astronomical Society
Secretary: Eric Hutton, 14 Folly Close, Hitchin, Hertfordshire.
Meetings: As arranged.

Lewes Amateur Astronomers
Secretary: Christa Sutton, 8 Tower Road, Lancing, West Sussex BN15 9HT.
Meetings: The Bakehouse Studio, Lewes. Last Wednesday each month.

Limerick Astronomy Club
Secretary: Tony O'Hanlon, 26 Ballycannon Heights, Meelick, Co. Clare, Eire.
Meetings: Limerick Senior College, Limerick. Monthly (except June and Aug.), 8 p.m.

Lincoln Astronomical Society
Secretary: David Swaey, 'Everglades', 13 Beaufort Close, Lincoln LN2 4SF.
Meetings: The Lecture Hall, off Westcliffe Street, Lincoln. 1st Tuesday each month.

Liverpool Astronomical Society
Secretary: Mr K. Clark, 31 Sandymount Drive, Wallasey, Merseyside L45 0LJ.
Meetings: Lecture Theatre, Liverpool Museum. 3rd Friday each month, 7 p.m.

Norman Lockyer Observatory Society
Secretary: G.E. White, PO Box 9, Sidmouth EX10 0YQ.
Website: www.ex.ac.uk/nlo/; *Email:* g.e.white@ex.ac.uk
Meetings: Norman Lockyer Observatory, Sidmouth. Fridays and 2nd Monday each month, 7.30 p.m.

Loughton Astronomical Society
Secretary: Charles Munton, 14a Manor Road, Wood Green, London N22 4YJ.
Meetings: 1st Theydon Bois Scout Hall, Loughton Lane, Theydon Bois. Weekly.

Lowestoft and Great Yarmouth Regional Astronomers (LYRA) Society
Secretary: Simon Briggs, 28 Sussex Road, Lowestoft, Suffolk.
Meetings: Community Wing, Kirkley High School, Kirkley Run, Lowestoft. 3rd Thursday each month, 7.30 p.m.

Luton Astronomical Society
Secretary: Mr G. Mitchell, Putteridge Bury, University of Luton, Hitchin Road, Luton.
Website: www.lutonastrosoc.org.uk; *Email:* user998491@aol.com
Meetings: Univ. of Luton, Putteridge Bury (except June, July and August), or Someries Junior School, Wigmore Lane, Luton (July and August only), last Thursday each month, 7.30–9.00 p.m.

Lytham St Annes Astronomical Association
Secretary: K.J. Porter, 141 Blackpool Road, Ansdell, Lytham St Anne's, Lancashire.
Meetings: College of Further Education, Clifton Drive South, Lytham St Anne's. 2nd Wednesday monthly Oct.–June.

Macclesfield Astronomical Society
Secretary: Mr John H. Thomson, 27 Woodbourne Road, Sale, Cheshire M33 3SY
Website: www.maccastro.com; *Email:* jhandlc@yahoo.com
Meetings: Jodrell Bank Science Centre, Goostrey, Cheshire. 1st Tuesday of every month, 7 p.m.

Maidenhead Astronomical Society
Secretary: Tim Haymes, Hill Rise, Knowl Hill Common, Knowl Hill, Reading RG10 9YD.
Meetings: Stubbings Church Hall, near Maidenhead. 1st Friday Sept.–June.

Maidstone Astronomical Society
Secretary: Stephen James, 4 The Cherry Orchard, Haddow, Tonbridge, Kent.
Meetings: Nettlestead Village Hall. 1st Tuesday in the month except July and Aug., 7.30 p.m.

Manchester Astronomical Society
Secretary: Mr Kevin J. Kilburn FRAS, Godlee Observatory, UMIST, Sackville Street, Manchester M60 1QD.
Website: www.u-net.com/ph/mas/; *Email:* kkilburn@globalnet.co.uk
Meetings: At the Godlee Observatory. Thursdays, 7 p.m., except below.
Free Public Lectures: Renold Building UMIST, third Thursday Sept.–Mar., 7.30 p.m.

Mansfield and Sutton Astronomical Society
Secretary: Angus Wright, Sherwood Observatory, Coxmoor Road, Sutton-in-Ashfield, Nottinghamshire NG17 5LF.
Meetings: Sherwood Observatory, Coxmoor Road. Last Tuesday each month, 7.30 p.m.

Mexborough and Swinton Astronomical Society
Secretary: Mark R. Benton, 14 Sandalwood Rise, Swinton, Mexborough, South Yorkshire S64 8PN.
Website: www.msas.org.uk; *Email:* mark@masas.f9.co.uk
Meetings: Swinton WMC. Thursdays, 7.30 p.m.

Mid-Kent Astronomical Society
Secretary: Peter Bassett, 167 Shakespeare Road, Gillingham, Kent ME7 5QB.
Meetings: Riverside Country Park, Lower Rainham Road, Gillingham. 2nd and last Fridays each month, 7.45 p.m.

Milton Keynes Astronomical Society
Secretary: Mike Leggett, 19 Matilda Gardens, Shenley Church End, Milton Keynes MK5 6HT.
Website: www.mkas.org.uk; *Email:* mike-pat-leggett@shenley9.fsnet.co.uk
Meetings: Rectory Cottage, Bletchley. Alternate Fridays.

Moray Astronomical Society
Secretary: Richard Pearce, 1 Forsyth Street, Hopeman, Elgin, Moray, Scotland.
Meetings: Village Hall Close, Co. Elgin.

Newbury Amateur Astronomical Society (NAAS)
Secretary: Mrs Monica Balstone, 37 Mount Pleasant, Tadley RG26 4BG.
Meetings: United Reformed Church Hall, Cromwell Place, Newbury. 1st Friday of month, Sept.–June.

Newcastle-on-Tyne Astronomical Society
Secretary: C.E. Willits, 24 Acomb Avenue, Seaton Delaval, Tyne and Wear.
Meetings: Zoology Lecture Theatre, Newcastle University. Monthly.

North Aston Space & Astronomical Club
Secretary: W.R. Chadburn, 14 Oakdale Road, North Aston, Sheffield.
Meetings: To be notified.

Northamptonshire Natural History Society (Astronomy Section)
Secretary: R.A. Marriott, 24 Thirlestane Road, Northampton NN4 8HD.
Email: ram@hamal.demon.co.uk
Meetings: Humfrey Rooms, Castilian Terrace, Northampton. 2nd and last Mondays, most months, 7.30 p.m.

Northants Amateur Astronomers
Secretary: Mervyn Lloyd, 76 Havelock Street, Kettering, Northamptonshire.
Meetings: 1st and 3rd Tuesdays each month, 7.30 p.m.

North Devon Astronomical Society
Secretary: P.G. Vickery, 12 Broad Park Crescent, Ilfracombe, Devon EX34 8DX.
Meetings: Methodist Hall, Rhododendron Avenue, Sticklepath, Barnstaple. 1st Wednesday each month, 7.15 p.m.

North Dorset Astronomical Society
Secretary: J.E.M. Coward, The Pharmacy, Stalbridge, Dorset.
Meetings: Charterhay, Stourton, Caundle, Dorset. 2nd Wednesday each month.

North Downs Astronomical Society
Secretary: Martin Akers, 36 Timber Tops, Lordswood, Chatham, Kent ME5 8XQ.
Meetings: Vigo Village Hall. 3rd Thursday each month. 7.30 p.m.

North-East London Astronomical Society
Secretary: Mr B. Beeston, 38 Abbey Road, Bush Hill Park, Enfield EN1 2QN.
Meetings: Wanstead House, The Green, Wanstead. 3rd Sunday each month (except Aug.), 3 p.m.

North Gwent and District Astronomical Society
Secretary: Jonathan Powell, 14 Lancaster Drive, Gilwern, nr Abergavenny, Monmouthshire NP7 0AA.
Meetings: Gilwern Community Centre. 15th of each month, 7.30 p.m.

North Staffordshire Astronomical Society
Secretary: Duncan Richardson, Halmerend Hall Farm, Halmerend, Stoke-on-Trent, Staffordshire ST7 8AW.
Email: dwr@enterprise.net
Meetings: 21st Hartstill Scout Group HQ, Mount Pleasant, Newcastle-under-Lyme ST5 1DR. 1st Tuesday each month (except July and Aug.), 7–9.30 p.m.

North Western Association of Variable Star Observers
Secretary: Jeremy Bullivant, 2 Beaminster Road, Heaton Mersey, Stockport, Cheshire.
Meetings: Four annually.

Norwich Astronomical Society
Secretary: Dave Balcombe, 52 Folly Road, Wymondham, Norfolk NR18 0QR.
Website: www.norwich.astronomical.society.org.uk
Meetings: Seething Observatory, Toad Lane, Thwaite St Mary, Norfolk. Every Friday, 7.30 p.m.

Nottingham Astronomical Society
Secretary: C. Brennan, 40 Swindon Close, The Vale, Giltbrook, Nottingham NG16 2WD.
Meetings: Djanogly City Technology College, Sherwood Rise (B682). 1st and 3rd Thursdays each month, 7.30 p.m.

Oldham Astronomical Society
Secretary: P.J. Collins, 25 Park Crescent, Chadderton, Oldham.
Meetings: Werneth Park Study Centre, Frederick Street, Oldham. Fortnightly, Friday.

Open University Astronomical Society
Secretary: Dr Andrew Norton, Department of Physics and Astronomy, The Open University, Walton Hall, Milton Keynes MK7 6AA.
Website: www.physics.open.ac.uk/research/astro/a_club.html
Meetings: Open University, Milton Keynes. 1st Tuesday of every month, 7.30 p.m.

Orpington Astronomical Society
Secretary: Dr Ian Carstairs, 38 Brabourne Rise, Beckenham, Kent BR3 2SG.
Meetings: High Elms Nature Centre, High Elms Country Park, High Elms Road, Farnborough, Kent. 4th Thursday each month, Sept.–July, 7.30 p.m.

Papworth Astronomy Club
Contact: Keith Tritton, Magpie Cottage, Fox Street, Great Gransden, Sandy, Bedfordshire SG19 3AA.
Email: kpt2@tutor.open.ac.uk
Meetings: Bradbury Progression Centre, Church Lane, Papworth Everard, nr Huntingdon. 1st Wednesday each month, 7 p.m.

Peterborough Astronomical Society
Secretary: Sheila Thorpe, 6 Cypress Close, Longthorpe, Peterborough.
Meetings: 1st Thursday every month, 7.30 p.m.

Plymouth Astronomical Society
Secretary: Alan G. Penman, 12 St Maurice View, Plympton, Plymouth, Devon PL7 1FQ.
Email: oakmount12@aol.com
Meetings: Glynis Kingham Centre, YMCA Annex, Lockyer Street, Plymouth. 2nd Friday each month, 7.30 p.m.

PONLAF
Secretary: Matthew Hepburn, 6 Court Road, Caterham, Surrey CR3 5RD.
Meetings: Room 5, 6th floor, Tower Block, University of North London. Last Friday each month during term time, 6.30 p.m.

Port Talbot Astronomical Society (formerly **Astronomical Society of Wales**)
Secretary: Mr J. Hawes, 15 Lodge Drive, Baglan, Port Talbot, West Glamorgan SA12 8UD.
Meetings: Port Talbot Arts Centre. 1st Tuesday each month, 7.15 p.m.

Portsmouth Astronomical Society
Secretary: G.B. Bryant, 81 Ringwood Road, Southsea.
Meetings: Monday, fortnightly.

Preston & District Astronomical Society
Secretary: P. Sloane, 77 Ribby Road, Wrea Green, Kirkham, Preston, Lancashire.
Meetings: Moor Park (Jeremiah Horrocks) Observatory, Preston. 2nd Wednesday, last Friday each month, 7.30 p.m.

Reading Astronomical Society
Secretary: Mrs Ruth Sumner, 22 Anson Crescent, Shinfield, Reading RG2 8JT.
Meetings: St Peter's Church Hall, Church Road, Earley. 3rd Friday each month, 7 p.m.

Renfrewshire Astronomical Society
Secretary: Ian Martin, 10 Aitken Road, Hamilton, South Lanarkshire ML3 7YA.
Website: www.renfrewshire-as.co.uk; *Email:* RenfrewAS@aol.com
Meetings: Coats Observatory, Oakshaw Street, Paisley. Fridays, 7.30 p.m.

Rower Astronomical Society
Secretary: Mary Kelly, Knockatore, The Rower, Thomastown, Co. Kilkenny, Eire.

St Helens Amateur Astronomical Society
Secretary: Carl Dingsdale, 125 Canberra Avenue, Thatto Heath, St Helens, Merseyside WA9 5RT.
Meetings: As arranged.

Salford Astronomical Society
Secretary: Mrs Kath Redford, 2 Albermarle Road, Swinton, Manchester M27 5ST.
Meetings: The Observatory, Chaseley Road, Salford. Wednesdays.

Salisbury Astronomical Society
Secretary: Mrs R. Collins, 3 Fairview Road, Salisbury, Wiltshire SP1 1JX.
Meetings: Glebe Hall, Winterbourne Earls, Salisbury. 1st Tuesday each month.

Sandbach Astronomical Society
Secretary: Phil Benson, 8 Gawsworth Drive, Sandbach, Cheshire.
Meetings: Sandbach School, as arranged.

Sawtry & District Astronomical Society
Secretary: Brooke Norton, 2 Newton Road, Sawtry, Huntingdon, Cambridgeshire PE17 5UT.
Meetings: Greenfields Cricket Pavilion, Sawtry Fen. Last Friday each month.

Scarborough & District Astronomical Society
Secretary: Mrs S. Anderson, Basin House Farm, Sawdon, Scarborough, North Yorkshire.
Meetings: Scarborough Public Library. Last Saturday each month, 7–9 p.m.

Scottish Astronomers Group
Secretary: Dr Ken Mackay, Hayford House, Cambusbarron, Stirling FK7 9PR.
Meetings: North of Hadrian's Wall, twice yearly.

Sheffield Astronomical Society
Secretary: Darren Swindels, 102 Sheffield Road, Woodhouse, Sheffield, South Yorkshire S13 7EU.
Website: www.sheffieldastro.org.uk; *Email:* info@sheffieldastro.org.uk
Meetings: Twice monthly at Mayfield Environmental Education Centre, David Lane, Fulwood, Sheffield S10, 7.30–10 p.m.

Shetland Astronomical Society
Secretary: Peter Kelly, The Glebe, Fetlar, Shetland ZE2 9DJ.
Email: theglebe@zetnet.co.uk
Meetings: Fetlar, Fridays, Oct.–Mar.

Shropshire Astronomical Society
Contact: Mr David Woodward, 20 Station Road, Condover, Shrewsbury, Shropshire SY5 7BQ.
Website: http://www.shropshire-astro.com; *Email:* jacquidodds@ntlworld.com
Meetings: Quarterly talks at the Gateway Arts and Education Centre, Chester Street, Shrewsbury and monthly observing meetings at Rodington Village Hall.

Sidmouth and District Astronomical Society
Secretary: M. Grant, Salters Meadow, Sidmouth, Devon.
Meetings: Norman Lockyer Observatory, Salcombe Hill. 1st Monday in each month.

Solent Amateur Astronomers
Secretary: Ken Medway, 443 Burgess Road, Swaythling, Southampton SO16 3BL.
Web site: www.delscope.demon.co.uk;
Email: kenmedway@kenmedway.demon.co.uk
Meetings: Room 8, Oaklands Community School, Fairisle Road, Lordshill, Southampton. 3rd Tuesday each month, 7.30 p.m.

Southampton Astronomical Society
Secretary: John Thompson, 4 Heathfield, Hythe, Southampton SO45 5BJ.
Web site: www.home.clara.net/lmhobbs/sas.html;
Email: John.G.Thompson@Tesco.net
Meetings: Conference Room 3, The Civic Centre, Southampton. 2nd Thursday each month (except Aug.), 7.30 p.m.

South Downs Astronomical Society
Secretary: J. Green, 46 Central Avenue, Bognor Regis, West Sussex PO21 5HH.
Website: www.southdowns.org.uk
Meetings: Chichester High School for Boys. 1st Friday in each month (except Aug.).

South-East Essex Astronomical Society
Secretary: C.P. Jones, 29 Buller Road, Laindon, Essex.
Website: www.seeas.dabsol.co.uk/; *Email:* cpj@cix.co.uk
Meetings: Lecture Theatre, Central Library, Victoria Avenue, Southend-on-Sea. Generally 1st Thursday in month, Sept.–May, 7.30 p.m.

South-East Kent Astronomical Society
Secretary: Andrew McCarthy, 25 St Paul's Way, Sandgate, near Folkestone, Kent CT20 3NT.
Meetings: Monthly.

South Lincolnshire Astronomical & Geophysical Society
Secretary: Ian Farley, 12 West Road, Bourne, Lincolnshire PE10 9PS.
Meetings: Adult Education Study Centre, Pinchbeck. 3rd Wednesday each month, 7.30 p.m.

Southport Astronomical Society
Secretary: Patrick Brannon, Willow Cottage, 90 Jacksmere Lane, Scarisbrick, Ormskirk, Lancashire L40 9RS.
Meetings: Monthly Sept.–May, plus observing sessions.

Southport, Ormskirk and District Astronomical Society
Secretary: J.T. Harrison, 92 Cottage Lane, Ormskirk, Lancashire L39 3NJ.
Meetings: Saturday evenings, monthly, as arranged.

South Shields Astronomical Society
Secretary: c/o South Tyneside College, St George's Avenue, South Shields.
Meetings: Marine and Technical College. Each Thursday, 7.30 p.m.

South Somerset Astronomical Society
Secretary: G. McNelly, 11 Laxton Close, Taunton, Somerset.
Meetings: Victoria Inn, Skittle Alley, East Reach, Taunton, Somerset. Last Saturday each month, 7.30 p.m.

South-West Hertfordshire Astronomical Society
Secretary: Tom Walsh, 'Finches', Coleshill Lane, Winchmore Hill, Amersham, Buckinghamshire HP7 0NP.
Meetings: Rickmansworth. Last Friday each month, Sept.–May.

Stafford and District Astronomical Society
Secretary: Miss L. Hodkinson, 6 Elm Walk, Penkridge, Staffordshire ST19 5NL.
Meetings: Weston Road High School, Stafford. Every 3rd Thursday, Sept.–May, 7.15 p.m.

Stirling Astronomical Society
Secretary: Hamish MacPhee, 10 Causewayhead Road, Stirling FK9 5ER.
Meetings: Smith Museum & Art Gallery, Dumbarton Road, Stirling. 2nd Friday each month, 7.30 p.m.

Stoke-on-Trent Astronomical Society
Secretary: M. Pace, Sundale, Dunnocksfold, Alsager, Stoke-on-Trent.
Meetings: Cartwright House, Broad Street, Hanley. Monthly.

Stratford-upon-Avon Astronomical Society
Secretary: Robin Swinbourne, 18 Old Milverton, Leamington Spa, Warwickshire CV32 6SA.
Meetings: Tiddington Home Guard Club. 4th Tuesday each month, 7.30 p.m.

Sunderland Astronomical Society
Contact: Don Simpson, 78 Stratford Avenue, Grangetown, Sunderland SR2 8RZ.
Meetings: Friends Meeting House, Roker. 1st, 2nd and 3rd Sundays each month.

Sussex Astronomical Society
Secretary: Mrs C.G. Sutton, 75 Vale Road, Portslade, Sussex.
Meetings: English Language Centre, Third Avenue, Hove. Every Wednesday, 7.30–9.30 p.m., Sept.–May.

Swansea Astronomical Society
Secretary: Dr Michael Morales, 238 Heol Dulais, Birch Grove, Swansea SA7 9LH.
Website: www.crysania.co.uk/sas/astro/star
Meetings: Lecture Room C, Science Tower, University of Swansea. 2nd and 4th Thursday each month from Sept.–June, 7 p.m.

Tavistock Astronomical Society
Secretary: Mrs Ellie Coombes, Rosemount, Under Road, Gunnislake, Cornwall PL18 9JL.
Meetings: Science Laboratory, Kelly College, Tavistock. 1st Wednesday each month, 7.30 p.m.

Thames Valley Astronomical Group
Secretary: K.J. Pallet, 82a Tennyson Street, South Lambeth, London SW8 3TH.
Meetings: As arranged.

Thanet Amateur Astronomical Society
Secretary: P.F. Jordan, 85 Crescent Road, Ramsgate.
Meetings: Hilderstone House, Broadstairs, Kent. Monthly.

Torbay Astronomical Society
Secretary: Tim Moffat, 31 Netley Road, Newton Abbot, Devon TQ12 2LL.
Meetings: Torquay Boys' Grammar School, 1st Thursday in month; and Town Hall, Torquay, 3rd Thursday in month, Oct.–May, 7.30 p.m.

Tullamore Astronomical Society
Secretary: Tom Walsh, 25 Harbour Walk, Tullamore, Co. Offaly, Eire.
Website: www.iol.ie/seanmck/tas.htm; *Email:* tcwalsh25@yahoo.co.uk
Meetings: Order of Malta Lecture Hall, Tanyard, Tullamore, Co. Offaly, Eire. Mondays at 8 p.m., every fortnight.

Tyrone Astronomical Society
Secretary: John Ryan, 105 Coolnafranky Park, Cookstown, Co. Tyrone, Northern Ireland.
Meetings: Contact Secretary.

Usk Astronomical Society
Secretary: Bob Wright, 'Llwyn Celyn', 75 Woodland Road, Croesyceiliog, Cwmbran NP44 2OX.
Meetings: Usk Community Education Centre, Maryport Street, Usk. Every Thursday during school term, 7 p.m.

Vectis Astronomical Society
Secretary: Rosemary Pears, 1 Rockmount Cottages, Undercliff Drive, St Lawrence, Ventnor, Isle of Wight PO38 1XG.
Website: www.wightskies.fsnet.co.uk/main.html;
Email: may@tatemma.freeserve.co.uk
Meetings: Lord Louis Library Meeting Room, Newport. 4th Friday each month except Dec., 7.30 p.m.

Vigo Astronomical Society
Secretary: Robert Wilson, 43 Admers Wood, Vigo Village, Meopham, Kent DA13 0SP.
Meetings: Vigo Village Hall. As arranged.

Walsall Astronomical Society
Secretary: Bob Cleverley, 40 Mayfield Road, Sutton Coldfield B74 3PZ.
Meetings: Freetrade Inn, Wood Lane, Pelsall North Common. Every Thursday.

Wellingborough District Astronomical Society
Secretary: S.M. Williams, 120 Brickhill Road, Wellingborough, Northamptonshire.
Meetings: Gloucester Hall, Church Street, Wellingborough. 2nd Wednesday each month, 7.30 p.m.

Wessex Astronomical Society
Secretary: Leslie Fry, 14 Hanhum Road, Corfe Mullen, Dorset.
Meetings: Allendale Centre, Wimborne, Dorset. 1st Tuesday of each month.

West Cornwall Astronomical Society
Secretary: Dr R. Waddling, The Pines, Pennance Road, Falmouth, Cornwall TR11 4ED.
Meetings: Helston Football Club, 3rd Thursday each month, and St Michall's Hotel, 1st Wednesday each month, 7.30 p.m.

West of London Astronomical Society
Secretary: Duncan Radbourne, 28 Tavistock Road, Edgware, Middlesex HA8 6DA.
Website: www.wocas.org.uk
Meetings: Monthly, alternately in Uxbridge and North Harrow. 2nd Monday in month, except Aug.

West Midlands Astronomical Association
Secretary: Miss S. Bundy, 93 Greenridge Road, Handsworth Wood, Birmingham.
Meetings: Dr Johnson House, Bull Street, Birmingham. As arranged.

West Yorkshire Astronomical Society
Secretary: Pete Lunn, 21 Crawford Drive, Wakefield, West Yorkshire.
Meetings: Rosse Observatory, Carleton Community Centre, Carleton Road, Pontefract. Each Tuesday, 7.15 p.m.

Whitby and District Astronomical Society
Secretary: Rosemary Bowman, The Cottage, Larpool Drive, Whitby, North Yorkshire YO22 4ND.
Meetings: Whitby Mission, Seafarers' Centre, Haggersgate, Whitby. 1st Tuesday of the month, 7.30 p.m.

Whittington Astronomical Society
Secretary: Peter Williamson, The Observatory, Top Street, Whittington, Shropshire.
Meetings: The Observatory. Every month.

Wiltshire Astronomical Society
Secretary: Simon Barnes, 25 Woodcombe, Melksham, Wiltshire SN12 6HA.
Meetings: St Andrew's Church Hall, Church Lane, off Forest Road, Melksham, Wiltshire.

Wolverhampton Astronomical Society
Secretary: Mr M. Bryce, Iona, 16 Yellowhammer Court, Kidderminster, Worcestershire DY10 4RR.
Website: www.wolvas.org.uk; *Email:* michaelbryce@wolvas.org.uk
Meetings: Beckminster Methodist Church Hall, Birches Barn Road, Wolverhampton. Alternate Mondays, Sept.–Apr., extra dates in summer, 7.30 p.m.

Worcester Astronomical Society
Secretary: Mr S. Bateman, 12 Bozward Street, Worcester WR2 5DE.
Meetings: Room 117, Worcester College of Higher Education, Henwick Grove, Worcester. 2nd Thursday each month, 8 p.m.

Worthing Astronomical Society
Contact: G. Boots, 101 Ardingly Drive, Worthing, West Sussex BN12 4TW.
Website: www.worthingastro.freeserve.co.uk;
Email: gboots@observatory99.freeserve.co.uk
Meetings: Heene Church Rooms, Heene Road, Worthing. 1st Wednesday each month (except Aug.), 7.30 p.m.

Wycombe Astronomical Society
Secretary: Mr P. Treherne, 34 Honeysuckle Road, Widmer End, High Wycombe, Buckinghamshire HP15 6BW.
Meetings: Woodrow High House, Amersham. 3rd Wednesday each month, 7.45 p.m.

The York Astronomical Society
Contact: Hazel Collett, Public Relations Officer
Tel: 07944 751277
Website: www.yorkastro.freeserve.co.uk; *Email:* info@yorkastro.co.uk
Meetings: The Knavesmire Room, York Priory Street Centre, Priory Street, York. 1st and 3rd Friday of each month (except Aug.), 8 p.m.

Any society wishing to be included in this list of local societies or to update details, including any website addresses, is invited to write to the Editor (c/o Pan Macmillan, 20 New Wharf Road, London N1 9RR), so that the relevant information may be included in the next edition of the *Yearbook*.

The William Herschel Society maintains the museum established at 19 New King Street, Bath BA1 2BL – the only surviving Herschel House. It also undertakes activities of various kinds. New members would be welcome; those interested are asked to contact the Membership Secretary at the museum.

The South Downs Planetarium (Kingsham Farm, Kingsham Road, Chichester, West Sussex PO19 8RP) is now fully operational. For further information, visit www.southdowns.org.uk/sdpt or telephone (01243) 774400